BIG HISTORY

DK

BIG HISTORY

MACQUARIE UNIVERSITY
BIG HISTORY
INSTITUTE | SYDNEY · AUSTRALIA

FOREWORD BY **DAVID CHRISTIAN**

DK | Penguin Random House

Lead Senior Editor Helen Fewster
Senior Editors Peter Frances, Dr. Rob Houston
Senior Art Editors Amy Child, Phil Gamble, Sharon Spencer
Project Art Editors Paul Drislane, Mik Gates, Duncan Turner, Francis Wong
Project Editors Wendy Horobin, Andy Szudek
Editor Kaiya Shang
Editorial Assistant Francesco Piscitelli
Picture Researcher Liz Moore
Cartography Ron and Dee Blakey, Ed Merritt, Simon Mumford
Jacket Designers Mark Cavanagh, Suhita Dharamjit
Jacket Editor Claire Gell
Senior DTP Designer (Delhi) Harish Aggarwal
Jacket Design Development Manager Sophia MTT
Managing Jackets Editor (Delhi) Saloni Singh

Producer, pre-production Jacqueline Street-Elkayam
Producer Mary Slater

Managing Art Editor Michael Duffy
Managing Editor Angeles Gavira Guerrero
Art Director Karen Self
Design Director Phil Ormerod
Publisher Liz Wheeler
Publishing Director Jonathan Metcalf
Illustrators
Rajeev Doshi (Medi-mation)
Peter Bull (Peter Bull Art Studio)
Arran Lewis
Dominic Clifford
Jason Pickersgill (Acute Graphics)
Mark Clifton
Special Sales & Custom Publishing Manager Michelle Baxter

First published in Great Britain in 2016 by
Dorling Kindersley Limited 80 Strand,
London WC2R 0RL

Copyright © 2016 Dorling Kindersley Limited
A Penguin Random House Company

2 4 6 8 10 9 7 5 3 1

001–287353–October/2016

A CIP catalogue record for this book is available from the British Library.

ISBN: 978-0-2412-9547-2

Printed and bound in Hong Kong

A WORLD OF IDEAS:
SEE ALL THERE IS TO KNOW
www.dk.com

Big History Institute

MACQUARIE UNIVERSITY
BIG HISTORY
INSTITUTE | SYDNEY · AUSTRALIA

Macquarie University was founded with a unique purpose: to bring minds together unhindered by tradition. Created to challenge the education establishment, Macquarie has a rich track record of innovation – Big History is such an innovation. The Big History Institute builds upon the pioneering role that Macquarie University has played in the evolution of the new field of Big History. It brings together a community of scholars and students from both the sciences and the humanities who pursue research questions across disciplinary boundaries and discover new ways of thinking. The Big History Institute is also a global hub for educators, members of the public, and partners from the research, government, non-profit, and business sectors.

Consultants

David Christian, Director, Big History Institute
Professor David Christian (DPhil Oxford, 1974) is the founder of Big History. David is a Distinguished Professor at Macquarie University, co-founder with Bill Gates of the Big History Project, presenter of one of the 11 classic TED Talks with over 6 million views, and instructor in the world's first Big History MOOC on COURSERA®. David has given hundreds of presentations internationally, including Davos World Economic Forum in 2012, 2014, and 2015. He is a member of the Australian Academy of the Humanities and the Royal Holland Society of Sciences and Humanities, and a member of the editorial boards of the Journal of Global History and The Cambridge World History.

Andrew McKenna, Executive Director, Big History Institute
Andrew McKenna (BCom LLB UNSW, MIntRel Macquarie) coordinates Big History as an integrated initiative encompassing research, teaching, and outreach. Andrew leads the strategic growth and development of the Big History Institute globally.

Tracy Sullivan, Education Leader, Big History Institute
Tracy Sullivan (BA GradDipEd UWS, MA Macquarie) was on the curriculum development team for Big History Project, and oversees implementation in Australian schools. Tracy coordinates educational initiatives to support the growth and development of Big History globally.

Contributors

Introduction – Elise Bohan
Threshold 1 – Robert Dinwiddie
Threshold 2 – Jack Challoner
Thresholds 3 and 4 – Colin Stuart
Threshold 5 – Derek Harvey
Threshold 6 – Rebecca Wragg-Sykes
Threshold 7 – Peter Chrisp
Threshold 8 – Ben Hubbard

CONTENTS

5 LIFE EMERGES

6 HUMANS EVOLVE

7 CIVILIZATIONS DEVELOP

8 INDUSTRY RISES

FOREWORD

I vividly remember a globe map of the world sitting in a classroom when I was a child. I also remember a geography class, taught in a school in Somerset in England, where we learnt how to draw sections through the earth, showing the various layers of soil beneath our feet, and how they connected to other parts of England. For me, the most exciting thing in school was always the sudden connections, realizing that layers of chalk beneath our feet were made from the remains of billions of tiny organisms – called coccolithophores – that had lived millions of years ago, and that the same remains could also be found in layers of chalk in other parts of England and other countries much further away. What was Somerset like when the coccolithophores were alive? For that matter, where was Somerset back then? That's a question I couldn't even ask when I was at school because at that time scientists didn't know for sure that the continents moved around the surface of the earth.

For me, the globe in the corner of my classroom was a key to all this knowledge. It helped me see the place of Somerset in Britain, of Britain in Europe – so *that's* where the Vikings came from! – and of Europe in the world. Big History is like the globe, but it's much bigger: it includes all the observable universe and all observable time, so it reaches back in time for 13.8 billion years to the astonishing moment of the Big Bang, when an entire Universe was smaller than an atom. Big History includes the story of stars and galaxies, of new elements from carbon – the magical molecule that made life possible – to uranium, whose radioactivity enabled us not just to make bombs, but also to figure out when our earth was formed. It is like a map of all of space and time. And once you start exploring that map, you will be able, eventually, to say: "So that's what I'm a tiny part of! That's my place in the grand scheme of things! So what's next?"

Today, more and more schools and universities are teaching Big History, and it's a story we all need to know. In the book you are holding in your hands, you will find a beautifully illustrated account of this story, a sort of globe in words and pictures that links knowledge from many different disciplines. *Big History* shows how our world developed, threshold by threshold, from a very simple early Universe, to the emergence of stars and chemistry, and on to a cosmos that contained places like our earth on which life itself could emerge.

And you'll also see the strange role played by our own species, humans, in this huge story. We appear at the very end of the story, but our impact has been so colossal that we are beginning to change the planet. We have done something else that is perhaps even more astonishing: from our tiny vantage point in the vast Universe, we have figured out how that universe was created, how it evolved, and how it became as it is today. That is an amazing achievement, and in this book you will explore the discoveries that allowed us to piece together this story. This is the world globe that we need today, early in the 21st century, as we try to manage the huge challenges of maintaining our beautiful planet and keeping it in good condition for those who will come after us.

DAVID CHRISTIAN
FOUNDER OF BIG HISTORY
DIRECTOR, BIG HISTORY INSTITUTE
CO-FOUNDER OF THE BIG HISTORY PROJECT

"

Big History provides a framework for understanding literally all of history, ever, from the Big Bang to the present day. So often subjects in science and history are taught one at a time – physics in one class, the rise of civilization in another – but Big History breaks down those barriers. Today, whenever I learn something new about biology or history or just about any other subject, I try to fit it into the framework I got from Big History. No other course has had as big an impact on how I think about the world.

"

BILL GATES, WWW.GATESNOTES.COM
CO-FOUNDER OF THE BIG HISTORY PROJECT

WHAT IS BIG HISTORY?

BIG HISTORY IS THE STORY OF HOW YOU AND I CAME TO BE.

It is a modern origin story for a modern age. This grand evolutionary epic rouses our curiosity, confronts our ingrained intuitions, and marries science, reason and empiricism with vivid and dynamic storytelling. Best of all, Big History provides the scope and scientific foundations to help us ponder some of the most exciting and enduring questions about life, the Universe, and everything.

These universally compelling questions include: How did life on Earth evolve? What makes humans unique? Are we alone in the Universe? Why do we look and think and behave the way we do? And what does the future hold for our species, our planet and the cosmos? Throw a dart at any point in the history of the Universe and it will land on a page of the Big History story. No matter how obscure this page, or how far removed it may seem from the world we know, it will invariably describe a fragment of this grand scientific narrative, in which all events and all chapters are connected.

In this volume we traverse the stars, the galaxies, the cells inside your body, and the complex interactions between all living and non-living things. We stretch our minds to the limits of human understanding in order to see reality from many angles, and on many scales. What is truly remarkable about looking at the world from such an expansive perspective is that we begin to engage with many facets of the natural world that we often miss, or take for granted.

How often do we think about the fact that every atom inside each of our

HOW OFTEN DO WE THINK ABOUT THE FACT THAT EVERY ATOM INSIDE EACH OF OUR BODIES WAS MADE INSIDE A DYING STAR?

bodies was made inside a dying star? Or that ancient celestial implosions gave rise to the kinds of chemistry that makes life possible? How frequently do we zoom out far enough in our historical musings to see connections that transcend the actions of kings, armies, politicians, and peasants?

Our minds do not instinctively follow the threads of our evolutionary history to the point where all national, tribal, and species boundaries fall away. But when we allow ourselves to explore beyond these domains we come face to face with a single family tree, which shows that every one of us shares a common ancestor with every living organism on the planet: from worms, to fish, to reptiles, to chimpanzees, to a bird singing on the other side of the world, and the strangers who sleep through its refrain.

naked eye. It is also important to remember that Big History is not a static tale that proclaims how things are and will be for all time. It is a provisional narrative that is constantly being updated as our knowledge about the natural world grows, and as our needs as a species evolve.

From a cosmic perspective, we see that humans are a novel species that appear on the scene very late in this evolutionary history. We were not there at the beginning, and we are almost certainly not the species with whom the evolutionary buck stops. Yet Big History is still very much a human story, written by humans, for humans. At a certain point in this tale we choose to focus on our species and our corner of the galaxy, because from our point of view, this is where the action and the meaning is.

In the grand scheme of space and time, humanity may seem like little more than a cosmic footnote. But when we look closely at our blue planet we see that our species is responsible for some very remarkable things, which no other species has achieved in the 3–4 billion years that life has existed on Earth. As far as we know, *Homo sapiens* is the first and only species to represent the Universe becoming self-aware. Humans are now the dominant force altering the planetary biosphere, and we have kicked the pace of terrestrial evolution into a dramatic new gear.

BIG HISTORY HELPS US TO QUESTION EVERYTHING WE SEE, AND EVERYTHING WE THINK WE KNOW.

Big History helps us question everything we see, and everything we think we know. In the process, we discover that the Universe is far stranger than we often imagine, and that the shape of history is moulded by forces that are often surprising, and hard to see with the

As you explore this remarkable narrative, you will discover that our species has been so successful in expanding and colonising the globe, in large part because of our capacity for what big historians call collective learning. Although we cannot impart

our accumulated knowledge and experiences to new generations via DNA, we have developed the means to transmit this information culturally. Such a radical innovation in information sharing was made possible by the human invention of symbolic language.

At first this meant sharing ideas through the oral tradition. But eventually we developed writing, which reduced the error rate in the transmission of information and left humans in possession of a tool resembling a crude external hard drive. For the first time we could store large bodies of information without having to use the limited memory capacity of our brains.

With the ability to build upon existing information over many generations, humans learned ever faster, and knowledge and innovation proliferated. While many civilizations collapsed and some discoveries were lost for centuries, the overall trend was a feedback loop of accelerating cultural change: the invention of ever faster and more accurate methods of information sharing generated rapid bursts of innovation, and vice versa.

While the oral tradition persisted for tens of thousands of years, it only took a few hundred years for humans to transition from the age of the printing press to the digital world of today. If the pace of cultural evolution continues at such a rate we may see the emergence of a new evolutionary paradigm in mere decades.

Because of our astounding capacity for collective learning and cultural development, humans have made a

WITH THE ABILITY TO BUILD UPON EXISTING INFORMATION OVER MANY GENERATIONS, HUMANS LEARNED EVER FASTER, AND KNOWLEDGE AND INNOVATION PROLIFERATED.

giant evolutionary leap in a relatively short period of time. We have transitioned from our initial role as one of evolution's many simple players, to a fledgling director engaged in the task of consciously shaping the trajectory of evolution on Earth. While this is a very exciting role, it also presents immense challenges.

It is sobering to look back at our extensive family tree and recall that 99 per cent of species that have ever lived are now extinct. In light of this, it is natural and beneficial to consider whether our species will be able to live sustainably and prosperously for many years into the future. And if we can achieve this, how might it be possible?

Will we reduce our consumption of energy and live more simply? Or will we harness our immense collective brainpower to engineer more sophisticated ways of producing clean energy and sustainable products and services? Will our modern

technological arms race leave us liberated or enslaved? And how long will most of us continue to exist as fully biological beings, unenhanced by technological modifications?

These are the kinds of questions that the Big History story prompts us to consider. There is no doubt that in terms of its scope, content, and method, Big History is a truly modern story, fit for the needs of a modern age.

Like all origin stories of previous ages, this narrative is designed to help orient us with where we come from, what we are, and where we might be going. But unlike ancient origin stories that were built upon myth and intuition, this evolutionary epic relies on the theories of modern science to help us get to grips with the world around us.

For most of us, thinking about things that are very big, very small, and very old does not come naturally. But pursuing big ideas and chasing the answers to profound universal questions

BIG HISTORY IS A TRULY MODERN ORIGIN STORY, FIT FOR THE NEEDS OF A MODERN AGE.

does! We cannot help wanting to know what else is out there: whether it be among the stars, inside black holes, or in the mysterious workings of our brains, our DNA, or the remarkable bacterial ecosystems that live on, around, and inside us.

The Big History story helps to facilitate our exploration of these and other exciting domains. It allows us to focus on an array of subjects and historical moments and encourages us to ponder the nature of reality on many different scales. We learn to relate the details to the big picture, and observe how broad trends can contextualise local phenomena and events. By exploring the viewpoints of both the generalist and the specialist, we are able to think more carefully and creatively about cause and effect, and devise more innovative responses and solutions to the many challenges we face in the world today.

Big History's unified perspective also helps us to see the present in dynamic terms, and shows us that we are not only the successors of previous evolutionary thresholds, but also the possible progenitors of those to come.

Our story is divided into eight thresholds of increasing complexity, which highlight some of the key transitionary phases in this cosmic evolutionary history. As we move from threshold to threshold you will see how profoundly each stage is connected, and how matter and information in the Universe grow denser and more complex in various pockets of cosmic order. This story helps us to see that our planet and our species emerged among a rare set of goldilocks conditions, where the balance and stability of elements was "just right" to sustain life.

Once you explore this book and get a feel for the big picture it presents, we hope you will be left pondering many new and rousing questions. As you sit, poised to embark on this journey of discovery, there is one question in particular that we hope you will consider.

What role will you play in determining how events unfold in the next threshold of the this great cosmic drama?

"BENEATH THE AWESOME DIVERSITY AND COMPLEXITY OF MODERN KNOWLEDGE, THERE IS AN UNDERLYING UNITY AND COHERENCE, ENSURING THAT DIFFERENT TIMESCALES REALLY DO HAVE SOMETHING TO SAY TO EACH OTHER."

DAVID CHRISTIAN, BIG HISTORIAN

THRESHOLD

THE BIG **BANG**

What are the origins of our Universe?
It is a question that has captivated humans
probably since we emerged as a species
and began trying to make sense of our
place in nature. Centuries of observation,
investigation, and scientific endeavour have
led us to the Big Bang theory – but that too
leaves questions unanswered, and our quest
for further explanation continues.

GOLDILOCKS CONDITIONS

The Universe formed in the Big Bang. We do not know if anything existed before it, and we only have a glimpse of what happened in the fraction of a second immediately afterwards. But over the next 380,000 years, the Universe expanded and cooled, and the fundamental forces and forms of matter that we know today emerged.

What changed?
Suddenly, space, time, energy, and matter came into existence in the Big Bang.

Before the Big Bang
We don't know what existed before the Big Bang. There might have been nothing. But there are other possibilities. For example, one alternative theory proposes a multiverse – a vast realm from which universes keep appearing.

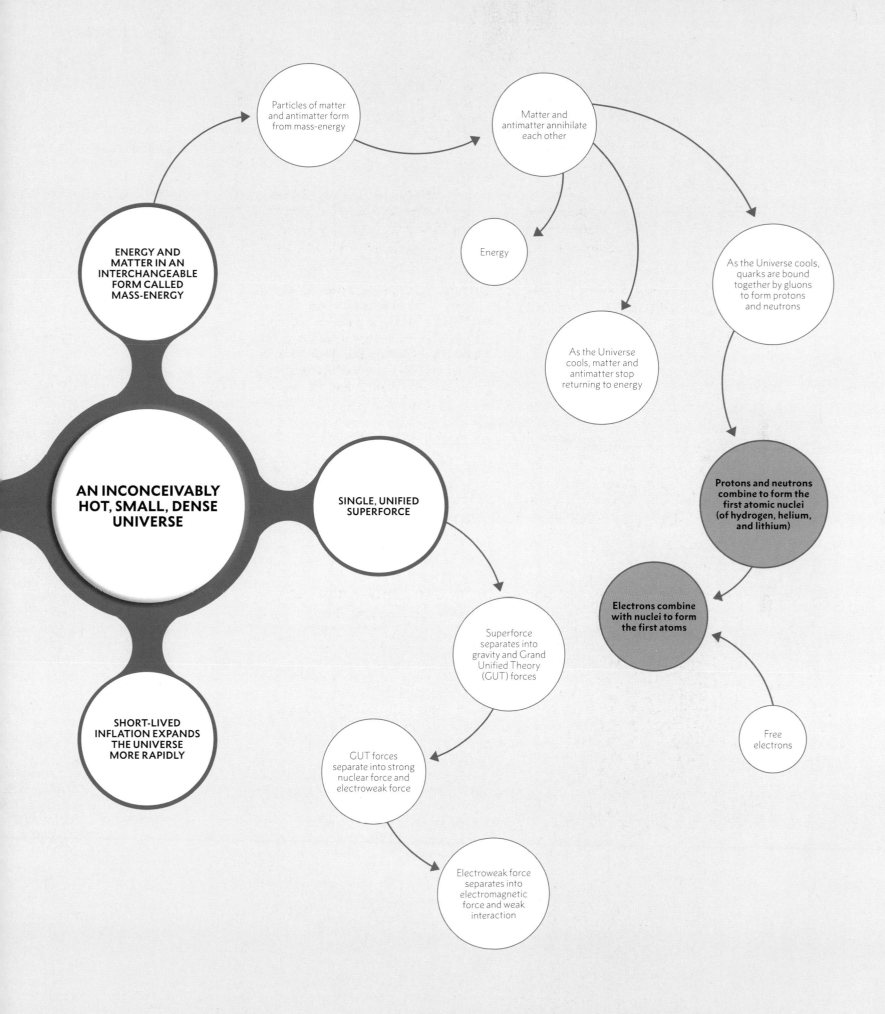

Particles of matter and antimatter form from mass-energy

Matter and antimatter annihilate each other

Energy

As the Universe cools, quarks are bound together by gluons to form protons and neutrons

ENERGY AND MATTER IN AN INTERCHANGEABLE FORM CALLED MASS-ENERGY

As the Universe cools, matter and antimatter stop returning to energy

Protons and neutrons combine to form the first atomic nuclei (of hydrogen, helium, and lithium)

AN INCONCEIVABLY HOT, SMALL, DENSE UNIVERSE

SINGLE, UNIFIED SUPERFORCE

Electrons combine with nuclei to form the first atoms

Superforce separates into gravity and Grand Unified Theory (GUT) forces

Free electrons

SHORT-LIVED INFLATION EXPANDS THE UNIVERSE MORE RAPIDLY

GUT forces separate into strong nuclear force and electroweak force

Electroweak force separates into electromagnetic force and weak interaction

ORIGIN **STORIES**

Nearly all human cultures and religious traditions have nurtured origin stories – symbolic accounts that describe how the world came about. These stories or narratives were most often passed from one generation to the next in the form of folk tales or ballads and sometimes through writing or pictures.

O rigin stories are extremely varied in detail, but they tend to include some common themes. Often they tell how the Universe acquired order from an original state of either darkness or deep chaos. In several versions, including the Old Testament's *Book of Genesis*, this order is imposed by a supreme being or deity. In some stories, creation is a cyclical process. For example, in Hindu thought, order is generated only to be destroyed and then regenerated. Many stories begin with Earth. In some, people and gods emerge from the Earth. In others, an animal dives into a boundless primeval ocean and retrieves a portion of Earth from which the cosmos is created.

ORIGINS OF THE SKY, SUN, AND MOON

Many origin stories describe how the sky was created along with Earth, often by splitting off from another primeval object. In a common form of the Maori creation myth, the Universe is created from nothing by a supreme being, Io. He also creates

> WE HAVE INHERITED FROM OUR FOREFATHERS THE KEEN LONGING FOR **UNIFIED, ALL-EMBRACING KNOWLEDGE**.
>
> Erwin Schrödinger, Austrian theoretical physicist, 1887–1961

Ranginui (Rangi) and Papatuanuku (Papa), the Sky Father and Earth Mother. Rangi and Papa remain physically cleaved together until pushed apart by their six offspring to create the separate realms of Earth and sky. Many stories also account for the creation of celestial bodies such as the Sun and Moon. For example, in a story from China, the first living being, Pangu, hatches from a cosmic egg. Half the shell lies under him as the Earth; the rest arcs above him as the sky. Each day for thousands of years he grows, gradually pushing Earth and sky apart until they reach their correct places. But then Pangu disintegrates. His arms and legs become mountains, his breath the wind, his eyes turn into the Sun and Moon. Often

MORE THAN **100 DISTINCT ORIGIN STORIES** HAVE BEEN IDENTIFIED FROM VARIOUS PEOPLES AND CULTURES ACROSS THE WORLD

celestial objects originate as physical representations of gods. For example, an origin story from ancient Egypt begins with Nun, the primeval ocean, from which the god Amen rises. He takes the alternative name Re and breeds more gods. While his tears become mankind, Amen-Re retires to the heavens, to reign eternally as the Sun.

Origin stories such as these developed because early humans needed to find an explanation for their own existence and for everything that they saw around them. The cultures that fostered these stories regarded them as true, and for their adherents they usually carried great importance and emotional power. But such perceptions were based on faith and not on accurate observations or scientific reasoning.

THE EARLIEST ASTRONOMERS

At points in history that vary according to the culture, but typically from about 4000 BCE in Europe and the Middle East, it seems that humans began to tire of merely gazing at, and devising stories about, objects such as the stars, Sun, and Moon. Instead some individuals began making detailed recordings of celestial phenomena. These investigations were carried out for a variety of mostly practical reasons. An ability to identify a few stars, and to understand sky movements, proved useful for navigation. It was also realized that the sky is a sort of

ASTRONOMERS IN CHINA RECORDED OBSERVATIONS OF **MORE THAN 1,600 SOLAR ECLIPSES** FROM 750 BCE ONWARDS

clock that could be used, for example, to tell farmers when to sow crops or to give warning of important natural events. In ancient Egypt, for example, the rising of the bright star Sirius around the same time as the Sun heralded the annual flooding of the Nile. A final reason for studying the heavens was to predict solar eclipses. Chinese astronomers are thought to have attempted this as long ago as 2500 BCE, but it was not until the 1st century BCE that the ancient Greeks reached the level of astronomical sophistication needed to do it accurately. Successful eclipse prediction had little specific practical use but it did confer on the predictor very significant mystical powers and, as a result, considerable peer respect.

In some early cultures, accurate observation not only had practical uses but was also intertwined with religion. Some of the most sophisticated observations before the invention of the telescope were made by the Maya, who colonized parts of Central America between 250 and 900 CE. They made accurate calculations of the length of the solar year, compiled precise tables of the positions of Venus and the Moon, and were able to predict eclipses. They used their calendar to time the sowing and harvesting of crops. But they also saw a link between the cycles they observed and the place of their gods in the natural order. Specific events in the night sky were seen as representing particular deities. The Maya also practised a form of astrology, drawing a connection between cycles in the sky and the everyday life and concerns of the individual.

A MODERN NARRATIVE

Big History is a modern-day origin story. Part of this story is an account of how the Universe formed provided by the Big Bang theory of cosmology. The theory describes the formation of a Universe with a beginning and a structure. Modern cosmology as a whole also contains an account of a Universe that changes over time, as matter and energy take on different forms, new particles come into existence, space itself expands, and structures such as stars and galaxies emerge. The Big Bang theory, as part of the Big History narrative, shares some other features with traditional origin stories. For example, in common with several of the stories, it proposes that everything – all matter, energy, space, and time – originated from nothing. Big Bang theory and the traditional stories also set out to answer many of the same questions – including how did the Universe begin? The theory does not give a complete account of how the Universe came to be the way it is now. For example, it does not explain the origin of life or the evolution of humans. But it does form part of the larger framework of Big History that attempts to answer these and other questions.

However, in one crucial respect, Big Bang theory, like Big History in general, differs from traditional origin stories in that it seeks to provide a literal and accurate account of the Universe's origins. It represents the current state of scientific thinking, arrived at after many centuries of both gradual change and sudden leaps forward. Like other scientific theories in Big History, the theory also makes predictions that can be tested against evidence, allowing it to be refined or even disproved and overturned. Some questions remain unanswered by Big Bang theory. But, at least for now, it offers the most convincing account of when and how the Universe began.

▶ **Brahma the creator** According to some older forms of Hinduism, the god Brahma, who is usually depicted with four heads, was born from a golden egg and created Earth and everything in it.

> " THERE WAS NEITHER **NON-EXISTENCE NOR EXISTENCE** THEN; THERE WAS NEITHER THE REALM OF **SPACE NOR THE SKY** WHICH IS BEYOND. "

The Rig Veda,
a collection of Sanskrit hymns, 2nd millenium BCE

THE NEBRA
SKY DISC

During the European Bronze Age, people developed their knowledge of astronomy and put it to practical uses. The Nebra Sky Disc is a key piece of evidence for observation of the sky at this time. Analysis of the disc's materials also reveals information about metalworking and trade.

The Bronze Age in Europe began around 3200 BCE. Dug up near Nebra in central Germany in 1999, the 3,600-year-old Nebra Sky Disc depicts the Sun, Moon, and 32 stars, including possibly the Pleiades star cluster. It is the oldest known portrayal of such a variety of sky objects. The disc also reveals that its owners had measured the angle between the rising and setting points of the Sun at the summer and winter solstices – the days of greatest and least daylight each year.

There are two schools of thought as to what the disc was used for or represents. Some archaeologists think that it was an astronomical clock, which could have been used to indicate times for sowing and harvesting crops and to coordinate the solar and lunar calendars. Alternatively, the objects on the disc may illustrate a significant astronomical event – a solar eclipse on 16 April 1699 BCE. On that date, the Sun, as it was eclipsed by the Moon, was close in the sky both to the Pleiades and to a tight grouping of three planets – Mercury, Venus, and Mars.

Whatever its exact use, the Nebra Sky Disc provides clear evidence that some Bronze Age people had made detailed sky observations and also developed tools to help them mark the passage of time and the seasons.

Small discs may denote stars, but most appear to be decorative, as they do not match known star patterns

Large gold disc probably represents the Sun

Holes were punched into the rim after other additions for an unknown purpose

Pleiades
Sun or full Moon
Waxing Moon or partially eclipsed Sun

PHASE 1

Arcs added, one of them covering two stars

PHASE 2

Sunboat added

PHASE 3

▲ **Phases in construction** The disc was made in three phases, significantly separated in time, suggesting it underwent some repurposing. The addition of the sunboat indicates that it may have taken on religious significance.

If the disc was held horizontally, its edge would represent the horizon

Sunset point at summer solstice

Sunrise point at summer solstice

▶ **The golden arcs** The two arcs on the disc span 82°, the angle between the points on the horizon where the Sun sets (or rises) at the summer and winter solstices for the location where the disc was found.

82° 82°

Sunset point at winter solstice

Sunrise point at winter solstice

Metal sources

The disc's copper came from the Austrian Alps. Its tin – used with copper to make bronze – and its original gold were from Cornwall, England. The gold in the arcs and sunboat came from the Carpathian Mountains in eastern Europe. Evidently there were well-established trade routes across Europe at the time.

Gold nugget

The Pleiades

A group of stars on the disc may represent the Pleiades star cluster, of which the brightest stars could have been seen with the naked eye by Bronze Age skygazers. In central Europe, the Pleiades would have been a prominent evening feature in the southeastern sky around harvest time.

Stars and dust in the Pleiades

Golden arcs span the angle between the setting (or rising) points of the Sun at summer and winter solstices

The Nebra hoard

The disc was buried with other objects, including two swords made of bronze with copper and gold inlays, a chisel, two axeheads, and two armbands, collectively called the Nebra hoard. It is not known why the disc was placed with these objects. The hoard was buried in around 1600 BCE, but the disc could be older. When first examined by archaeologists, it was suspected to be an elaborate fake, but corrosion tests, excavation of the burial site, and examination of the other artefacts pointed to its authenticity.

Bronze Age sword from the Nebra hoard

Gold crescent may signify either a crescent Moon or the Sun during a solar eclipse

Blue-green patina, caused by oxidation of disc's copper content, was probably an intentional decorative feature

The sunboat

The arc of gold at the bottom of the Nebra sky disc is thought to be a sunboat – the means by which some ancient people imagined the Sun was conveyed from its setting point in the west to its rising point in the east during the night. The hairlike protrusions around the edge of the arc might represent oars. If the arc is indeed a sunboat, it would be the earliest known representation of one.

Gold arc, with hundreds of tiny protrusions, may represent a sunboat and oars

ASTRONOMY
BEGINS

For most of human history, people were too busy surviving to spend much time thinking about the world's underlying nature and origins. But from around 1000 BCE, a few began to try answering key questions about the Universe without recourse to supernatural explanations.

These thinkers – initially concentrated in Mediterranean lands, especially Greece – realized that to understand the world it is necessary to know its nature, and that natural phenomena should have logical explanations. Although they did not always find the correct answers, this leap marked the start of a 3,000-year journey that has led in the modern world to such key theories as the Big Bang model of the Universe.

THE NATURE OF MATTER

The fundamental questions of what the world is made of, and where matter came from, are some of the oldest. In the 6th century BCE, Greek philosophers such as Thales and Anaximenes proposed that all substances were modifications of more intrinsic substances, the main candidates being water, air, earth, and fire. In the 5th century BCE, Empedocles claimed that everything was a mixture of all four of these substances, or elements. His near-contemporary Democritus developed the idea that the Universe is made of an infinite number of indivisible particles called atoms. Finally, in the 4th century BCE the influential scholar Aristotle added a fifth element, aether, to Empedocles' four. Although Aristotle was sceptical of the idea of atoms, it is remarkable that the concepts of both atoms and elements had been proposed more than 2,000 years before either was proved to exist.

EARTH'S SHAPE AND SIZE

Among many other ideas that Aristotle gave his views on was the concept that Earth is a sphere. Earlier Greek scholars, such as Pythagoras, had already argued this, but Aristotle was the first to summarize the

> THE IDEA THAT **EARTH IS FLAT** WAS STILL THE PREVAILING VIEW IN **CHINA UP TO THE EARLY 17TH CENTURY**

main points of evidence. Chief among them was that travellers to southern lands could see stars that could not be seen by those living further north – explainable only if Earth's surface is curved. In 240 BCE, by comparing how the Sun's rays reach Earth at Syene and Alexandria, the mathematician Eratosthenes was able to estimate Earth's circumference. He came up with a figure of about 40,000km (25,000 miles) – close to the true value known today.

EARTH AND THE SUN

Aristotle thought that Earth was at the centre of the Universe and that the Sun, planets, and stars move around it. This seemed like common sense given that every night various celestial objects (and during the day, the Sun) could be seen moving across the sky from

Sun's rays

Tower in Alexandria

Tower's shadow

Height of tower

800km (500 miles) from Alexandria to Syene

Length of shadow

Well at Syene

Angle at Earth's centre is equal to angle at which shadow is cast in Alexandria

7°

7°

Centre of Earth

◀ **Estimating Earth's circumference**
When the Sun was overhead above a well at Syene, it cast a shadow at an angle of about 7° in Alexandria. Dividing this angle into 360°, then multiplying the result by the distance between the two places gave an estimate of Earth's circumference of about 40,000km (25,000 miles).

ORBIUM PLA
TERRAM COM
TIUM SCENO

SPHÆRA

SPHÆRA

SCOR
PIVS

CAPRI
CORNVS

HYPOTHESIS PTOLEMAICA

▲ **Earth-centred Universe**
This 17th-century illustration by Andreas Cellarius depicts Aristotle and Ptolemy's model. Working out from the centre, the Moon, Mercury, Venus, the Sun, Mars, Jupiter, Saturn, and the stars move in circular orbits around Earth.

east to west, whereas Earth itself did not seem to move. An alternative view, put forward by the astronomer Aristarchus, was that the Sun is at the centre and that Earth orbits it, but this idea did not gain much credence. In 150 CE, Claudius Ptolemy – an eminent Greek scholar living in Alexandria – published a book called the *Almagest*, which

NETARUM PLECTEN GRAPHIA.

HYPOTHESIS BRAHEA. *in quâ centrum Lunæ et Firmamenti est Terra; reliquorum quinq; Planetarum Sol.*

A STATIONARY OR A SPINNING EARTH?

Linked to the issue of what is at the centre of the Universe, the question of whether or not Earth rotates was debated for around 2,000 years up to the 17th century CE. The prevailing view was that Earth does not spin, as this fitted best with the idea of an Earth-centred Universe. However, there were opponents to this view, including Greek philosopher and astronomer Heraclides Ponticus in the 4th century BCE, as well as an Indian astronomer, Aryabhata, and Persian astronomers (Al-Sijzi and Al-Biruni) between the 5th and 15th centuries CE. Each proposed that Earth rotates and that the stars' apparent movement is just a relative motion caused by Earth's spin. But it was not until the Copernican Revolution (see pp.24–25) that Earth's rotation became accepted as fact, and it was not until the 19th century that it was categorically proved.

▲ **Ulugh Beg**
Working at his observatory at Samarkand, Ulugh Beg and other astronomers determined matters such as the tilt of Earth's spin axis and an accurate value for the length of the year.

THE SIZE AND AGE OF THE UNIVERSE

A final popular subject for speculation among early philosophers was the question of whether the Universe is finite (limited) or infinite, both in extent and in time. Aristotle proposed that the Universe is infinite in time (so it has always existed) but finite in extent – he believed that all the stars were at a fixed distance, embedded in a crystal sphere, beyond which was nothing. The mathematician Archimedes made a reasoned estimate of the distance to the fixed stars and realized it was vast (at least what we would now call 2 light years) but stopped short of claiming it to be infinite. In the 6th century CE, Egyptian philosopher John Philoponus opposed the prevailing Aristotelian view by arguing that the Universe is finite in time. It was not until the 20th century that scientists began to find answers to these questions.

affirmed the prevailing view that Earth is at the centre. Ptolemy's detailed model fitted with all known observations but in order to do so contained complex modifications to Aristotle's original ideas. For about the next 14 centuries, the Earth-centred view of Aristotle and Ptolemy totally dominated astronomical theory, and it was adopted throughout Europe by medieval Christianity. During this time, Islamic astronomers such as Ulugh Beg (who worked from a great observatory in Samarkand, in what is now Uzbekistan, during the 15th century) made major contributions to knowledge of the Solar System and in particular to cataloguing star positions.

> " IN POSITION **EARTH LIES IN THE MIDDLE OF THE HEAVENS** VERY MUCH LIKE ITS CENTRE. "

Claudius Ptolemy, astronomer and geographer, 90–168 CE

To the people of medieval Europe up to the mid-16th century, the question of how the Universe is organized had been answered centuries before by Ptolemy, in his modifications to ideas first asserted by Aristotle (see pp.22–23). According to Ptolemy, Earth stood still at the centre of the Universe. Stars were "fixed" or embedded in an invisible, distant sphere that rotated rapidly, approximately daily, around Earth. The Sun, Moon, and planets also revolved around Earth, attached to other invisible spheres. For most people, this explanation seemed reasonable – after all, looking up at the sky at night, it did seem that Earth was quite still, while all other objects in the sky, including the Sun and stars, rose up in the east, moved across the sky, and then set below the western horizon.

EARTH **ORBITS THE SUN**

▼ **The Solar System in miniature**
This model of the Solar System, called an armillary sphere, is a Copernican version, showing the Sun at the centre and the planets revolving around it.

In the 16th and early 17th centuries, the prevailing view of an Earth-centred, or geocentric, Universe, as first put forward by the Greek scholars Aristotle and Ptolemy, was challenged by a simpler Sun-centred, heliocentric, model. This single idea eventually led to the scientific revolution, a whole new way of thinking about the Universe.

DOUBTS ABOUT GEOCENTRISM
The geocentric model of the Universe did not satisfy everyone, however. A serious doubt focused on what it predicted about the planets. According to the original Aristotelian version of geocentrism, the planets rotated around Earth in perfect circles, each at its own steady speed. But if this was true, the planets should move across the sky with unvarying speed and brightness because they were always the same distance from Earth – and this wasn't what was observed. Some planets, such as Mars, varied hugely in brightness over time, and when their movements were compared with those of the outer sphere of fixed stars, the planets sometimes reversed direction – a behaviour called retrograde motion. To deal with these problems, Ptolemy had modified the Aristotelian model. For example, he had planets attached not to

COPERNICUS WAS A DOCTOR, CLERIC, DIPLOMAT, AND ECONOMIST AS WELL AS AN **ASTRONOMER**

the spheres themselves, but to circles called epicycles attached to the spheres. To some astronomers, these modifications looked like "fixes" to fit the model to observational data. From time to time, they suggested alternative ideas, such as that Earth orbits the Sun. But supporters of geocentrism had what seemed an excellent reason for ruling this out. They argued that if Earth moves, the stars should be seen shifting a little relative to each other over the course of a year – but no such shifts could be detected and so, they answered, Earth cannot move.

THE COPERNICAN MODEL
In the face of these arguments – and the power of the Catholic Church, which supported the established view – for centuries there was little opposition to the idea of a geocentric Universe. However, around 1545, rumours began circulating in Europe that a new and convincing challenge – in the form of a Sun-centred theory of the Universe – had appeared in a book,

De Revolutionibus Orbium Coelestium ("On the Revolutions of the Celestial Spheres"), by a Polish scholar, Nicolaus Copernicus.

Copernicus based his theory on several assumptions. The first was that Earth spins on its axis, and it is this rotation that accounts for most of the daily motion of the stars, planets, Moon, and Sun across the sky. Copernicus considered that it was inconceivable that thousands of stars were rotating rapidly around Earth. Instead, he proposed that their apparent motion was an illusion caused by Earth's spin. He discounted an objection that this would create catastrophic winds, pointing out that Earth's atmosphere was part of the planet and so part of the motion.

Copernicus's core assumption was that the Sun, not Earth, is at or near the centre of the Universe, and that the planets – including Earth, just another planet – circle the Sun at differing speeds. This system could explain, in a simpler way, the motions and variation in brightness of the planets without recourse to any of Ptolemy's "fixes". A third important assumption was that the stars are much further from Earth and the Sun than had previously been accepted. This explained why the relative positions of the stars as seen from Earth appeared to remain fixed over the course of a year.

THE THEORY DEVELOPS

De Revolutionibus was published when Copernicus was dying, and it was a century or more before his theory became widely accepted. One problem was that his model contained misconceptions that had to be corrected by later astronomers. Copernicus clung to the idea that all movements of celestial bodies occur with the objects embedded in invisible spheres. In 1576, the English astronomer Thomas Digges suggested modifying the Copernican system by removing the outermost sphere, in which stars are embedded, and replacing it with a star-filled unbound space. In the 1580s, the Danish astronomer Tycho Brahe banished the rest of the spheres in favour of planets

moving freely in orbits. Brahe had observed comets apparently passing through the spheres, which convinced him that they did not actually exist. He also observed a supernova, contradicting a long-held idea that no change takes place in the heavens.

Another shortcoming in Copernicus's theory was his belief that all celestial objects must move in circles, which forced him to retain some of Ptolemy's "fixes". But in the 1620s, the work of the German astronomer Johannes Kepler showed that orbits were elliptical, not circular. By removing most of the remaining "fixes", this simplified and improved the heliocentric model. In the late 17th century, Isaac Newton expanded on Kepler's work, and with his laws of motion and newly introduced force of gravity (see pp.46–47), Newton was able to explain exactly why celestial objects move in the way they do. His work *Principia* effectively removed the last doubts about heliocentrism.

These improvements in the Copernican theory took place against the backdrop of

CHURCH REACTION

In 1616, the Roman Catholic Church banned *De Revolutionibus* – a ban that was enforced for more than 200 years. This probably came about as a result of a dispute the Church was having with the astronomer Galileo Galilei, a champion of the Copernican theory who had made discoveries that supported heliocentrism. In particular, in about 1610, Galileo had discovered moons circling Jupiter, proving that some celestial objects do not orbit Earth. The dispute with Galileo caused *De Revolutionibus* to undergo intense scrutiny by the Church, and because some of its ideas

seemed to go against biblical statements, it was banned. In 1633, Galileo himself was eventually put on trial and forced to recant his views.

THE SCIENTIFIC REVOLUTION

Banned by the Catholic Church and viewed ambivalently at first by astronomers, the Copernican theory took time to catch on. More than 150 years passed before some of its basic assumptions were shown to be true

other important advances in cosmology. In the early 17th century, the development of telescopes helped establish that stars are far more distant than planets and exist in vast numbers. It was even suggested that the Universe could be infinite. Kepler, however, pointed out that it cannot be infinite, static, and eternal, otherwise the night sky would look uniformly bright due to there being a star emitting light from every direction.

beyond dispute. But what was important about the theory was that it established cosmology as a science and represented a serious blow to some old, traditional ideas about how the Universe works, many dating from Aristotle. As such, it is often viewed as ushering in the scientific revolution – a series of advances between the 16th and 18th centuries that transformed views of nature and society in the early modern world.

William Herschel completes a 12m (40ft) long reflecting telescope, 1789.

Fraunhofer's spectroscope

Spectroscope invented 1814, by Joseph von Fraunhofer, who notices dark (absorption) lines in the Sun's spectrum. Later known as Fraunhofer lines, they help astronomers to determine the chemical makeup of stars.

Reflecting telescopes improved by James Short, 1730s–1760s. Several are used to observe transits of Venus.

First practical reflecting telescope built by John Hadley, 1721. A parabolic mirror avoids spherical aberration, improving image quality.

Various nebulous objects, now known to be mostly star clusters and galaxies, identified by Charles Messier, 1760s–1780s.

1800

First use of photography in astronomy, 1839, allowing fainter objects to be seen and efficient, permanent recording.

Newton's reflector

First working reflecting telescope produced by Isaac Newton, 1668. The design avoids a drawback of refractors called chromatic aberration, but another problem, spherical aberration, renders it impractical.

1700

New record for the largest telescope set in 1686 by Christiaan Huygens, who builds a 95m (310ft) long aerial, tubeless refractor.

First measurement of a star's parallax, made by Friedrich Bessel, 1838. This becomes the standard method for measuring distances to nearby stars.

Telescopic sight and micrometer invented by William Gascoigne, 1638, facilitating more accurate plotting and measurement of celestial objects.

Refractor 3.5m (11½ft) long built by Johannes Hevelius, 1647. Hevelius subsequently builds even longer telescopes and uses them to make the first accurate map of the Moon.

SEEING THE LIGHT

The telescope, and a lesser-known instrument, the spectroscope, are the main tools with which astronomers have expanded knowledge of the Universe and its beginnings.

The first telescopes were designed to gather visible light only, and within 100 years had split into two main types – refractors and reflectors. In the 19th century, the spectroscope – which can be used to study the composition and motions of celestial objects – was invented. During the 20th century, bigger optical telescopes came along, followed by radio telescopes. Innovations since the 1970s have included launching telescopes into space and, in the case of radio telescopes, arranging them on the ground in arrays.

Galileo builds a 20-power telescope, 1609. Some of his observations made by telescope later throw him into conflict with the Catholic Church.

Patent filed for a refracting telescope, 1608, by Hans Lippershey.

VISIBLE LIGHT TELESCOPE ASTRONOMY

1600

VISIBLE LIGHT TELESCOPE TECHNOLOGY

Massive reflector, with a 1.5m (5ft) wide mirror, built by William Parsons, 1845.

James Webb Space Telescope is due to launch, 2018.

2000

First Keck Telescope begins operation in Hawaii, 1993. The telescope, and its twin, has a 10m (33ft) wide mirror made of 36 segments and uses a technology called adaptive optics to adjust for atmospheric turbulence by altering the mirror's shape.

Cosmic microwave background radiation mapped from space, 1993. This first map is made by the Cosmic Background Explorer (COBE).

Hipparcos Satellite makes its first observations, 1989. Hipparcos makes highly accurate measurements of the positions of stars.

SPACE TELESCOPES

First pulsar discovered, 1967, by Jocelyn Bell and Antony Hewish using a radio telescope at the University of Cambridge.

Cosmic microwave background radiation detected, 1964, by Arno Penzias and Robert Wilson using a radio telescope at Bell Telephone Laboratories, New Jersey. It helps to confirm the Big Bang theory.

First parabolic dish radio telescope in Wheaton, built by Grote Reber in Wheaton, Illinois, 1937. Reber then makes an all-sky map of radio emissions from space.

Edwin Hubble uses the Hooker Telescope in the 1920s to show there are galaxies outside our own and to relate the distances and recessional velocities of galaxies – leading to the discovery that the Universe is expanding.

The Hubble Space Telescope placed in orbit, 1990. It has peered deep into space and time, providing astonishing images of objects in our galaxy and beyond, and improved measurements of the Universe's age.

Elements in the Sun's atmosphere identified by Gustav Kirchoff, 1851. He notices dark lines in its spectrum match wavelengths of light emitted by elements burned in a flame.

First photograph of a star's spectrum taken by Henry Draper, 1872. The star is Vega, and the photograph shows its absorption lines.

Yerkes Refractor is completed in Wisconsin, 1895. The largest refractor ever used for research, it is involved in discoveries such as the spiral nature of the Milky Way.

BEYOND VISIBLE LIGHT

The Very Large Array (VLA), work together to form images, a group of 27 radio telescopes that begins operations in New Mexico, 1980.

1900

Spectra of nebulae, stars, and galaxies are studied by William and Margaret Huggins, 1860s. They measure the redshifts of stars, showing how fast they are moving.

Pluto discovered, 1930, at the Lowell Observatory, Arizona, by Clyde Tombaugh, who makes his discovery after comparing photographic plates, taken about a week apart.

THE **ATOM** AND THE **UNIVERSE**

From the early 19th century to the late 1920s, a series of breakthroughs occurred in the physical sciences. They transformed our understanding of the workings and structure of the world at both infinitesimally small scales and at the very largest, raising the possibility of an infinite cosmos.

These discoveries paved the way for the advances of the 1930s to the 1950s, from the realization that the Universe is expanding to the development of ideas on how energy and matter interact at the subatomic level. Through the coming together of ideas in cosmology and particle physics, these breakthroughs eventually led to the development of the Big Bang theory.

PROBING MATTER AND ENERGY

The idea that matter consists of atoms was first suggested by the ancient Greek, Democritus (see p.22). In the early 1800s, an Englishman, John Dalton, revived the idea. Dalton regarded atoms as indivisible, but around the turn of the 20th century experiments by scientists such as the New Zealander Ernest Rutherford proved that they have a substructure. Around the same

time, the German theoretical physicist Albert Einstein showed that matter and energy have an equivalence. Simultaneously, a new field of physics, quantum theory, was proposing (among other things) that light can behave either as a wave or as a stream of particles. By the late 1920s, it was known

◄ **Henrietta Leavitt**
Over 20 years, Leavitt studied 1,777 variable stars at the Harvard College Observatory before stumbling upon her key discovery.

> 66
>
> WHAT WE OBSERVE AS **MATERIAL BODIES AND FORCES** ARE NOTHING BUT **SHAPES AND VARIATIONS IN THE STRUCTURE OF SPACE**.
>
> 99

Erwin Schrödinger, Austrian theoretical physicist, 1887–1961

▶ **Understanding the atom**
From around 1800 until the mid-1920s, a step-by-step evolution occurred in the understanding of atomic structure. Later, from the late 1920s, physicists found that atomic nuclei have a substructure.

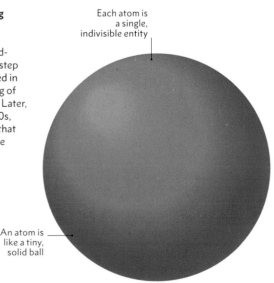

Each atom is a single, indivisible entity

An atom is like a tiny, solid ball

Dalton's atom (1803) English chemist John Dalton pictures atoms as extremely small spheres, like tiny billiard balls, that have no internal structure and cannot be subdivided, created, or destroyed.

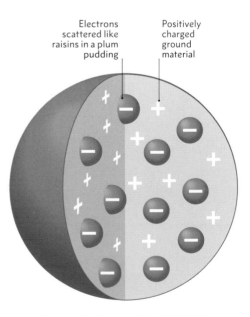

Electrons scattered like raisins in a plum pudding

Positively charged ground material

Thomson's plum pudding (1904) The discoverer of the electron, British physicist J.J. Thomson, suggests a "plum-pudding" model, with negatively charged electrons embedded in a positively charged sphere.

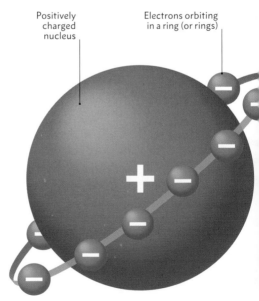

Positively charged nucleus

Electrons orbiting in a ring (or rings)

Nagaoka's Saturnian model (1904) Japanese physicist Hantaro Nagaoka proposes an atom has a central nucleus, around which the electrons orbit in one or more rings, like the rings of Saturn.

that atomic nuclei consist of protons and neutrons and are held together by a newly detected force, the strong force. Also discovered at this time was antimatter – subatomic particles that are identical to their matter equivalents except for opposite electrical change – and that the coming together of matter and antimatter can annihilate both, producing pure energy.

THE DISTANCES TO STARS

During roughly the same period, great advances were made in understanding the true scale of the cosmos. In 1838, the German astronomer Friedrich Bessell made the first reliable measurement of the distance to a star other than the Sun, using a method called stellar parallax. The star, although one of the closest to the Sun, seemed at the

A LIGHT-YEAR – THE DISTANCE LIGHT TRAVELS THROUGH SPACE IN A YEAR – IS ABOUT **9.5 TRILLION KILOMETRES (6 TRILLION MILES)**

time almost unimaginably far-off – what would now be called 10.3 light-years away. It was 1912 before a system was discovered for estimating the distance to many more remote stars. The discoverer was an

American called Henrietta Leavitt. Her breakthrough concerned a class of star called Cepheid variables, which cyclically vary in brightness. Leavitt found a link between the cycle period and brightness of these stars, meaning that if both could be measured a good estimate could be made of their distance from Earth. Within a few years, it became apparent that some stars are tens of thousands of light-years away, while some vaguely spiral-shaped nebulous patches in the sky, known at the time as "spiral nebulae", seemed to be millions of light-years away.

SHIFTING NEBULAE

Between 1912 and 1917, the American astronomer Vesto Slipher studied several "spiral nebulae" and realized that many were moving away from Earth at high speed, while a few were approaching Earth. He found this out by measuring a property of the light from the nebulae called redshift or blueshift. It seemed odd that the nebulae were moving at such speed relative to the rest of the galaxy. Partly prompted by Slipher's findings, in 1920 a formal debate was held in Washington, DC on whether these nebulae might be separate galaxies outside our own. The debate was inconclusive. But within a few years, the answer had been found by another American astronomer called Edwin Hubble (see pp.30–31).

Galaxy moving away from observer

Wavelength is stretched

Galaxy appears slightly redder to observer

Line in original spectrum

Redshifted spectrum line

REDSHIFT

◀ **Redshift**
When an object such as a galaxy is receding at high speed, light waves from it appear stretched. This causes features in the galaxy's spectrum, such as prominent lines, to shift towards the red (long wavelength) end. This is a redshift.

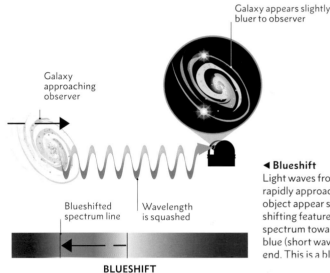

Galaxy approaching observer

Galaxy appears slightly bluer to observer

Blueshifted spectrum line

Wavelength is squashed

BLUESHIFT

◀ **Blueshift**
Light waves from a rapidly approaching object appear squashed, shifting features in the spectrum towards the blue (short wavelength) end. This is a blueshift.

Empty space

Electrons gain or lose energy on moving between orbits

Tiny, very dense, positively charged nucleus

Electrons moving around randomly

Nucleus as in Rutherford model

Electron orbit

Rutherford and the nucleus (1911)
Rutherford proves experimentally that an atom's nucleus is much smaller and denser than previously thought – and that much of an atom is empty space.

Bohr's electron orbits (1913) Danish physicist Niels Bohr proposes that electrons can move in spherical orbits, at fixed distances from the nucleus, and can "jump" between orbits.

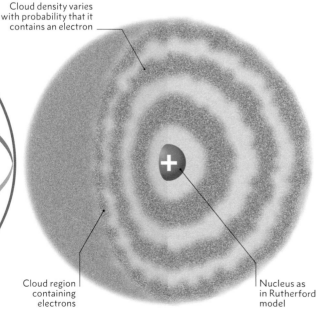

Cloud density varies with probability that it contains an electron

Cloud region containing electrons

Nucleus as in Rutherford model

Schrödinger's electron cloud model (1926) According to Austrian physicist Erwin Schrödinger's model, the locations of electrons in an atom are never certain and can be stated only in terms of probabilities.

THE UNIVERSE
GETS BIGGER

During the 1920s, two key breakthroughs led to a revolution in understanding of the size and nature of the Universe. Both were the result of discoveries made by the astronomer Edwin Hubble.

In 1919, Hubble arrived at Mount Wilson Observatory in California, aged 30. His arrival coincided with the completion of what was then the largest telescope in the world, a reflector with a 2.5m (100in) wide mirror, called the Hooker Telescope.

ENDING THE GALAXY DEBATE

At that time, the prevailing view was that the Universe consisted of just the Milky Way Galaxy, although in 1920 a famous debate (see p.29) had considered whether or not some vaguely spiral-shaped nebulae – fuzzy, star-containing objects – in the night sky might be collections of stars outside our own galaxy. Hubble, who had been studying these nebulae, already strongly suspected that they were outside our galaxy. In 1922–23, he used the Hooker Telescope to observe a class of stars called Cepheid variables in some of the nebulae, including what today is called the Andromeda Galaxy. Cepheid variables stars whose distances can be estimated by measuring their average brightness and the lengths of their cycles of brightness variation. As a result of his observations, in 1924 Hubble was able to announce that the Andromeda nebula and other spiral nebulae were far too distant to be part of the Milky Way and so must be galaxies outside our own. Almost overnight, the Universe had become a much bigger place than anyone had previously imagined.

RECEDING GALAXIES

Hubble next studied a phenomenon that had already been noted by an astronomer called Vesto Slipher: many of the spiral galaxies had large "redshifts" in their spectra, meaning that they were moving away from Earth at high speed (see p.29). Again by observing Cepheid variables, Hubble began measuring the distances to these galaxies and compared the distances to their redshifts. He noticed something remarkable: the more distant a galaxy was, the greater was its recessional velocity – a relationship that became known as Hubble's Law. Hubble published his results in 1929. Although he himself was initially sceptical, to other astronomers it was clear that only one conclusion could be drawn – the whole Universe must be expanding!

▼ **Photographic evidence**
These two (negative) photographic plates were used by Hubble to identify a specific Cepheid variable star in the Andromeda Galaxy. Studies on this star were crucial in confirming that the Andromeda Galaxy is outside the Milky Way.

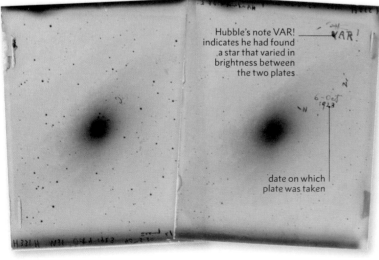

Hubble's note VAR! indicates he had found a star that varied in brightness between the two plates

date on which plate was taken

> ## THE **HISTORY OF ASTRONOMY** IS A **HISTORY OF RECEDING HORIZONS**.

Edwin Hubble, American astronomer, 1889–1953

10⁻⁶ SECONDS | THE FIRST PROTONS AND
AFTER BIG BANG | NEUTRONS FORM

3 MINUTES | THE FIRST ATOMIC
AFTER BIG BANG | NUCLEI FORM

380,000 YEARS | THE UNIVERSE BECOMES
AFTER BIG BANG | TRANSPARENT

13.6 BYA | THE FIRST
STARS FORM

The world's largest telescope
Completed in 1917, the Hooker Telescope was the world's largest telescope for about 30 years. Its glass mirrors, which had to be cast to an accuracy of a few millionths of an inch, had to be kept cool to prevent them warming up and becoming distorted.

13.8 BYA | THE UNIVERSE FORMS
IN THE BIG BANG

**10⁻³⁶ SECONDS
AFTER BIG BANG** | INFLATION
BEGINS

**10⁻³² SECONDS
AFTER BIG BANG** | INFLATION
ENDS

**10⁻¹² SECONDS
AFTER BIG BANG** | SEPARATION OF FUNDAMENTAL
FORCES IS COMPLETED

THE **EXPANDING** UNIVERSE

Edwin Hubble's work showed that many galaxies are receding from us at a rate proportional to their distance. It was soon deduced that the Universe must be expanding, but astronomers still had to understand the nature of this expansion and what the Universe is expanding from.

By the beginning of the 1930s, scientists were also starting to address a question that philosophers had been pondering for several millennia – has our Universe always existed or did it have a beginning? Physicists, mathematicians, and astronomers were now in a position to try answering this question.

it became clear to many astronomers that the Universe must indeed be expanding, although neither Hubble nor Einstein was convinced at first. Despite this, for many years credit for the discovery was given to Hubble, but today most experts agree it should be equally shared with Lemaître.

a "primeval atom" as he called it – which disintegrated in an explosion, giving rise to space and time and the expansion of the Universe. By 1933, Einstein (who had by now abandoned his cosmological constant) was in full agreement with Lemaître's theory, calling it "the most beautiful and satisfactory explanation of creation to which I have ever listened".

Simple physics dictates that the Universe compressed into a tiny point would be extremely hot. During the 1940s, Russian-American physicist George Gamow, and colleagues, worked out details of what might have happened during the exceedingly hot first few moments of a Lemaître-style universe. This included working out how the nuclei of light elements, such as helium, might have been forged, starting with just protons and neutrons. The work showed that a "hot" early universe, evolving into what is observed today, is at least theoretically feasible. In a 1949 radio interview, the British astronomer Fred Hoyle coined the term "Big Bang" for the model of the Universe Lemaître and Gamow had been developing. At last, Lemaître's startling hypothesis had a name, which has stuck ever since.

> "
> THE **RADIUS OF SPACE BEGAN AT ZERO**; THE FIRST STAGES OF THE EXPANSION CONSISTED OF A **RAPID EXPANSION** DETERMINED BY THE MASS OF THE INITIAL ATOM.
> "
>
> **Georges Lemaître**, astronomer, 1894–1966

EINSTEIN'S POSSIBLE UNIVERSES
The story of how scientists came to realize that the Universe is expanding began in 1915 with the publication of Albert Einstein's general theory of relativity. This theory is a description of how gravity works at the largest scales, and it defines what possible universes can exist. Part of Einstein's theory consists of a set of equations that have to be solved to give a description of the long-term, large-scale behaviour of the Universe.

Einstein's initial solution to his equations suggested the Universe is contracting, but he could not believe this, so he introduced a "fix" – an expansion-inducing factor called the cosmological constant – into his theory to allow for a static universe. In 1927, the Belgian astronomer Georges Lemaître, who had studied Einstein's equations and heard of Hubble's measurements of galaxy distances, proposed that the whole of space is expanding – but his hypothesis failed to attract widespread attention. After Hubble released his findings about receding galaxies in 1929,

DISCOVERING THE BIG BANG
If the Universe is expanding, and the clock is run backwards, then the further back in time you look, the denser the Universe becomes. But, as Lemaître reasoned, one can only go so far before the Universe is crushed into an infinitely dense point. So in 1931, he suggested that the Universe was initially a single, extremely dense particle –

▶ **Expanding space**
The Universe's expansion is most accurately thought of in terms of space itself expanding and carrying objects with it – called cosmological expansion – rather than galaxies and galaxy clusters moving away from each other "through" space.

▼ **Georges Lemaître**
Arguably the first person to propose that the Universe is expanding, Lemaître was a priest and physicist as well as an astronomer.

At the beginning of time, all matter was concentrated in a tiny particle – Lemaître's "primeval atom" – which exploded

Early galaxy clusters were closer together than they are today

Free gas and dust not yet absorbed into galaxies

Each disc represents a galaxy

A galaxy's velocity is estimated from measurements of its redshift

The slope of the line gives a value for the Hubble Constant

A galaxy's distance is estimated by taking measurements from some of its variable stars

RECESSIONAL VELOCITY (km per second) — 20,000 / 15,000 / 10,000 / 5,000

DISTANCE FROM EARTH (millions of light-years) — 0 / 30 / 60 / 90 / 120

▲ The Hubble Constant

If the velocities of a number of galaxies are plotted against their distances, a "best fit" line can be drawn close to all the plotted points. The slope of the line is an estimate of the Hubble Constant, itself a measure of the rate of the Universe's expansion.

At a local scale, gravity dominates over expansion, holding galaxy clusters together

Over time, the space between galaxies and galaxy clusters empties out as free gas and dust are pulled into galaxies

In the 1930s, it was assumed that the rate of expansion was at or near a uniform rate – with just slight slowing due to gravity

All galaxy clusters are gradually moving away from each other – there is no centre to the expansion

Some galaxies gradually develop spiral shapes

THE **BIG BANG**

Since the 1930s, when the Big Bang theory was first proposed, physicists and cosmologists have been testing and developing the theory and filling in the details of the first moments of the Universe.

Part of the work to improve Big Bang theory has been carried out by experiments in which high-energy particles are collided to re-create Big Bang-like conditions (see pp.36–37), and part has been purely theoretical, involving the formulation of equations and models. During the experimental side of this journey, many new subatomic particles have been discovered. Another focus of research has been the fundamental forces that govern particle interactions. It has been known since the 1930s that there are four of these forces: gravity, the electromagnetic force, the strong force, and the weak interaction. During the Big Bang, it is theorized that these forces were initially unified. Then, as the Universe cooled, they split off, possibly triggering new phases of the Big Bang. Gradually, physicists have fitted all the known particles and the forces into a scheme called the Standard Model of particle physics.

One important change to the original theory was made in the 1980s by the American physicist Alan Guth. He proposed that at a very early stage a part of the Universe underwent an extremely fast expansion called cosmic inflation. Guth's idea helped explain some aspects of the Universe today, including why at the largest scales matter and energy seem to be distributed very smoothly. The reality of cosmic inflation is now widely accepted.

 Up quark   Down quark — There are six types of quark. Up and down quarks are the most stable and common.

 Electron — This tiny subatomic particle has a negative electrical charge.

 Gluon — By carrying the strong nuclear force, gluons hold quarks together.

Photon — A photon is a tiny packet of light or other electromagnetic radiation.

 Higgs boson — This particle is associated with a field that gives mass to other particles.

▲ Fundamental particles
These particles are not, so far as is known, made of smaller particles. Some, such as quarks, are building blocks of matter. Others, like gluons and photons, are force-carrier particles.

 Proton — A proton is made of two up quarks and one down quark plus gluons.

 Neutron — Two down quarks and one up quark, plus gluons, make up a neutron.

▲ Composite particles
These particles are composed of other smaller particles. Scores of different composite particles have been identified, but protons and neutrons are the only stable types.

 Up antiquark   Down antiquark — For each of the six types of quark there is a corresponding type called an antiquark.

 Positron — A positron is the positively charged equivalent of the electron.

 Anti-proton — Two up antiquarks and one down antiquark, plus gluons, form an anti-proton.

 Anti-neutron — This consists of two down antiquarks and one up antiquark, plus gluons.

▲ Antiparticles
These are particles with the same mass but an opposite electric charge to their equivalent particles.

HYDROGEN ATOM

HELIUM-4 ATOM

HELIUM-3 ATOM

DEUTERIUM ATOM

100 million light-years diameter

2,700°C

380,000 YEARS

8 FIRST ATOMS
Electrons combine with protons to form hydrogen atoms and with other nuclei to form deuterium (heavy hydrogen), helium, and lithium atoms. As electrons are now bound up in atoms, they no longer interfere with photons, which are free to travel through space as radiation, and the Universe becomes transparent.

Photons can now move freely without colliding with free electrons

LITHIUM 7 NUCLEUS

10,000°C

1000 YEARS

100,000°C

DEUTERIUM NUCLEUS

1 YEAR

HELIUM-4 NUCLEUS

HYDROGEN NUCLEUS (FREE PROTON)

1 million °C

HELIUM-3 NUCLEUS

1 DAY

10 million °C

7 FIRST NUCLEI
Collisions between protons and neutrons begin forming the nuclei of helium-4 and small amounts of other nuclei, such as helium-3 and lithium-7. All the neutrons are mopped up by these reactions, but many free protons remain.

1 hour

100 million °C

3 MINUTES

1 billion °C

60 seconds

LITHIUM-7 ATOM

1 billion trillion°C

HIGGS BOSON

2 GRAND UNIFIED ERA

This era begins when gravity splits off from the other fundamental forces. During this short time, matter and energy are in a fluidly interchangeable form called mass-energy.

FORCES

Gravity separates out

10⁻⁴³ SECONDS

1km diameter

1 THE BIG BANG

Space, time, and an intense burst of energy appear suddenly and simultaneously. The state of the Universe during the first 10⁻⁴³ seconds – the Planck Era – is uncertain, but it is inconceivably hot and the four fundamental forces are unified.

DIAMETER

PARTICLES

TEMPERATURE

10⁻³⁶ SECONDS

Pairs of quarks and antiquarks form and then immediately annihilate each other

3 INFLATION BEGINS

The Universe undergoes a short period of extreme inflation, during which a fantastic amount of mass-energy comes into existence. Around this time, the strong force splits off from the two remaining fundamental forces. The Universe at this point is dominated by photons (packets of electromagnetic energy).

10⁻¹² SECONDS

Strong nuclear force separates out

100 million km diameter

1,000km diameter

1 million km diameter

1 million trillion°C

100,000 trillion°C

10,000 trillion°C

1,000 trillion°C

100 trillion°C

5 FINAL SEPARATION

The weak interaction separates from the electromagnetic force, and the fundamental forces and laws of physics become as they are today.

10⁻³² SECONDS

10 trillion trillion°C

4 INFLATION ENDS

As inflation ends, a seething mass of particles and antiparticles, such as quark-antiquark pairs, form spontaneously from energy and then annihilate back to energy. The sea of particles is sometimes referred to as a quark-gluon plasma. The temperature of the Universe at this stage is still many trillion trillion degrees Celsius.

Residue of particles results from slight excess of particles over antiparticles

Antimatter freezeout The Universe has cooled to the point where no more particle-antiparticle pairs form out of energy.

1 trillion km diameter

Quarks are bound into heavier particles, such as protons, by gluons

100 billion km diameter

10⁻⁶ SECONDS

10 trillion°C

6 FIRST PROTONS AND NEUTRONS

The Universe has cooled sufficiently that quarks start becoming bound together by gluons into composite particles, such as protons and neutrons, and antiquarks form into antiprotons and antineutrons.

1 SECOND

0 billion°C

Physics on a grand scale
The large, barrel-shaped machine undergoing a refit here is a part of the LHC called the electromagnetic calorimeter. It measures the energies of electrons and photons to a high degree of accuracy.

RE-CREATING THE **BIG BANG**

For years, researchers at the European Organization for Nuclear Research (CERN) have used the world's largest particle accelerator – the Large Hadron Collider (LHC) – to smash particles together at extreme speeds to re-create conditions that existed shortly after the Big Bang.

The LHC is the largest, most sophisticated scientific instrument ever built. Located underground on the French-Swiss border, it accelerates two beams of high-energy particles, moving in opposite directions, through pipes connected in a ring with a circumference of almost 27km (17 miles). From time to time, the beams are made to collide, and the results – which typically include the appearance of short-lived, exotic particles – are recorded by detectors around the ring. The purpose of the LHC is to study the range of subatomic particles that can exist and the laws governing their interactions.

Physicists hope these experiments will refine their ideas about what happened in the Big Bang and help them to investigate some poorly understood cosmic phenomena. The Big Bang-type conditions are re-created only in miniature – so there is no chance the experiments could trigger a new Big Bang and the appearance of a new Universe.

NEW DISCOVERIES
One success of the LHC has been to create a quark-gluon plasma, a maelstrom of free quarks and gluons (see p.34) that is thought to have existed for up to a microsecond (a millionth of a second) after the start of the Big Bang. This was achieved in 2015 by colliding protons with lead nuclei, creating minuscule fireballs in which everything broke down momentarily into quarks and gluons.

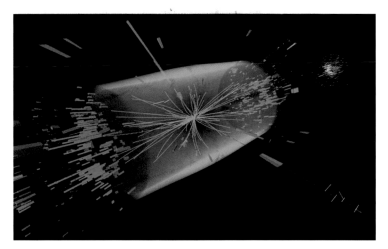

In 2012, a long sought-after, high-mass, extremely short-lived particle called the Higgs boson was detected. Its existence confirmed the presence of an energy field, the Higgs field, that imparts mass to particles passing through it. The significance of this for the Big Bang is that it explains how in the first moments of the Universe particles such as quarks acquired mass, causing them to slow down and combine to form composite particles, such as protons and neutrons.

Other notable successes include the detection in 2014 of a pentaquark (consisting of four quarks and an antiquark). This discovery may allow scientists to study in more detail the strong force that holds quarks together.

▲ **Seeking the Higgs boson**
This computer graphic shows a particle collision recorded during the search for the Higgs boson. It displays features that could be expected from the decay of a Higgs boson into two other bosons. One of these decays to a pair of electrons (green lines) and the other to a pair of particles called muons (red lines).

> ❝
> WE HAVE MADE THE DISCOVERY OF **A NEW PARTICLE** – A **COMPLETELY NEW PARTICLE** – WHICH IS MOST PROBABLY VERY DIFFERENT FROM ALL THE OTHER PARTICLES.
> ❞
>
> **Rolf-Dieter Heuer**, Director of CERN, 1948–, on the discovery of the Higgs boson

BEYOND THE BIG BANG

Although the Big Bang model is now accepted by the vast majority of astronomers, additional evidence is continually being sought to support it. There are also some problems with the theory that need to be addressed and some aspects that have yet to be understood.

Red-orange spots
These have a temperature just 0.0002°C higher than the average CMB temperature

All-sky projection
The map is a projection of measurements collected across the whole sky

A general point in favour of the Big Bang model is that an important assumption on which it is based, the cosmological principle (see opposite page), has so far held true. The model also works within the framework of general relativity (see p.32), which is today considered a pillar of cosmology. However, these facts do not necessarily mean the Big Bang theory is correct. To be sure of its validity, specific positive evidence is needed – but there is no shortage of this.

SPECIFIC EVIDENCE

The most important positive evidence for the Big Bang is an extremely faint but uniform thermal radiation coming from the sky called the cosmic microwave background (CMB). Early supporters of the Big Bang theory predicted that this radiation should exist, and in 1964 it was detected by two American radio astronomers. The CMB arose soon after the Big Bang, when photons (small packets of radiant energy) were freed from interacting with matter and began to travel unhindered through space.

Further strong evidence comes from observations of deep space, looking back billions of years in time. Such observations have revealed objects called quasars (the highly energetic centres of galaxies) that no longer seem to exist today. Furthermore, the most distant galaxies – that is, galaxies as they existed 10–13 billion years ago – look different from closer, modern galaxies. These observations suggest the Universe is of a finite age and has evolved over time rather than been static and unchanging.

One other important piece of evidence comes from the predominance and proportions of the chemical elements hydrogen and helium in the Universe. The ratios of these two elements in their different forms (called isotopes) agree very closely with what is predicted by the Big Bang theory.

▼ Dark matter
In this image of a galaxy cluster over 7 billion light-years from Earth, called El Gordo ("The Fat One"), the blue haze indicates the distribution of dark matter – hard-to-detect matter that appears to bind galaxy clusters together gravitationally. The pink haze indicates X-ray emissions.

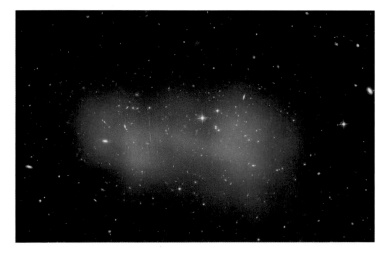

▲ The cosmic microwave background
The strength of the CMB measured by the Planck spacecraft is shown here as a temperature variation. Although the CMB is uniform across the sky, a finely graded scale has been used to show tiny variations as coloured spots.

UNANSWERED QUESTIONS

One major problem in cosmology in general is to shed light on the nature of "dark matter" and how it may have arisen in the Big Bang. Dark matter is an unknown substance that emits no light, heat, radio waves, nor any other kind of radiation – making it extremely hard to detect – but it does interact with other matter. Another challenge is to understand "dark energy". In 1998, it was discovered that the expansion of the Universe has been accelerating over the past 6 billion years. The reason for the acceleration is not known, but the mysterious phenomenon of dark energy has been proposed as the cause. Very little is known about it at present, but if dark energy exists, it must permeate the whole Universe.

> " WE CAN TRACE THINGS BACK TO **THE EARLIER STAGES OF THE BIG BANG**, BUT WE STILL DON'T KNOW **WHAT BANGED** AND **WHY IT BANGED**. THAT'S A CHALLENGE FOR **21ST-CENTURY SCIENCE**. "
>
> **Martin Rees**, British cosmologist, 1942–

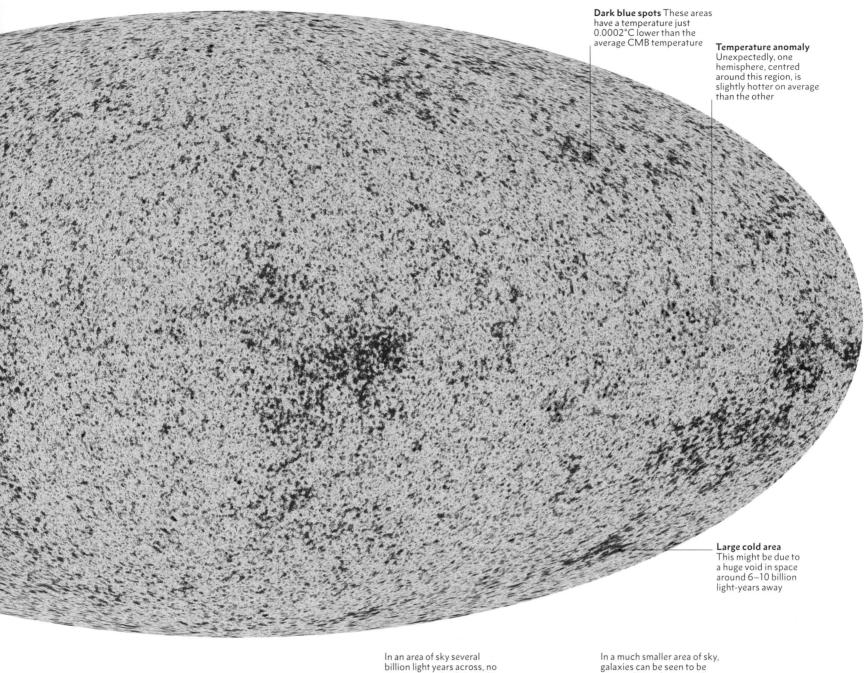

Dark blue spots These areas have a temperature just 0.0002°C lower than the average CMB temperature

Temperature anomaly Unexpectedly, one hemisphere, centred around this region, is slightly hotter on average than the other

Large cold area This might be due to a huge void in space around 6–10 billion light-years away

Other unanswered questions include why an excess of matter over antimatter appeared during the Universe's first few moments – without it, no atoms could ever have formed – and what caused the cosmic inflation that produced the smooth distribution of matter that we see in the Universe today. The final question is "what triggered the Big Bang?" and this, of course, may never be answered.

▶ **The cosmological principle**
This principle states that when viewed on a sufficiently large scale, the Universe is uniform, although on small scales there are clear variations in the distribution of objects such as galaxies. It follows from the cosmological principle that the Universe has no centre and no edges.

In an area of sky several billion light years across, no structure can be detected in the distribution of galaxies

In a much smaller area of sky, galaxies can be seen to be grouped into clusters rather than evenly distributed

5 BILLION LIGHT-YEARS ACROSS

150 MILLION LIGHT-YEARS ACROSS

4 MILLION LIGHT-YEARS ACROSS

THRESHOLD

STARS ARE **BORN**

With space, time, matter, and energy in place after the Big Bang, new powerhouses start to appear – stars. These form as matter is packed tighter and tighter together under the influence of gravity. The extremely high temperatures that result cause atoms to fuse together, releasing a huge amount of energy and opening the door to a new level of complexity in the Universe.

GOLDILOCKS CONDITIONS

The early Universe was shaped by two ingredients, both of which emerged while it was less than a second old. Gravity acted on tiny variations in the density of matter, setting in train processes that led to the formation of the first stars and galaxies and, ultimately, a far more complex Universe.

The nuclei of hydrogen atoms

The nuclei of helium atoms

Dark matter

Tiny variations in the density of matter

Gravity, which pulls matter together

Clumps of matter grow denser and hotter

What changed?

The early Universe consisted of hydrogen and helium – and another form of matter called dark matter. It was also completely without light. Under the influence of gravity, matter began to clump together. As it did so, it heated up until nuclear fusion reactions began, forming the first stars and lighting up the Universe. Over time, the new stars clustered together into galaxies.

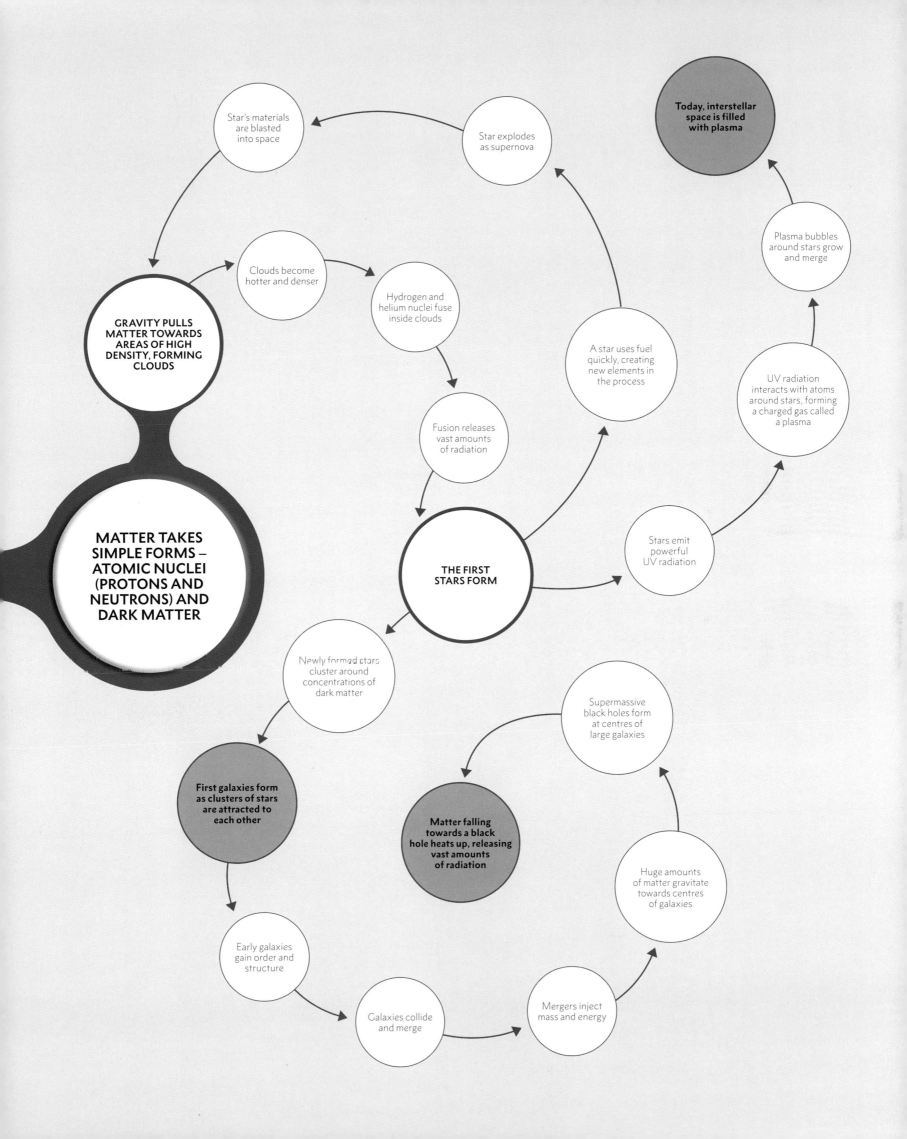

GRAVITY PULLS MATTER TOWARDS AREAS OF HIGH DENSITY, FORMING CLOUDS

MATTER TAKES SIMPLE FORMS – ATOMIC NUCLEI (PROTONS AND NEUTRONS) AND DARK MATTER

Star's materials are blasted into space

Star explodes as supernova

Today, interstellar space is filled with plasma

Clouds become hotter and denser

Hydrogen and helium nuclei fuse inside clouds

A star uses fuel quickly, creating new elements in the process

Plasma bubbles around stars grow and merge

Fusion releases vast amounts of radiation

UV radiation interacts with atoms around stars, forming a charged gas called a plasma

THE FIRST STARS FORM

Stars emit powerful UV radiation

Newly formed stars cluster around concentrations of dark matter

Supermassive black holes form at centres of large galaxies

First galaxies form as clusters of stars are attracted to each other

Matter falling towards a black hole heats up, releasing vast amounts of radiation

Huge amounts of matter gravitate towards centres of galaxies

Early galaxies gain order and structure

Galaxies collide and merge

Mergers inject mass and energy

THE **FIRST STARS**

TYPICAL FIRST-GENERATION STAR

THE SUN

For its first 200 million years, the Universe was a dark place. But things changed dramatically when clouds of gas collapsed to form the first stars. Inside, new chemical elements formed, and at the ends of their short lives the stars exploded, dispersing the elements into space.

During the Epoch of Recombination, 380,000 years after the Big Bang (see p.34), positively charged hydrogen and helium nuclei combined with negatively charged electrons to form neutral (uncharged) atoms. Until this point, collisions with free electrons had prevented photons of light from moving any distance in a straight line. Now the Universe became transparent to light,

although it was also dark, for there were no sources of light. It was a time cosmologists refer to as the Cosmic Dark Ages. Amid the dark soup of neutral gas was even darker stuff: dark matter. Scientists have little idea about the nature of dark matter, although they do know there is lots of it and that it is affected by gravity but doesn't interact with light or any other form of radiation.

HOW STARS FORM
Tiny variations in the density of the dark matter and the hydrogen and helium gases caused vast clouds of gas to collapse under the influence of gravity to form huge spherical clumps of matter. This would have happened without dark matter but much more slowly – so slowly that no stars would have formed to this day.

The enormous energy liberated in the collapse heated the balls of gas. At the increasing densities deep inside the balls of gas and as a result of the high temperatures

The Big Bang
13.8 BYA

The Universe is an opaque plasma of positively charged hydrogen and helium nuclei

Epoch of Recombination
380,000 years after Big Bang

Cosmic Dark Ages
13.796 to 13.4 BYA

The first stars form 13.6 BYA

Early star forming inside gas cloud

NEUTRAL HYDROGEN AND HELIUM ATOMS

Hydrogen and helium gases begin to clump together to form clouds

Filament of dark matter

▶ **Lighting up the early Universe**
The first stars formed about 200 million years after the Big Bang from clouds of hydrogen and helium gas. The intense ultraviolet light produced by these stars re-ionized the space around them, leaving behind charged atoms (or ions) and free electrons – and defining the character of interstellar space we see today.

▲ The size of early stars
According to astrophysicists' best models, most early stars were much larger than the Sun and hundreds of times as massive.

at their cores, hydrogen and helium nuclei collided, and some of them joined together, or fused. This nuclear fusion resulted in the production of more helium nuclei from the hydrogen nuclei, and new, heavier elements – including boron, carbon, and oxygen – from the helium nuclei (see pp.58–59).

The nuclear fusion inside the collapsing balls of gas released a huge amount of energy, enough to heat the gas to incredibly high temperatures. That made the gas expand, buoying it up against further collapse. The high temperature also made the balls of gas glow brightly – to become the first stars.

The extremely hot first stars emitted large amounts of powerful ultraviolet radiation that had far-reaching effects. When the intense radiation hit neutral hydrogen and

helium atoms still in space, its energy separated the electrons from their nuclei – just as they had been before the Epoch of Recombination. This "re-ionization" created a plasma bubble, of hydrogen ions, helium ions, and free electrons, in the space around each star. Interstellar space today is an extremely tenuous plasma that was created by this re-ionization, and nearly all radiation can pass through it.

SHORT LIVES
The first stars were large and massive: probably dozens of times the diameter of the Sun and with hundreds of times as much mass. Such stars burn out quickly. The first generation of stars probably only lived for a

◄ Early light
This is an artist's impression of CR7, a small, bright galaxy. At 12.7 billion light years away, CR7 appears as it was about a billion years after the Big Bang. It represents the best evidence so far of first-generation stars.

few million years, compared to several billion years for an average star in later generations. As the hydrogen and helium "fuel" began to dwindle at the cores of the stars, they cooled, enabling the collapse to begin again, eventually causing the stars to explode as supernovas (see pp.60–61). The explosions threw a cocktail of new elements and the remaining un-fused hydrogen and helium out into space. This cocktail formed the ingredients of a second generation of stars.

FIRST-GENERATION STARS LIVED ONLY **A FEW MILLION YEARS** BEFORE EXPLODING AS **VIOLENT SUPERNOVAS**

Stars form in clusters that coincide with concentrations of dark matter

The first stars explode as supernovas
13.5 BYA

Re-ionization starts
13.45 BYA

Ultraviolet radiation from hot star creates bubble of ionized plasma

Clusters of stars are drawn together into dwarf galaxies
13.4 BYA

Dwarf galaxies combine to form larger galaxies, including spiral galaxies

As re-ionization continues, bubbles of plasma merge, and eventually the Universe is filled with plasma

THE **PUZZLE** OF **GRAVITY**

▼ Isaac Newton
In the late 1680s, Newton published both his Universal Law of Gravitation – the first scientific theory of gravity – and his three laws of motion.

Gravity, or gravitation, plays a crucial role in the formation of stars and planets because it causes matter to clump together. The modern theory of gravity, Einstein's general theory of relativity, accurately explains its effects. Nevertheless, the true nature of gravity remains a mystery.

The ancient Greek philosopher Aristotle supposed that Earth is at the centre of the Universe and that everything has a natural tendency to move towards it. According to Aristotle, heavier things have more of this tendency and so fall faster. Although Aristotle's simple notion was superficially supported by observations, experiments by Italian scientist Galileo Galilei in the 17th century showed that he was wrong. Galileo's experiments led him to predict, correctly, that in the absence of air resistance, all falling objects would accelerate downwards at the same rate. English scientist Isaac Newton made sense of Galileo's prediction with his Universal Law of Gravitation.

NEWTON'S GRAVITY
Newton realised that what makes things fall to the ground here on Earth also keeps the Moon in orbit. He proposed that gravity is a force and derived an equation that could predict the strength of the force between any two objects. According to Newton's law, the force depends on the masses of the objects and the distance between their centres.

By combining his law of gravitation with his laws of motion, Newton was able to account for the motions of any object under the influence of gravity – from projectiles on Earth to planets in space. His theory was accepted for over 200 years – and scientists still use his equation in most situations where they need to calculate the effects of gravity. However, in the 19th century,

Under the influence of gravity, the planet falls towards the star, following a curved orbital path

Gravitational force on planet

Gravitational force on star is equal to force on planet

Star hardly moves because of its large mass

STAR

PLANET

Without gravity, the planet would follow a straight line path

▲ Newton's theory
In Newton's theory, a star and planet exert an attractive force on each other. Both are subject to an equal force, but the effect on the planet is more obvious because it has a lower mass.

> ❝
> **NEWTON** HIMSELF WAS BETTER AWARE OF THE **WEAKNESSES IN HIS INTELLECTUAL EDIFICE** THAN THE GENERATIONS OF LEARNED SCIENTISTS WHICH FOLLOWED HIM.
> ❞
>
> **Albert Einstein**, German physicist, 1879–1955

calculations of the orbit of planet Mercury, at odds with observations, showed Newton's theory to be flawed. In 1915, German physicist Albert Einstein proposed a radical new theory of gravitation – the general theory of relativity – that could accurately predict the orbit of Mercury. And according to Einstein's theory, gravity is not a force at all.

EINSTEIN'S GRAVITY

General relativity is an extension of special relativity, a theory Einstein published in 1905. Special relativity was an attempt to reconcile Newton's laws of motion with the theory of electromagnetism, developed in the 1860s. To do that, Einstein had to abandon the idea that space and time are absolute: people in motion relative to each other measure distances and intervals of time differently – the differences only become significant at extremely high relative speeds. One of the direct consequences of special relativity was the realization that time is a dimension, just like the three dimensions of space, and that all four exist in a four-dimensional grid called spacetime; objects therefore move through spacetime, not space.

In order to generalize special relativity to include gravity, Einstein realized that objects with mass distort spacetime. The more massive an object, the greater the distortion. Objects travelling freely through distorted spacetime follow curved paths. So projectiles and planets are simply following the equivalent of straight line paths, but in distorted spacetime. A force is needed to change an object's path. For example, the ground pushes upwards on a person's feet, which stops the person from following a path that would take him or her "freefalling" towards the centre of Earth. For a star, the expansion of the hot gas of which it is made provides the force necessary to stop it collapsing – expansion that lasts as long as the star produces heat (see pp.56–57).

EINSTEIN'S PREDICTIONS

The general theory of relativity has been tested many times, to extremely high precision. It has also made several important predictions, such as the idea that light must also follow the curved paths of distorted spacetime. The result is a phenomenon called gravitational lensing, which is evident in the distorted views of distant galaxies whose light has been bent as it passed close to nearby galaxies. Another key prediction is the existence of gravitational waves: ripples in spacetime emanating at the speed of light from any very energetic event. In 2015, scientists detected the first hard evidence of the existence of gravitational waves, produced by the merging of two black holes.

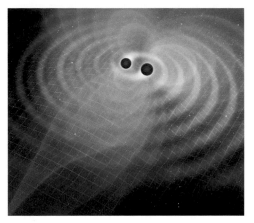

◄ **Gravitational waves**
The first gravitational waves ever detected resulted from the merger of two black holes. Here, the waves are represented as ripples in a two-dimensional sheet of spacetime. These ripples were detected by sensitive equipment on Earth.

Despite the success of general relativity, the theory is at odds with quantum mechanics, an equally well-tested cornerstone of modern science. Quantum mechanics accurately describes the behaviour of matter at the atomic and subatomic scales, while gravity accurately describes the behaviour of matter at much larger scales – but the two theories are incompatible. The search for a quantum theory of gravity is a major concern of modern physics, and it is likely that Einstein's theory of gravity will be reinterpreted or superseded as part of a grand theory that can describe the behaviour of matter at all scales. One thing is certain: the puzzle of gravity is not yet solved.

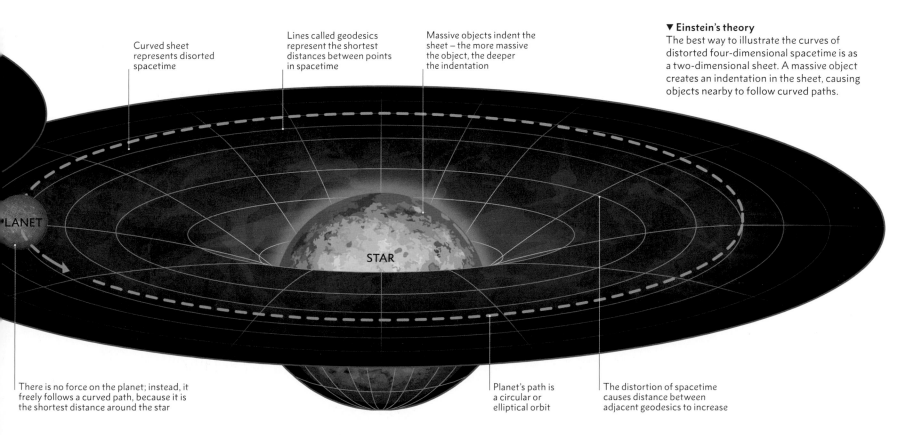

Curved sheet represents distorted spacetime

Lines called geodesics represent the shortest distances between points in spacetime

Massive objects indent the sheet – the more massive the object, the deeper the indentation

▼ **Einstein's theory**
The best way to illustrate the curves of distorted four-dimensional spacetime is as a two-dimensional sheet. A massive object creates an indentation in the sheet, causing objects nearby to follow curved paths.

PLANET

STAR

There is no force on the planet; instead, it freely follows a curved path, because it is the shortest distance around the star

Planet's path is a circular or elliptical orbit

The distortion of spacetime causes distance between adjacent geodesics to increase

THE **FIRST GALAXIES**

A galaxy is a vast congregation of stars orbiting a common centre. The first galaxies began to form soon after the first stars, around clumps of dark matter. Mutual gravitational attraction caused these small galaxies to merge, each merger sparking new flurries of star birth.

▼ Galaxy evolution
In the absence of direct observations, astrophysicists construct simulations to test their theories of how the first galaxies formed. The images below are snapshots from one of those simulations.

Dark matter was crucial in the creation of the first galaxies, just as it was for the formation of the first stars (see pp.44–45). Slight variations in the density of dark matter in the early Universe caused the dark matter and ordinary matter – in the form of hydrogen and helium gas – to clump together. The dark matter formed a network of sinuous filaments and nodes, or haloes, at various scales. The clumping process drove the formation of individual stars as the concentrations of matter began to rotate and heat up, eventually resulting in nuclear fusion (see pp.56–57). At a larger scale, the same process also produced clusters of stars. Each star cluster, plus its surrounding gas, was attracted to neighbouring clusters, and the Universe's first galaxies were born.

GROWING GALAXIES

As matter fell towards matter, the dark matter haloes grew in size, and so did the galaxies. Like water draining down a plug hole, much of the matter began to spin as it fell, so that it went into orbit around the most dense, central part of the halo. As a result, galaxies that began as irregularly shaped masses began to gain order and

DARK MATTER   ORDINARY MATTER

GALAXY

0.6 billion years old Dark matter clumps together due to gravity, attracting hydrogen and helium gas (red in the bottom image) into its filaments and nodes. Clusters of stars (blue dots) form where the density is particularly high.

1.0 billion years old The dark matter has further collapsed in on itself, increasing the gravitational attraction on stars and gas. A small, irregularly shaped galaxy forms, its stars orbiting a point at its centre.

structure. Many formed spinning discs, with spiral arms; others were egg-shaped elliptical galaxies. But with each merger, the structure was disrupted, only to be regained or developed millions or billions of years later. The mergers injected energy and mass, too, and the rate of star formation and star death increased. Each star inside a young galaxy inevitably ended its life in a powerful supernova explosion that filled the galaxy with the elements that would seed the next generation of stars and even planets.

SUPERMASSIVE BLACK HOLES

Although much of the gas and many of the stars stayed in orbit around the centre of each galaxy, huge amounts of the matter fell towards the centre. In large galaxies, the density at the centre increased so much that a supermassive black hole (see p.47) formed there. As matter jostled its way in towards the growing black hole, friction heated it to extremely high temperatures, releasing vast

amounts of energy as high-energy (short wavelength) X-rays, ultraviolet radiation, and bright visible light. Astronomers first detected these energetic galaxies in the 1950s; they made the discoveries with early radio telescopes, since the short-wavelength radiation has been stretched to such an extent by the expansion of space that it arrives as long-wavelength infrared and radio waves. Most large galaxies in the Universe today, including our own, still have supermassive black holes at their centres.

◀ **Merging galaxies**
Astronomers observe many merging galaxies. Shown here is NGC 4676 – also known as the Mice Galaxies – a pair of colliding galaxies around 290 million light-years away.

> " [IN SIMULATIONS] YOU CAN MAKE **STARS AND GALAXIES** THAT LOOK LIKE THE REAL THING. BUT IT IS THE **DARK MATTER** THAT IS **CALLING THE SHOTS**. "

Professor Carlos Frenk, cosmologist, 1951–

.7 **billion years old** Several galaxies have come together, forming a much larger structure millions of light-years across. Each small galaxy that merges brings new material, and the increasing density eads to a burst of star formation.

13.6 billion years old The galaxy has become stable, merging with others less often. It has a spiral shape, like that of a hurricane, and a supermassive black hole at its core. Fragmented debris of its progenitor galaxies lies around it.

HUBBLE EXTREME
DEEP FIELD

Taken by the Hubble Space Telescope, the eXtreme Deep Field records faint light from thousands of galaxies in a small area of sky. The deepest view of space ever captured, it provides the best evidence we have about the early Universe's stars and galaxies.

When we look out into space, we are looking back in time, because the light from distant objects left a long time ago. Light that left a galaxy 5 billion years ago will appear extremely faint, however bright the galaxy was at the time. Imaging such a dim object requires a long exposure time – not a fraction of a second, like a typical photograph, but millions of seconds.

In 1995, astronomers pointed NASA's Hubble Space Telescope at a tiny patch of sky for over 140 hours and combined a total of 342 images into a single, remarkable image called the Hubble Deep Field. In 2004, NASA scientists produced the even more remarkable Hubble Ultra Deep Field – an image with an even longer exposure, on a different patch of sky. Observations on that area continued over the next eight years, and the addition of an infrared camera to the telescope in 2009 meant that objects whose light has been redshifted (see p.29) beyond the visible spectrum and into the infrared could also be seen. The new observations were combined with the Ultra Deep Field, and the result was published in 2012 as the Hubble eXtreme Deep Field (XDF). Light from the most distant galaxies in the XDF took more than 13 billion years to reach us, and they appear one ten-billionth as bright as the dimmest thing visible to the naked eye.

Containing evidence of galaxy mergers (see p.49), extreme redshifting, and gravitational lensing (see p.47), the Hubble XDF is a significant piece of evidence in support of the most convincing theories we have about the evolution of the Universe.

Relatively nearby galaxy looks red as its stars are running low on hydrogen fuel

This foreground star is in our own galaxy

Light from this very faint galaxy, called UDFj-39546284, took 13.4 billion light-years to reach Earth

This relatively nearby object is a spiral galaxy, like the Milky Way, seen front-on

▶ **Looking back** The largest, brightest objects in the XDF include mature galaxies that appear as they were about 5–9 billion years ago – when they had grown by merging and were populated by second- or third-generation stars. Galaxies in the background are smaller: young, irregular galaxies seen as they were over 9 billion years ago. The foreground is relatively empty because the XDF team chose an area almost devoid of nearby galaxies and stars in our own galaxy.

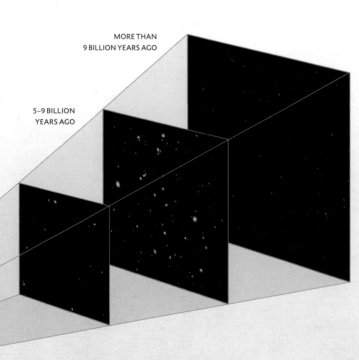

MORE THAN 9 BILLION YEARS AGO

5–9 BILLION YEARS AGO

LESS THAN 5 BILLION YEARS AGO

More recent galaxies are the result of mergers of smaller, older galaxies

Distant galaxy appears red due to redshifting of its light

Field of view

Next to the full Moon, the Hubble eXtreme Deep Field covers a tiny area: less than one twenty-millionth of the area of the whole sky. To see the image at its true size, you would need to hold this page about 300m (1,000ft) away. It is remarkable that more than 7,000 galaxies can be seen in such a small field of view – and to think that each tiny dot in the image is a collection of millions or billions of stars frozen in time.

XDF's field of view, with the Moon for comparison

Early galaxies

The XDF gives astronomers a unique view of galaxies as they were during the Universe's first few hundred millions of years, when they were relatively small, irregularly shaped groups of stars. As they collided and merged, most became spiral shaped because the collisions resulted in rotation. The Universe was smaller when the light captured in the XDF left the young galaxies. As space has expanded, the light has been "stretched", shifting its frequencies towards or even beyond the red end of the spectrum, which is why so many of the XDF galaxies appear reddish.

Close-up of heavily redshifted galaxy merger

ELEMENTS ARE
FORGED

We all come from dying stars. All the elements that make up our world originated there. Stars are hungry, and as some of them use up their fuel, age, and finally die, they collapse and go out with a tremendous explosion of energy. But from star death come new building blocks – the elements – pushed out into the Universe to start something new.

GOLDILOCKS CONDITIONS

The formation of the first stars had profound consequences. As well as lighting up the Universe, stars act as chemical factories, producing new chemical elements that provide the raw materials for everything else in the Universe, including living things.

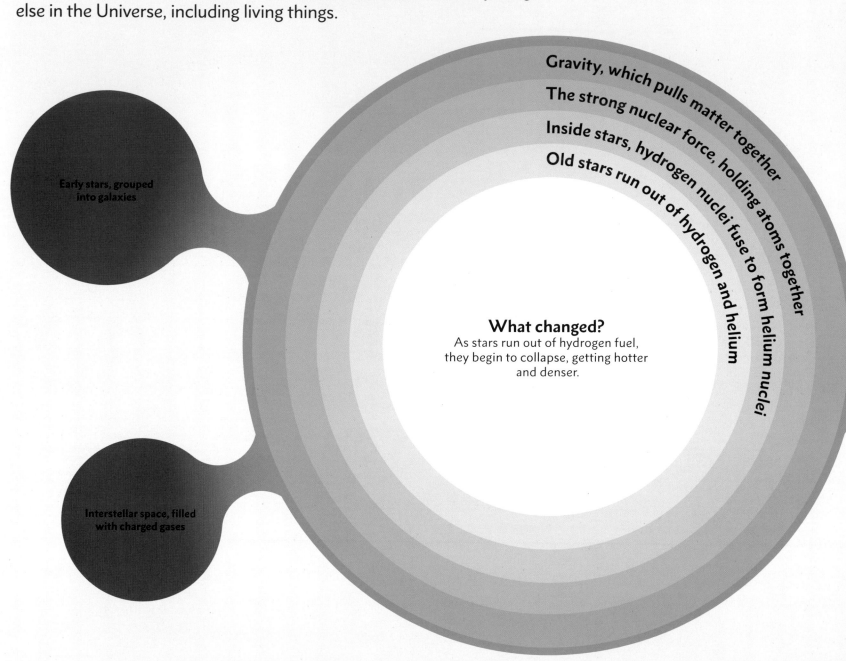

Early stars, grouped into galaxies

Interstellar space, filled with charged gases

Gravity, which pulls matter together

The strong nuclear force, holding atoms together

Inside stars, hydrogen nuclei fuse to form helium nuclei

Old stars run out of hydrogen and helium

What changed?
As stars run out of hydrogen fuel, they begin to collapse, getting hotter and denser.

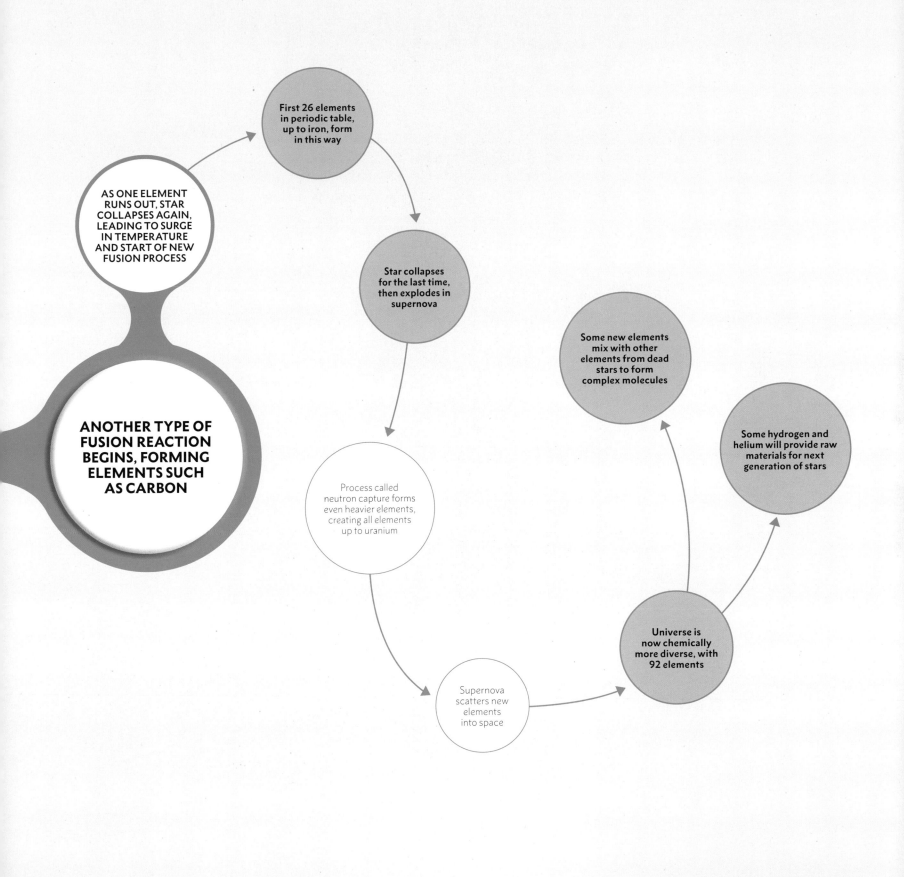

AS ONE ELEMENT RUNS OUT, STAR COLLAPSES AGAIN, LEADING TO SURGE IN TEMPERATURE AND START OF NEW FUSION PROCESS

First 26 elements in periodic table, up to iron, form in this way

ANOTHER TYPE OF FUSION REACTION BEGINS, FORMING ELEMENTS SUCH AS CARBON

Star collapses for the last time, then explodes in supernova

Some new elements mix with other elements from dead stars to form complex molecules

Some hydrogen and helium will provide raw materials for next generation of stars

Process called neutron capture forms even heavier elements, creating all elements up to uranium

Universe is now chemically more diverse, with 92 elements

Supernova scatters new elements into space

THE LIFE CYCLE OF A STAR

Just like humans, stars are born, grow old, and die. The way a star ends its days depends on its mass, with the largest stars exploding as supernovas. These detonations furnished, and continue to furnish, the Universe with heavier elements, recycling material ready for it to be turned into new stars.

Consequently, the life cycle of stars also played a crucial role in the emergence of life on Earth. Essential ingredients – including the calcium in your bones and the iron in your blood – were forged inside stars, only for supernovas to spread them far and wide.

Stars come in a vast array of sizes. Astronomers classify them into seven main groups from largest to smallest denoted by the letters O, B, A, F, G, K, and M. Our Sun is a G star, meaning there are bigger and smaller stars out there than our own. The smallest stars, known as dwarfs, are the most common. M stars, for example, make up more than 75 per cent of all stars. By contrast, O stars account for just 0.00003 per cent. The size of a star also

A **SUPERGIANT STAR** CAN HAVE A VOLUME **8 BILLION** TIMES THAT OF **THE SUN**

governs how long it will live. The larger the star, the quicker it will consume its nuclear material. O stars live fast and die young, often dying out within just a few million years, whereas the smallest stars can eke out their existence for trillions of years.

LIFE STAGES

Stars begin their lives as protostars, formed from clouds of interstellar dust (see pp.44–45). Nuclear processes in a star's core then shore it up against gravitational collapse. For most of a star's life, this

balance is maintained, but things change when fusion eventually stops. Astronomers refer to a star still fusing hydrogen into helium as a main-sequence star. Once this fusion ceases, the star evolves off the main sequence.

For all but the smallest stars, the core contracts and the temperature rises to around 100 million degrees Celsius. This is hot enough for helium to fuse into carbon, which creates enough energy to upset the balance the other way and the star bloats outwards. Then, depending on size, it will either turn into a planetary nebula with a white dwarf at the centre, or detonate as a supernova, leaving behind a neutron star or black hole.

▼ Sun-like star
Stars like the Sun typically live for around 10 billion years. After entering a red giant phase, they form a planetary nebula – and usually do not explode as supernovas.

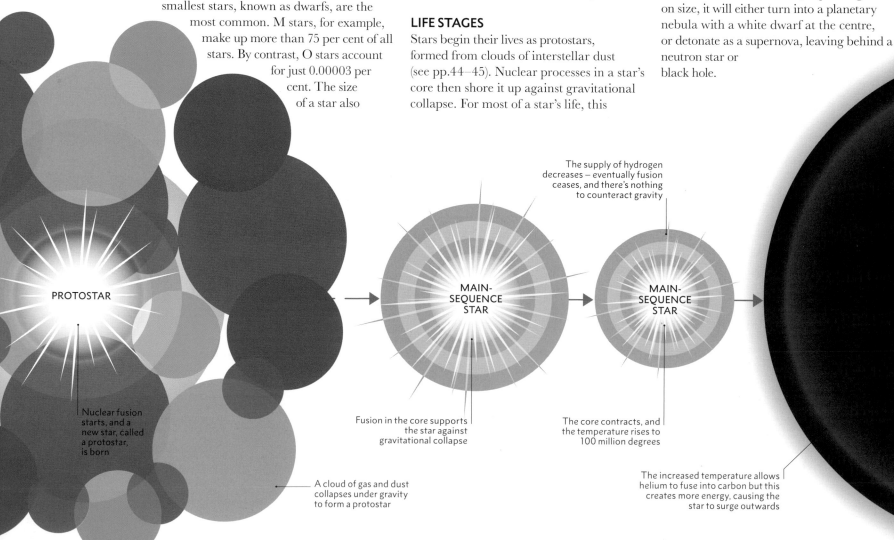

PROTOSTAR

Nuclear fusion starts, and a new star, called a protostar, is born

A cloud of gas and dust collapses under gravity to form a protostar

MAIN-SEQUENCE STAR

Fusion in the core supports the star against gravitational collapse

The supply of hydrogen decreases – eventually fusion ceases, and there's nothing to counteract gravity

MAIN-SEQUENCE STAR

The core contracts, and the temperature rises to 100 million degrees

The increased temperature allows helium to fuse into carbon but this creates more energy, causing the star to surge outwards

▶ **Low-mass star**

These smaller stars are able to mix their interiors, meaning that the core's supply of hydrogen gets replenished by the outer layers falling towards the centre – so the core doesn't contract to start helium fusion.

▶ **High-mass star**

The evolution of more massive stars is initially similar to that of Sun-like stars. But they form red supergiants, instead of red giants, and eventually supernovas. The star's ultimate fate depends on its mass.

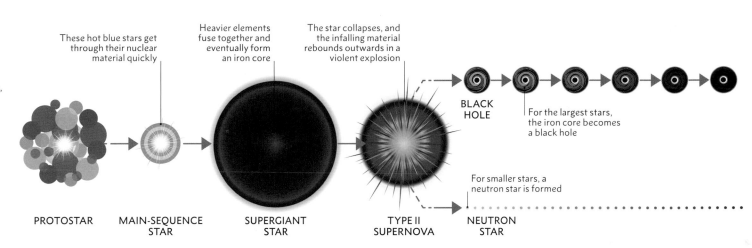

Stars less than a quarter of the Sun's mass don't become red giants

Hydrogen fusion can continue for trillions of years

The star finally runs out of fuel and forms a white dwarf

PROTOSTAR — MAIN-SEQUENCE STAR — ... — RED DWARF — WHITE DWARF

These hot blue stars get through their nuclear material quickly

Heavier elements fuse together and eventually form an iron core

The star collapses, and the infalling material rebounds outwards in a violent explosion

For the largest stars, the iron core becomes a black hole

For smaller stars, a neutron star is formed

PROTOSTAR — MAIN-SEQUENCE STAR — SUPERGIANT STAR — TYPE II SUPERNOVA — BLACK HOLE — NEUTRON STAR

> STARS ARE **BORN, LIVE** – OFTEN FOR BILLIONS OF YEARS – AND **DIE**...
> SOMETIMES IN A **SPECTACULAR MANNER**.

Carl Sagan, American astronomer, 1934–1996

RED GIANT

Half of the star's mass ends up in a central, Earth-sized core

Helium fusion is less stable, and the star sheds its outer layers

PLANETARY NEBULA

This white dwarf is orbiting a main-sequence star

The white dwarf can rip material from its partner

BINARY SYSTEM

Eventually, the white dwarf becomes unstable and explodes as a supernova

TYPE 1A SUPERNOVA

Initially, the white dwarf is hot and glows brightly

Over time, the white dwarf fades away into a black dwarf

WHITE DWARF ... BLACK DWARF

HOW **NEW ELEMENTS** FORM INSIDE **STARS**

Before the first stars shone, the Universe was just a sea of hydrogen, helium, and residual energy from the Big Bang. The chemical diversity in the Universe today is due to stars – effectively, vast atom factories – churning primitive materials into more complex elements and then flinging them outwards when they die.

Inside stars, the temperature is high enough to rip electrons away from the nuclei of atoms. In the case of hydrogen, this leaves solitary protons (and electrons) wandering around the star's interior. Matter in this state is known as plasma. Due to their like electric charges, protons repel each other, rather like similar poles of a magnet.

NEW ELEMENTS IN STARS

However, deep in the core of the star, the temperature and pressure are high enough to squash protons together. Known as nuclear fusion, this process releases energy and is the star's power source. It also exerts an outward pressure that counters the inward pull of gravity.

The simplest fusion mechanism is called the proton-proton (or pp) chain. In the first step, one of the fused protons turns into a neutron, creating a new proton-neutron pair called a deuteron. This is bombarded by another proton to create the nucleus of a helium-3 atom. When two of these helium-3 atoms collide, they create a helium-4 nucleus, along with two protons, which can start the whole process again. The German–American physicist Hans Bethe was a key player

in uncovering this process and was awarded the 1967 Nobel Prize in Physics for his work. Crucially, the total mass of the products of the pp-chain is less than the mass of the ingredients entering into it. In the Sun, for example, 620 million tonnes

of hydrogen (protons) is turned into 616 million tonnes of helium every second. The missing four million tonnes of mass is converted into energy according to Einstein's famous equation $E = mc^2$.

Eventually, the hydrogen in the star's core runs out and gravity contracts the core. The resulting temperature surge allows a new fusion mechanism to take over – the triple alpha process – one which uses helium-4 nuclei (alpha particles) as its main ingredient. This enables two helium nuclei to fuse into beryllium and then, with the addition of a third helium nucleus, into carbon. In smaller stars, such as the Sun, the atom construction process ends here.

However, larger stars can go on increasing the diversity of chemical elements; once one fusion path runs out, the core contracts and the temperature spikes to kick-start another. Next, carbon fuses with helium to form oxygen, which is bombarded by another helium nucleus to forge neon, which itself is fashioned into magnesium by a similar process. The sheer range of possible reactions is vast. Eventually, carbon and oxygen fuse together to form silicon.

At this point, the temperature in the core has soared to three billion degrees Celsius, which is enough to force two silicon nuclei together to form iron. In this way, a wealth of elements builds up in shells within the star, resembling the layers of an onion, with

> ❝
> ## FINALLY, I GOT TO **CARBON**, AND AS YOU ALL KNOW, IN THE CASE OF CARBON THE REACTION **WORKS OUT BEAUTIFULLY**.
> ❞
>
> **Hans Bethe**, German–American physicist, 1906–2005

▼ The triple alpha process
In this process, two helium-4 nuclei fuse into beryllium-8, which becomes carbon-12 when struck by a third helium-4 nucleus. Helium-4 nuclei are also called alpha particles, and so this mechanism is known as the triple alpha process.

Gamma ray emitted as two helium-4 nuclei fuse to form beryllium-8 nucleus

Helium-4 nucleus, or alpha particle

Helium-4 nucleus

Proton
Neutron

Helium-4 nucleus

Helium-4 and beryllium-8 nuclei fuse to form carbon-12 nucleus

Beryllium-8 nucleus

Helium-4 nucleus

Gamma ray (high-energy photons)

Carbon-12 nucleus

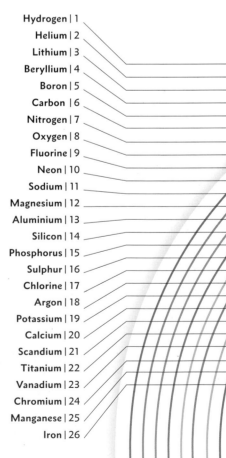

Hydrogen | 1
Helium | 2
Lithium | 3
Beryllium | 4
Boron | 5
Carbon | 6
Nitrogen | 7
Oxygen | 8
Fluorine | 9
Neon | 10
Sodium | 11
Magnesium | 12
Aluminium | 13
Silicon | 14
Phosphorus | 15
Sulphur | 16
Chlorine | 17
Argon | 18
Potassium | 19
Calcium | 20
Scandium | 21
Titanium | 22
Vanadium | 23
Chromium | 24
Manganese | 25
Iron | 26

9 BYA | THE UNIVERSE CONSISTS OF
VAST CLUSTERS OF GALAXIES

6 BYA | THE EXPANSION OF THE UNIVERSE
STARTS TO ACCELERATE

4.6 BYA | OUR SOLAR SYSTEM
STARTS TO FORM

iron at its heart. However, because iron is the most stable of all the elements, it cannot be fused into anything else and fusion ceases. As heavier elements form, the process gathers pace – it can take millions of years for a star to exhaust its hydrogen, but the fusion of silicon nuclei to form iron takes just a single day.

NEW ELEMENTS IN SUPERNOVAS

Elements heavier than iron can only be created when a massive star explodes in a supernova. The next heaviest elements are formed by the s-neutron-capture process – "s" stands for slow, as it typically takes hundreds of years. This process actually begins inside stars, but in stars the interactions are extremely slow – they only speed up once a supernova gets going. The earlier transformation of carbon into oxygen, and neon into magnesium, created a wealth of additional neutrons. The gradual combination of these excess particles with existing nuclei allows elements as heavy as bismuth to form. However, this process cannot produce any elements heavier than bismuth, because bismuth decays away into polonium before it can combine with a neutron. A much faster neutron capture mechanism is required – the r-process ("r" stands for

rapid). The r-process can only happen in the extreme conditions of a supernova. The density of neutrons increases greatly during the explosion, and new elements can be formed in a fraction of a second. Some of these r-process nuclei later decay away, creating new elements not fashioned directly by either neutron capture process.

COMPLEX CHEMISTRY

This profusion of material is dispersed into the wider Universe by the force of the supernova. It then mixes with interstellar material and debris from other dead stars to form giant molecular clouds that will eventually collapse to form new stars. Individual atoms can combine with others in the clouds to form complex molecules, some of which are crucial for life. Astronomers and astrochemists have already found evidence of these molecules. The simplest amino acid – glycine – has been detected in a cloud of gas towards the centre of our Milky Way galaxy, as well as in the nearby Orion Nebula. Amino acids are regarded as life's building blocks, so it is possible that the basic ingredients for life were fashioned long before the Sun lit up.

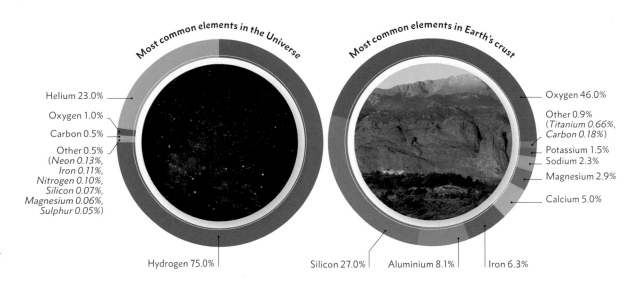

Most common elements in the Universe

Helium 23.0%
Oxygen 1.0%
Carbon 0.5%
Other 0.5%
(*Neon 0.13%,
Iron 0.11%,
Nitrogen 0.10%,
Silicon 0.07%,
Magnesium 0.06%,
Sulphur 0.05%*)
Hydrogen 75.0%

Most common elements in Earth's crust

Oxygen 46.0%
Other 0.9%
(*Titanium 0.66%,
Carbon 0.18%*)
Potassium 1.5%
Sodium 2.3%
Magnesium 2.9%
Calcium 5.0%
Silicon 27.0%
Aluminium 8.1%
Iron 6.3%

▲ **The distribution of the elements**
The combination of elements found on Earth differs greatly from the Universe at large. The lightest elements, hydrogen and helium, were expelled from Earth's orbit by the young Sun. Oxygen, the crust's most abundant element, was created as life turned carbon dioxide into sugar via photosynthesis.

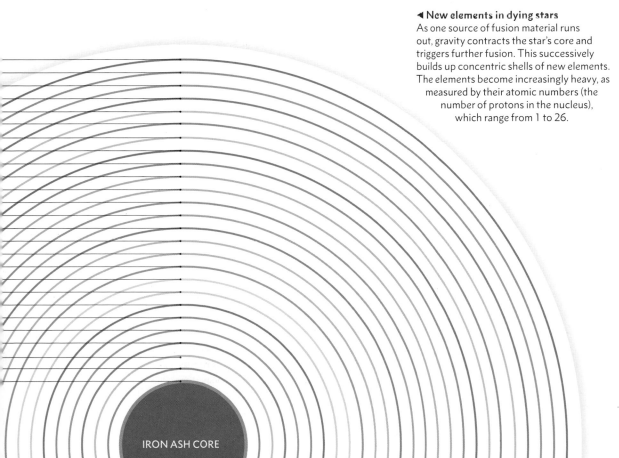

◄ **New elements in dying stars**
As one source of fusion material runs out, gravity contracts the star's core and triggers further fusion. This successively builds up concentric shells of new elements. The elements become increasingly heavy, as measured by their atomic numbers (the number of protons in the nucleus), which range from 1 to 26.

IRON ASH CORE

▲ **Life's cosmic origins**
The building blocks of life have been found in the nearest star-forming region to our Solar System, the Orion Nebula. Amino acids combine to create proteins and are a key component of DNA.

WHEN GIANT STARS **EXPLODE**

Today we know that supernovas pepper the Universe with elements heavier than iron. But our quest to understand these searing explosions dates back to a time long before the advent of our astronomical understanding. We've been documenting them for almost 2,000 years.

5 minutes after core collapse

166 minutes

The earliest recorded evidence of an observed supernova dates back to Chinese astronomers in 185 CE. They documented the appearance of a sudden bright light in the sky that took eight months to fade from view. A similar event occurred in 393 CE, and up to 20 other potential events appear

> JUST BEFORE A
> **SUPERGIANT STAR EXPLODES AS A SUPERNOVA**, ITS TEMPERATURE REACHES ABOUT **100 BILLION°C**

in Chinese records, although modern astronomers haven't been able to confirm they were all supernovas.

One definitive explosion – perhaps the most famous of the pre-telescope age – was seen to detonate in 1054. It was observed in Japan and the Middle East, as well as in China. Luminous enough to be seen during daylight hours for nearly a month,

it was a guest in the night sky for almost two years. The remnant of this colossal explosion is the spectacular Crab Nebula in the constellation Taurus.

ENTER THE TELESCOPE

The 1054 event was followed nearly six centuries later by the supernovas of 1572 and 1604, the last in the pre-telescope age. The latter, known as Tycho's supernova, was the last observed to explode in our Milky Way galaxy.

However, in more recent times, light reached us in 1987 from an explosion in one of our galaxy's satellites – the Large Magellanic Cloud. By then, astronomers were able to observe it with telescopes within days of detonation. The Voyager probe, then on its way to the furthest planets, was also pointed towards the explosion for a closer look. Designated SN 1987A, it surprised astronomers because the best theories of the day said the star that exploded shouldn't have done so. Consequently, it has become a valuable source of evidence against which astronomers can test their theories. Some of their ideas were backed up by SN 1987A, particularly that the radioactive decay of cobalt atoms keeps the supernova remnant bright long after the initial explosion. But some mysteries remain. For example, astronomers have yet to find the neutron star that should have formed at the heart of the dying star.

The 1054 supernova and SN 1987A were both Type II supernovas, formed by the core collapse of massive stars. In recent years, astronomers have also been able to pick out some relatively close Type 1a supernovas, which are formed by stars of lower mass. These include SN 2011fe in the Pinwheel Galaxy and SN 2014J in the nearby Cigar Galaxy.

▼ **Chaco Canyon** These wall markings in a New Mexico cave show a large star, a crescent Moon, and a handprint. It has been suggested that the local Anasazi people drew it as a record of the 1054 supernova.

9 BYA | THE UNIVERSE CONSISTS OF
VAST CLUSTERS OF GALAXIES

6 BYA | THE EXPANSION OF THE UNIVERSE
STARTS TO ACCELERATE

4.6 BYA | OUR SOLAR SYSTEM
STARTS TO FORM

27 minutes

50 minutes

120 minutes

Simulating a supernova
This computer model of SN 1987A
was made at the Max Planck Institute
for Astrophysics in Germany. Density
increases from black through red,
orange, and white. A shockwave is
expanding through the star's outer
layers of hydrogen. Metals (white) from
the core are being expelled rapidly, with
turbulence occurring as they collide
with gases in the star's interior.

▼ **The Periodic Table**
First presented to the Russian Chemical Society on 6 March 1869 as "the period system", this famous depiction of the primary components of matter organises the elements in an incredibly useful way.

Missing elements By arranging the table in terms of the behaviour and structure of elements, Mendeleev was able to spot gaps that suggested as-yet-unseen elements, including germanium

Atomic number This is the number of protons in the nucleus – just one in the case of hydrogen

ПЕРИОДИЧЕСКАЯ СИСТЕМА ЭЛЕМЕНТОВ Д. И. МЕНДЕЛЕЕВА

Group Vertical columns are called groups. Group members have similar electron configurations and so exhibit similar chemical properties. Today, 18 groups are officially recognized

Unstable elements Some elements are not stable and decay over time. Even the most stable form of kurchatovium (now called rutherfordium) will decay to half the original amount in just 1 hour 20 minutes

Relative atomic mass This is measured in atomic mass units (amu), where 1 amu is equal to $1/12$ of the mass of a carbon atom. This is why it is called relative – it helps compare the masses of different elements

MAKING SENSE OF THE ELEMENTS

The periodic table of the elements is one of the most recognizable icons in science. By organizing the elements according to their atomic structure, it provides a standard way to order and classify them. Of the 118 elements in the table, 92 form inside stars and supernovas.

Dmitri Mendeleev Mendeleev is the name most associated with the Periodic Table. He didn't win the Nobel Prize, but he does have an element named after him (Mendelevium), as well as a crater on the Moon

Period Rows are known as periods. Their main function is to make sure that elements with similar chemical properties appear in the correct group. There are currently seven periods

Tile Each tile displays a chemical symbol for the element (either one or two letters), along with information including atomic number and relative atomic mass number

As the scientific revolution gathered pace, so did the rate at which new elements were discovered. Over time, a pattern in their chemical behaviour was found. The first attempt to organize the elements into groups came in the late 18th century, when French chemist Antoine Lavoisier sorted them into four categories: gases, non-metals, metals, and earths. In 1829, the German Johann Döbereiner noted that trios of elements had similar chemical properties. Crucially, he realized that the attributes of one could be predicted from those of the other two. By the 1860s, the British chemist John Newlands had devised his Law of Octaves, which said that every eighth element exhibited similar chemical behaviour. However, on occasion he had to squeeze two elements into the same box, and he did not leave gaps for as-yet-undiscovered elements. This problem explains why the Russian Dmitri Mendeleev is often regarded as the father of the periodic table. In 1869, Mendeleev published a primitive version of the famous table, leaving gaps based on the "periodicity" of the known elements.

HOW THE TABLE WORKS

The elements are organized in order of increasing atomic mass. The horizontal rows are known as periods – a new period begins when the behaviour of an element repeats. For example, a new period starts after neon to ensure that sodium is in the same column as lithium (both are highly reactive). These columns, or groups, are the real key to the table. Mendeleev's table only had seven groups, but the power of his system was confirmed in the 1890s when the noble gases were discovered and fitted in perfectly as an eighth group.

WHERE THE ELEMENTS ARE FORGED

The searing heat in the first minutes after the Big Bang turned some of the cosmos's nascent hydrogen into helium via nuclear fusion (see p.58). After just 20 minutes, fusion stopped and the basic composition of the Universe was set down as about 75 per cent hydrogen and 25 per cent helium. It took millions of years for more elements to appear. The elements up to and including iron form by fusion in stars, whereas many beyond iron can only be made in the cataclysm of a supernova.

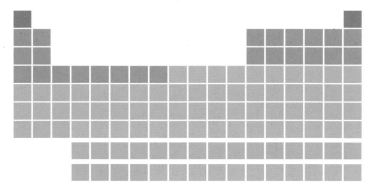

▲ **Organizing the elements** The elements can be grouped according to how they formed. Most of the elements up to uranium formed as a result of nuclear reactions in stars or supernovas. Elements heavier than uranium are unstable and rarely encountered.

KEY
- Formed in Big Bang (hydrogen and helium)
- Formed in stars by fusion (lithium to iron)
- Formed in stars by neutron capture (cobalt to uranium)
- Unstable elements

IT IS THE **FUNCTION OF SCIENCE** TO DISCOVER THE EXISTENCE OF A GENERAL REIGN OF ORDER IN NATURE AND **TO FIND THE CAUSES GOVERNING THIS ORDER**.

Dmitri Mendeleev, Russian chemist, 1834–1907

THRESHOLD

PLANETS **FORM**

As our own star – the Sun – ignites, its gravitational pull sweeps up the elements into orbit around it. As they crash together, planets begin to form. While the lighter elements are blown to the outer regions, forming gas giants, close to the Sun the heavier elements remain and form rocky planets, including Earth: our home is born.

GOLDILOCKS CONDITIONS

When stars were born from the debris of former stars, some chemically rich material was left in orbit. This debris clumped into balls of matter stuck together by gravity and chemical bonds. These structures were planets, and they were far more complex than anything seen before. We now know that this first happened long ago in solar systems far older than our own.

A newly formed sunlike star

New chemical elements and clouds of chemically rich matter orbiting the new star

Gravity, accretion, and random collisions

Matter from dying stars
The death of stars builds up an ever-increasing supply of heavier elements, supplementing the hydrogen and helium of the early Universe. This results in a more chemically complex world with 92 elements that can combine to form compounds.

What changed?
After the formation of a star, material was left orbiting in a disc. The star's fierce radiation blasted light, volatile material, particularly hydrogen and helium, far from the star. These gases would go on to form distant gas-giant planets. Nearer to the star, the heavier, chemically rich materials from the death of previous generations of stars remained solid or liquid and clumped into rocky planets. In our own Solar System, one of these planets was Earth.

Star nurseries
Clouds of dead star material, rich in heavy elements, such as carbon, oxygen, nitrogen, aluminium, nickel, and iron, gather under weak forces of gravity and electromagnetism. They become sites of new star formation.

Shockwave from a supernova
A disturbance, such as a shockwave from a neighbouring exploding star, may trigger a cloud to begin contracting to form a star. As it slowly collapses, the cloud begins spinning faster and faster, and takes on a disc shape.

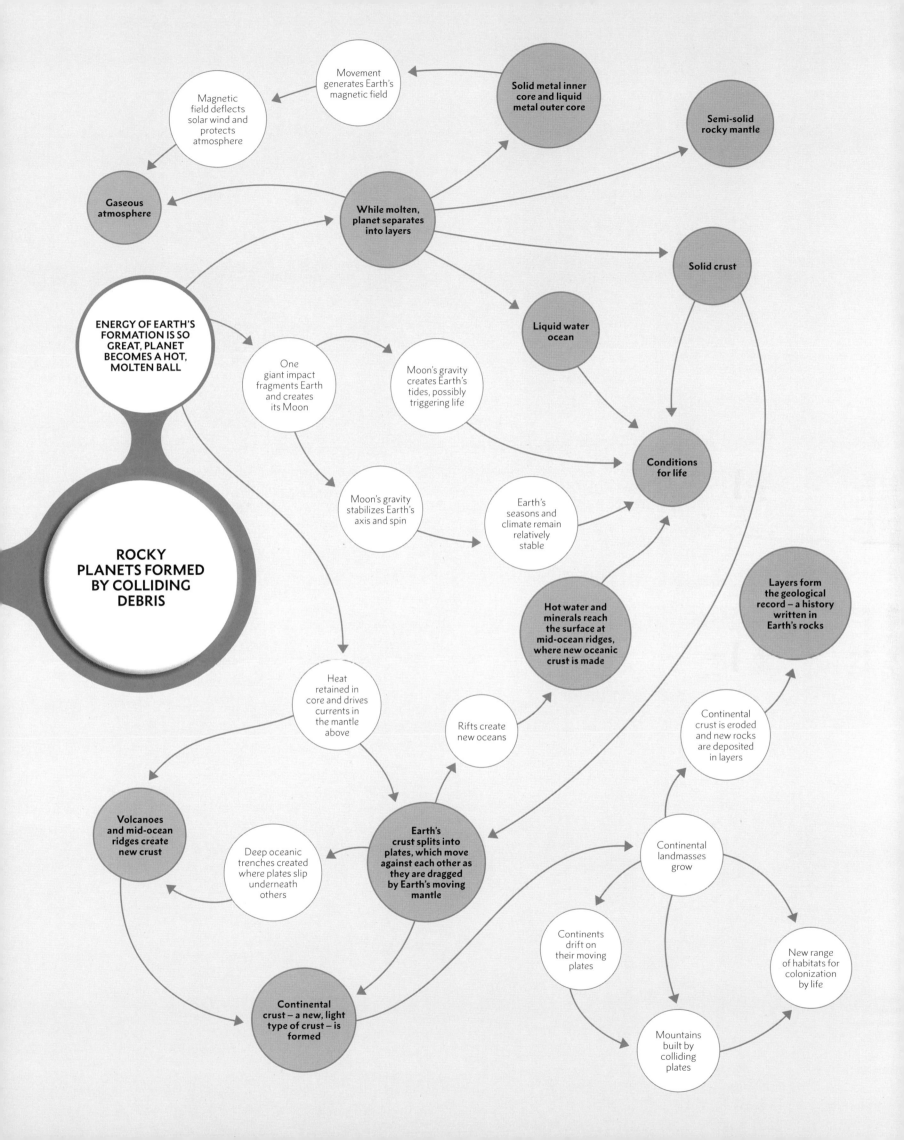

ROCKY PLANETS FORMED BY COLLIDING DEBRIS

ENERGY OF EARTH'S FORMATION IS SO GREAT, PLANET BECOMES A HOT, MOLTEN BALL

While molten, planet separates into layers

Movement generates Earth's magnetic field

Magnetic field deflects solar wind and protects atmosphere

Gaseous atmosphere

Solid metal inner core and liquid metal outer core

Semi-solid rocky mantle

Solid crust

Liquid water ocean

One giant impact fragments Earth and creates its Moon

Moon's gravity creates Earth's tides, possibly triggering life

Moon's gravity stabilizes Earth's axis and spin

Earth's seasons and climate remain relatively stable

Conditions for life

Layers form the geological record – a history written in Earth's rocks

Hot water and minerals reach the surface at mid-ocean ridges, where new oceanic crust is made

Heat retained in core and drives currents in the mantle above

Rifts create new oceans

Continental crust is eroded and new rocks are deposited in layers

Volcanoes and mid-ocean ridges create new crust

Deep oceanic trenches created where plates slip underneath others

Earth's crust splits into plates, which move against each other as they are dragged by Earth's moving mantle

Continental landmasses grow

Continents drift on their moving plates

Continental crust – a new, light type of crust – is formed

Mountains built by colliding plates

New range of habitats for colonization by life

OUR **SUN IGNITES**

In an otherwise inconspicuous region of our Milky Way galaxy, a giant cloud of matter began to coalesce. Our Sun had a tempestuous birth, heating up and spinning until it exploded into life.

An unassuming mass of gas and dust, measuring only a few gas molecules per cubic centimetre, floated aimlessly in space. Eventually, it started to collapse under the weight of its own gravity.

It is likely that this collapse was kick-started by a shockwave from a nearby supernova. A rare type of aluminium can be found across the solar system, which may be a potential trace of this supernova.

UNSTOPPABLE FORCE

Whatever the cause, what we do know is that over tens of millions of years the cloud progressively became more dense. In the centre, the cloud was at its densest and hottest – this was the protosun, and it was composed of about 75 per cent hydrogen and 25 per cent helium. Extreme temperatures and pressures counteracted its own gravitational force, blasting ice, rock, and gas away from the centre. These materials flattened in a spinning disc that began to orbit the protosun.

Entering a new phase of intense activity, the protosun began to eject jets of radiation from its poles. Fierce winds blasted lighter elements such as hydrogen and helium to the edge of the protosun's orbit. Soon, the protosun's temperature, pressure, and size rose even higher, until it had absorbed 99.9 per cent of material from the original solar nebula.

Despite these events occuring almost 5 billion years ago, we can gather clues as to how our Sun was born because we can watch new stars being created elsewhere in the galaxy.

> THE **SUN**, WITH ALL OF THOSE PLANETS REVOLVING AROUND IT... CAN STILL **RIPEN A BUNCH OF GRAPES** AS IF IT HAD **NOTHING ELSE** IN THE **UNIVERSE TO DO**.

Galileo Galilei, astronomer, 1564–1642

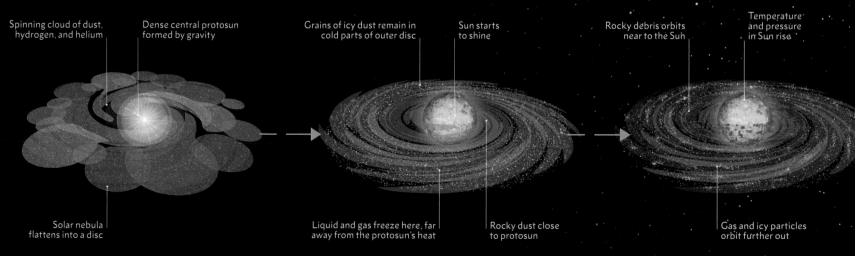

Spinning cloud of dust, hydrogen, and helium

Dense central protosun formed by gravity

Grains of icy dust remain in cold parts of outer disc

Sun starts to shine

Rocky debris orbits near to the Sun

Temperature and pressure in Sun rise

Solar nebula flattens into a disc

Liquid and gas freeze here, far away from the protosun's heat

Rocky dust close to protosun

Gas and icy particles orbit further out

An interstellar cloud of gas and dust begins to collapse under gravity, spinning and heating up as it does so. In the hot, dense centre, a protosun forms.

Extreme temperatures inside the protosun generate energy that counteracts its own gravity. Ice and gas near the protosun burn away, leaving rocky dust particles.

The protosun's temperature and internal pressure rise, and it becomes an early Sun. Lumps of rock and ice orbiting the Sun start to collide.

4.1 BYA | FIRST TRACE OF
POSSIBLE LIFE

4 BYA | EARTH SETTLES
INTO LAYERS

3.8 BYA | EARTH'S CONTINENTS
START TO FORM

Bursting into life
Intense jets of radiation erupt from the
protosun's poles as it swallows up dust
and gas. Fierce winds collide with the
surrounding rock and ice that will later
form planets.

Rocky worlds are born
As planetesimals within the frost line orbited the young Sun, incoming materials approached with ever greater speed. The constant impacts accelerated their growth, pulling even more material towards them.

THE PLANETS FORM

The planets in our Solar System started their lives as gas and tiny grains of dust. Formed into a whirling disc by the young Sun's gravitational pull, millions of years of violent collisions would eventually mould the gas and dust into impressive planets, one of which would become our home.

Before the modern planets came the planetesimals – the building blocks from which planets are made. The gathering together of smaller chunks to form larger ones is a process known as accretion.

ASSEMBLING A PLANET

The irregular orbits of the mostly solid materials around the young Sun led to frequent impacts, causing accretion. Initially, centimetre-sized grains grew to metre-sized lumps. It took tens to hundreds of millions of years for their collective gravity to accumulate materials that resulted in planetesimals that stretched kilometres across.

The largest planetesimals had enough gravitational power to attract additional material relentlessly. The planetesimals formed by this process of runaway accretion created the embryos of planets.

DIFFERENT TYPES OF WORLD

The distance at which these planetary seeds formed from the Sun determined whether the eventual planet was made primarily of rock or gas.

In the hot ring of the inner Solar System, only materials with very high melting points, such as iron, nickel, and silicon, could survive to be incorporated into the rocky planets, Mercury, Venus, our home planet Earth, and Mars.

In the outer Solar System, beyond what astronomers refer to as the frost line, materials such as water and methane froze in the frigid temperatures. With more solid material available, the gravitational pulls of these larger planetesimals were stronger. Consequently, lighter elements such as hydrogen and helium were more easily captured, resulting in the vast gaseous atmospheres typical of Jupiter, Saturn, Uranus, and Neptune.

> ❝
> THE **FORMATION OF THE PLANETS** IS LIKE A **GIGANTIC SNOWBALL FIGHT**... A PLANET-BALL THAT HAS **GATHERED ALL THE SNOWFLAKES** IN THE SURROUNDING AREA. ❞
>
> Claude Allègre, scientist and politician, 1937–

Gravity draws rock and dust into rings around Sun

Rock and dust clump together to form planetesimals

Sun

Frost line

Sun blasts vapour and other gases beyond the frost line

Sun's radiation boils away most water and other volatile substances

Little debris remains in inner Solar System

Fully formed rocky inner planet

Icy material and gas remains in outer Solar System

Distant planet continues to pull in ice and gas, becoming a bloated gaseous world

Sun

Uranus

Mercury

Earth

Mars

Kuiper Belt

Saturn

Venus

Neptune

Jupiter

Asteroid Belt

Materials and debris left over from the Sun's formation orbited the young Sun in rings. The inner rings were composed of metals and rock; outer rings beyond the frost line held rock, frozen water, and gases.

Large planetesimals attracted smaller particles. Their gravitational fields grew stronger as they continued to grow larger. Most of the orbiting material was eventually swept up.

Stabilization of the Solar System took hundreds of millions of years (see pp.74–75). The gravitational interactions of the infant planets settled, eventually forming the stable orbits we see today.

THE IMILAC
METEORITE

Meteorites – pieces of material that have flown through space and landed on Earth – deliver small time capsules of ancient data. They have drifted since the birth of the Solar System, so the information they contain is often older than Earth.

Artefacts that were around after the Solar System formed are still orbiting our Sun today, as comets and asteroids. They are relics of the early Solar System that have remained relatively unchanged due to the absence of geological activity. When they land on Earth as meteorites, studying them allows us to journey into the past and test out our theories of how our Solar System, and our planet, came to be. Tens of thousands of meteorites weighing more than 10g (¼ oz) land on Earth every year, each parachuting down precious information on what the Solar System was like billions of years ago.

This sample is a slice of a meteorite named "Imilac", which was itself a small fragment of almost a tonne of material that fell into the Atacama Desert, Chile, as part of a single impact event. Imilac is classified

as a pallasite meteorite due to its matrix of metal encapsulating its crystals. Like all pallasites, it originated from the boundary between the metallic core and the rocky mantle of a planetesimal, which broke apart during the formation of our Solar System, possibly due to the early Sun's gravitational pull. Some small pieces of the mantle fell into the molten core during this process. It then took at least a million years for these chunks to cool into the crystals scattered throughout the metal you can see here.

Not only can pallasite meteorites help determine the age of the Solar System, they can also provide clues as to its early chemical composition. Pallasites such as this one are incredibly rare in our Earthly collection – they make up just 0.4 per cent of the meteorites scientists have gathered up.

Metal matrix is made of iron and nickel

See-through parts are olivine crystals

▲ Orbiting evidence
These ice mountains on Comet 67p, studied by probes in 2014–15, are as old as our Solar System. The presence of ice in the comet's interior demonstrates that water or ice was present during the Solar System's formation.

How do we know its age?

Calculating the age of these cosmic fragments allows geologists to date the birth of the Solar System. This meteorite was once part of an asteroid's or planetesimal's hot interior. When the asteroid cooled sufficiently for its molten rock and metal to freeze, it also sealed in isotopes – unstable, radioactive atoms. Scientists can use a process called radiometric dating (see pp.88–89) to put a date on this event. By measuring the present-day densities of the isotopes, geologists can calculate how much radioactive decay has occurred and estimate that the asteroid solidified 4.5 BYA – soon after the birth of the Sun.

What happened on impact?

During this meteorite's descent to Earth, it split into fragments as it entered our planet's atmosphere. Friction heated the surface of this fragment, and a thin crust melted. Outer crystals melted out of the matrix, but crystals in the interior remained cool and intact, because it only took a few seconds to pass through Earth's atmosphere.

Earth's building block?

By comparing the composition of these meteorites to the composition of Earth, geologists can identify the type of planetesimals that came together to form our planet. Like Earth, this meteorite contains iron and nickel – both of which are thought to constitute Earth's core. Asteroids, dwarf planets, and this pallasite meteorite have remained unchanged since the early Solar System and therefore can be key pieces of evidence in determining its history.

Planetesimal forming from smaller bodies

Crystals from the rocky mantle

The crystals are made of olivine and peridot – materials found in tetrataenite, a mineral that can record magnetic fields. Microscopic analysis of these particles demonstrates that when the meteorite was part of an asteroid, the asteroid had a magnetic field – until its core solidified.

A thin slice of meteorite under a microscope

KEY

◻ Sun's gravitational field in g (where 1 g = Earth's gravity at sea level)

◼ Sunlight intensity in Watts per sq m (Watts per sq ft)

Solar wind
The outer layer of the Sun's atmosphere, the chromosphere, emits a stream of highly charged and extremely hot (1 million °C) particles outwards throughout the Solar System. Earth's magnetic field (see pp.80–81) protects it from this solar wind

Comets and their tails
As a comet nears the Sun, heat vaporizes ice, letting loose dusty material, forming the dust tail that bends as it orbits the Sun. A second ion tail that streaks directly behind the comet's path is formed through interactions between the comet and the solar wind

Asteroid belt
In this region, the opposing gravitational pulls of Jupiter and the Sun cancel each other out, and pull the asteroids in opposite directions. This means they cannot clump together under their own gravity and form new planets

Gravity 0.004

0.001

0.0006

0.0003

0.00002

0.000006

Venus
Although Venus is the hottest planet, it does not receive the most intense sunlight: Mercury is bathed in much greater solar radiation. Venus is hotter because it traps heat from the Sun in its dense atmosphere, which is rich in carbon dioxide

SATURN

JUPITER

MERCURY   EARTH   MARS

VENUS

Mars
Rover data suggest Mars was once much warmer and wetter, with a thicker atmosphere. Mars is smaller than Earth, so its inner heat and activity may have cooled more rapidly, causing its protective magnetic field to switch off. Solar wind would have stripped most of the atmosphere away

Jupiter
When our Sun ignited (see pp.68–69), light gases were blasted into the furthest parts of the inner Solar System. As Jupiter grew larger, its gravitational pull captured a huge amount of gas to form a giant atmosphere 5,000km (3,100 miles) high

15 (1.4)

51 (4.7)

590 (55)

1,370 (127)

2,610 (243)

Sunlight intensity 9,120 (848)

ASTEROID BELT

Inner Solar System
he realm of the eight planets is eferred to as the inner Solar System. However, that is by no means the end of the Sun's family of orbiting objects. There are many objects beyond Neptune, including dwarf planets and comets. Light and gravity spread out from the Sun in all directions – each rapidly losing intensity with distance

0.000002

URANUS

0.0000007

NEPTUNE

1.5 (0.14)

3.7 (0.35)

Uranus
The intensity of light fades over distance: at twice the distance, sunlight is four times weaker. Uranus's orbit is 20 times further from the Sun than Earth's, so the intensity of sunlight is just 1/400th of that on Earth

THE SUN
TAKES CONTROL

Between 4.1 and 3.8 BYA, planets shifted their orbits in a cascade of gravitational disruption. The process left eight major planets in orbits that remain stable to this day. However, the Sun controls much more in its neighbouring space than just these planets.

Scientists have long grappled with the problem of how the modern Solar System came to be. When modelling the evolution of the Sun's environment, it was hard to explain its present form if the planets had always been where they are now.

NICE MODEL
The present arrangement of the Solar System fits with the explanation that the four gas giants started out much closer together: Jupiter moved inwards while the other three backed away from the Sun. It is even possible that Uranus and Neptune may have swapped order. The outward migration of Neptune would have scattered many of the Solar System's smaller objects into a region known as the Kuiper Belt.

This simulation is known as the Nice Model, after the city in France where it was devised. If the migration of the gas giants took place about 600 million years after the formation of the Solar System, then it might also account for the event known as the Late

Heavy Bombardment. This occurred when a sudden shift in the movements of the gas giants and their gravitational fields caused a catastrophic torrent of asteroids to fall on the inner Solar System, including Earth. Lunar rock samples returned to Earth by the Apollo astronauts point to a clustering of meteor impacts around 3.9 BYA. According to the Nice Model, the giant planet migration was to blame.

A MISSING PLANET
Simulations of the Solar System's infancy also suggest that our Sun once had more planets. By adding a fifth gas planet to the model, researchers found they could get a much better match for the modern arrangement of planets. We do not have five gas planets today, however, so the fifth must have been ejected from the Solar System. Given that astronomers have recently found rogue planets – which wander through empty space with no host star – the idea is not as bizarre as it may at first appear.

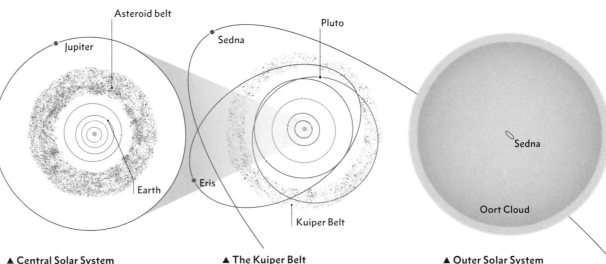

▲ Central Solar System
The Sun's gravity holds four rocky planets – Mercury, Venus, Earth, and Mars – and an asteroid belt. Beyond that, the gas giants Jupiter, Saturn, Uranus, and Neptune also orbit the Sun.

▲ The Kuiper Belt
The band of icy objects – including Pluto – that sits 30–50 times further from the Sun than Earth is known as the Kuiper Belt. Objects including Eris and Sedna orbit even further out.

▲ Outer Solar System
The Oort Cloud is a large, spherical region sparsely populated by comets. The Sun's gravity controls their orbits up to one light year away, which is the extent of our Solar System.

HOW WE FIND
SOLAR SYSTEMS

For centuries astronomers have recognized the stars as distant versions of our own Sun. The stars are so far away that it took until the late 20th century to tease out the presence of planets orbiting them and to discover new solar systems.

Stars are often millions of times bigger than planets, and their considerable brightness easily overwhelms any light their suites of planets happen to reflect. The stars themselves appear only as tiny flecks of light from Earth due to their vast distances – the closest one is over 40 trillion km (25 trillion miles) away. It is only in the last few decades that scientists have developed the technology to spot the alien worlds orbiting them.

BLOCKING THE LIGHT
While too small and dark to be observed directly, a planet blocks some of its host star's light when passing, or "transiting", in front of it. Astronomers can glean a wealth of information from this simple event. The planet's size, for example, is betrayed by the amount of light that is blocked out. A transiting Earth would cause a 0.01 per cent change in the brightness of the Sun.

The time between successive transits reveals the duration of the planet's orbit, which in turn discloses its orbital distance:

shorter orbits mean closer planets. Consequently, astronomers use this distance to estimate the planet's temperature and whether it might be habitable.

GRAVITATIONAL WOBBLE
The other main way of finding other solar systems is to exploit the two-way nature of gravity. While stars famously pull on planets, planets also pull back on their suns. This slight tugging causes the star to wobble slightly on the spot. These small changes in the star's motion have an effect on the way we see the light it emits. If wobbling towards us, the star's light is shifted towards the blue end of the colour spectrum. Conversely, if it is moving away from us, the shift is towards the red end (see pp.28–29). As more massive planets pull on their stars with a greater gravitational force, these colour shifts are more pronounced for heavier planets, allowing astronomers to estimate the planet's mass.

Communication hub transmits data to Earth for eight hours a day and at speeds of five megabits per second

Two dual-speed focuser telescopes with billion-pixel cameras housed in spacecraft's cylindrical body

Exoplanet blocks some of its star's light reaching Earth as it orbits

Star

Earth

Brightness

Star brightness falls as exoplanet passes in front

Time

▲ **Finding distant planets**
Star brightness (red dots) is sampled many times. The line shows the average as it dips due to the passing planet.

Star's orbit   Star

Exoplanet's orbit

Blue light emitted as star moves towards us

Exoplanet's gravity causes alien star's orbit to wobble

Red light emitted as star moves away

Earth

▲ **Tracking distant stars**
As the star wobbles, colour shifts in its light tell us its speed of travel towards or away from us.

Temperature-resistant materials cope with conditions between -170°C and 70°C (-270°F–160°F)

Satellite telescope
is 3m (9¾ft) tall

Silicon carbide
structure provides
strength and stability

◀ **Gaia satellite**
Launched by the European Space Agency
(ESA), this spacecraft is able to precisely
pinpoint the location of exoplanets by
measuring their star's brightness and
the colour of its light.

Sun-shield measures
10m (33ft) wide

▼ **Habitable zones**
Most solar systems have a habitable zone, where
liquid water and life could exist. Earth orbits in our
Solar System's habitable zone, and other planets
in alien solar systems, for example Kepler-452b,
orbit in habitable zones of their own. The planet
has spent 6 billion years orbiting within its star's
habitable zone – longer than Earth has in its own.

Kepler-452b

Venus   Earth

Mercury   Mars

Sensor within cylinder
can detect stars
400,000 times dimmer
than human eyes can see

Kepler-452

Sun

Kepler-452 system

Habitable zone

Solar system

EARTH **COOLS**

Early Earth was very different from the warm, blue planet we know today. Its tumultuous first years were dominated by almost constant collisions from elsewhere in the Solar System. Initially a giant molten ball of magma, it gradually became a world fit for life.

Around 4,560 million years ago, rock and ice orbiting the early Sun collided into a small, rocky planet under the force of gravity. Earth would have looked very different, with no atmosphere and no oceans. The collisions were far from over – our infant planet was still being battered by many objects, some the size of planets. One collision, with an impactor about the size of Mars, is thought to have formed our Moon 100 million years later (see pp.82–83).

BOMBARDMENT OF EARTH

The energy of these collisions, along with that emitted by the radioactive decay of heavier elements, kept early Earth incredibly hot. Much of its material remained molten. This allowed heavier materials, such as iron and nickel, to sink deep towards the planet's core. Less dense, rocky materials, such as molten magnesium and silicon oxides,

floated to the surface. Geologists call this process "differentiation" and it would stabilize Earth's structure (see pp.80–81).

HELLISH PLANET

Earth's earliest period was once believed to be so hellish that it is named the Hadean Era – after Hades, the god of the underworld. It was thought that much of Earth's surface remained molten for hundreds of millions of years, but recent findings are overturning this notion and suggest our planet began to cool more rapidly. It may have had oceans less than 200 million years after it formed, as vapour released by volcanic activity condensed into water.

Localized heating and melting of rock

Spherical shape due to larger mass and gravitational field

Craters from impacts

Rock

Larger clumps of rock and ice formed

Ice

Gravity pulled rock and ice together

▲ **A tiny Earth began to form,** bearing the scars of continual impacts. Its bumpy surface was a result of recent additional material. Gravity moulded it into a roughly spherical shape.

▲ **The gravitational potency** of early Earth increased and it attracted impactors, such as asteroids, that were hurtling around the Solar System. Each impactor that joined Earth added to the planet's mass and gravitational force. This increased the acceleration and energy of the next impactor.

▲ **Accretion** over many millions of years pulled increasingly large clumps of rock and ice (planetesimals) together. They formed a planetary embryo, which then attracted more material. Lumps of ice that remained intact despite the Sun's heat would later become the initial source of water on Earth.

THE **HADEAN ERA**, IN WHICH **EARTH FORMED,** AND IN WHICH ITS **LAYERS STARTED TO STABILIZE**, OCCURRED **4.6–4 BYA**

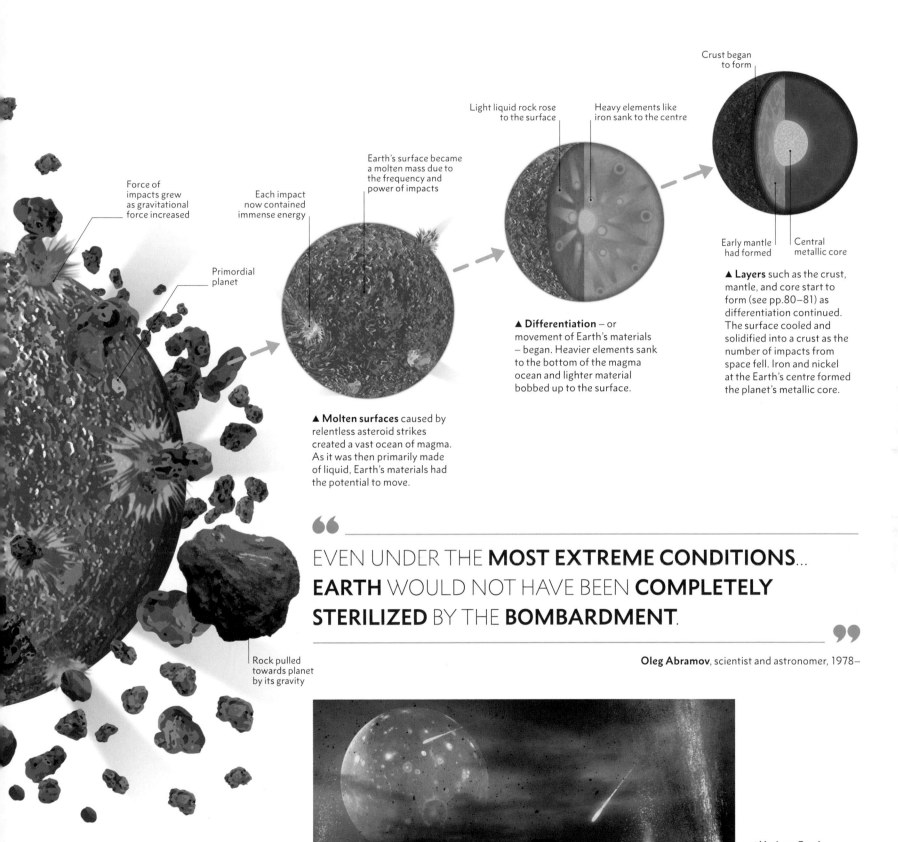

Force of impacts grew as gravitational force increased

Each impact now contained immense energy

Earth's surface became a molten mass due to the frequency and power of impacts

Light liquid rock rose to the surface

Heavy elements like iron sank to the centre

Crust began to form

Primordial planet

Early mantle had formed

Central metallic core

Rock pulled towards planet by its gravity

▲ **Molten surfaces** caused by relentless asteroid strikes created a vast ocean of magma. As it was then primarily made of liquid, Earth's materials had the potential to move.

▲ **Differentiation** – or movement of Earth's materials – began. Heavier elements sank to the bottom of the magma ocean and lighter material bobbed up to the surface.

▲ **Layers** such as the crust, mantle, and core start to form (see pp.80–81) as differentiation continued. The surface cooled and solidified into a crust as the number of impacts from space fell. Iron and nickel at the Earth's centre formed the planet's metallic core.

> ❝
> EVEN UNDER THE **MOST EXTREME CONDITIONS**... **EARTH** WOULD NOT HAVE BEEN **COMPLETELY STERILIZED** BY THE **BOMBARDMENT**.
> ❞
>
> **Oleg Abramov**, scientist and astronomer, 1978–

◀ **Hadean Earth**
During the Hadean Era, molten lava dominated the surface, and Earth's atmosphere was devoid of oxygen. The Moon, far nearer than it is today, caused huge tides, as a deluge of impactors rained from above.

EARTH SETTLES INTO LAYERS

The Earth is formed of distinct layers, and each is made of different materials. The processes responsible for this structure began billions of years ago and continue to shape and influence our planet today.

For hundreds of millions of years after the planet formed, Earth was a molten mass. It was still contracting under its own gravity and material left over from the Solar System's formation was still bombarding it. Both processes generated heat. Earth's crust solidified, but the planet continued to differentiate, settling into its present layers.

FROM CORE TO ATMOSPHERE

Material in the centre hardened to form a solid inner core, surrounded by a largely liquid outer core. The fluid in the outer core flowed easily, and turbulence within it is

TEMPERATURES IN EARTH'S CORE ARE ESTIMATED TO BE HIGHER THAN 6,700°C (12,000°F)

thought to contribute to Earth's magnetic field to this day. Above the outer core sits the thickest of the layers – the mantle. The next layer, formed by molten rock erupting from the mantle, is the crust, which accounts for only 0.5 per cent of the planet's thickness.

Differentiation continued as water vapour released by early volcanic activity condensed into water and became the first

oceans. The Late Heavy Bombardment about 4.1–3.9 BYA (see pp.74–75) saw a significant, secondary spike in the number of impacts thumping into Earth. These asteroids and comets are thought to have added much of the water that contributed to the primordial oceans.

The lightest materials – gases – escaped from the mantle via volcanoes and became part of our planet's carbon dioxide-rich atmosphere. Hydrogen and helium were blasted away by the solar wind, but Earth's gravity was strong enough to hold onto carbon dioxide, nitrogen, water vapour, and argon. Gaseous oxygen was absent from the atmosphere – all of Earth's oxygen was bound into its rocks and water.

EXPLORING INSIDE EARTH

Our planet's depths are so hot and under such extreme pressure that we have never even penetrated the crust. Instead, scientists have used other methods to deduce what is inside Earth. They knew that there must be significantly heavier material at the centre, because the average density of Earth is greater than the density at its surface. Studies of the way earthquakes travel and how our magnetic field emerges provide additional clues about the inner structure of Earth.

▼ **Earth's layers**
Layers began to form 4.4–3.8 BYA. Our planet is divided here into six layers: the solid inner core, liquid outer core, semi-solid mantle, solid crust, liquid ocean, and gaseous atmosphere.

Solid core made of iron and nickel sank to the centre soon after Earth formed

INNER CORE

The flow of liquid iron and nickel in the outer core creates Earth's magnetic field

OUTER CORE

MANTLE

▶ **Seismic waves**
Vibrations from earthquakes are either primary (P) waves or secondary (S) waves. The speed at which they travel through the planet during seismic events can help to determine Earth's structure.

Crust

Epicentre of earthquake

S-waves cannot travel through liquid outer core

Paths of P-waves refract and wobble as they travel through each layer

Shadow zone where no waves can travel due to a change in the direction of travel at the boundary between mantle and core

Inner core

Outer core

Mantle

Heavier, thinner oceanic crust sits lower on the mantle and forms the deep ocean basins

Lighter, thicker continental crust floats higher on the hot mantle and forms dry land, flooded at the edges by shallow seas

ATMOSPHERE

Gaseous layer around 120km (75 miles) thick contains oxygen, nitrogen, argon, and a small amount of carbon dioxide

Layer of water with an average depth of 3.7km (12,100ft) covers two-thirds of Earth's surface

OCEAN

CRUST

Semi-solid rock in the mantle flows very slowly in convection currents, which cause plate movements in the crust (see pp.92–93)

Region of charged particles held in place by magnetic field; it is sometimes visible as aurorae (Northern Lights)

Bow shock

EARTH

SUN

Magnetic field lines show shape and strength of field

▲ Natural shield
A stream of harmful particles from the Sun – solar wind – is deflected by Earth's magnetic field. This field is created by currents in the liquid-iron core.

Solar wind deflected by Earth's magnetic field

THE **MOON'S ROLE**

Despite being a relatively small planet, Earth is blessed with a particularly large moon – the fifth largest in the Solar System. The Moon is our only natural satellite and has had such a significant influence on our planet that it may even have played a role in kick-starting life on Earth.

If the length of Earth's existence was condensed into a single day, the Moon would have formed when the Earth was 10 minutes old. The Moon is our planet's steadfast partner and it is likely that we would not be here without it.

It is thought that a giant piece of rock smashed into our infant planet during its early days. Rock from the impact, while in Earth's orbit, gathered together to form the Moon. As it formed, it was 10 times closer to Earth than it is currently.

THE MOON AND LIFE

During Earth's childhood, the Moon's close proximity would have created a considerably mightier gravitational pull than we feel now.

Tides were extreme, and biologists have speculated that the intense churning during these super tides was a key factor in the mixing of ingredients that led to life in the first oceans. Over millions of years, the Moon retreated from Earth due to the Moon's gradually increasing orbital velocity. Today, the Moon is the main driver of the roughly daily cycle of high and low tide, and continues to drift away from Earth at a rate of 3.8cm (1.5in) per year. As it edges further away, tidal strength falls.

The tides swirled the oceans, and this helped to spread heat from polar to equatorial regions, regulating the young Earth's temperature. The Moon's gravity also keeps the tilt of Earth's axis constant, which means our seasons are steady and repeat predictably. The Moon stabilized Earth over time and this has given life a chance to thrive.

PULLING ON THE PLATES

Geologists have speculated that Earth is the only planet with plate tectonics (see pp.92–93) because of the early Moon's strong gravitational pull. During Earth's hellish Hadean Era, our Moon would have pulled on the primordial oceans of magma. Theories suggest that the wrench of the Moon on the cooling liquid rock helped separate it into the distinct pieces of crust our planet possesses today.

▼ **Extreme tides**
The Bay of Fundy on Canada's Atlantic coast boasts the widest tidal ranges on Earth. The water rises and falls twice each day by up to 16 m (52 ft), regularly submerging the Hopewell Rocks.

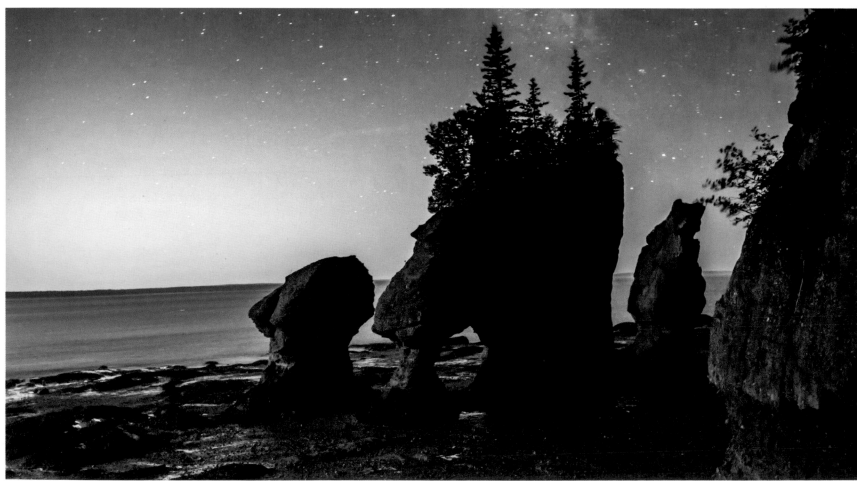

▼ Pull of the Moon

The Moon's gravitational force creates tidal bulges on both sides of Earth. On the side facing the Moon, the Moon's gravity pulls the oceans towards it, resulting in high tides. As well as attraction, however, gravity exerts a stretching force on Earth. Counterintuitively, this results in a second high tide facing away from the Moon.

> " THE POSSIBILITY DESERVES CONSIDERATION THAT **THE FORMATION OF THE MOON... PROVOKED THE ORIGIN OF LIFE** ON EARTH. "

Richard Lathe, molecular biologist, c.1950–

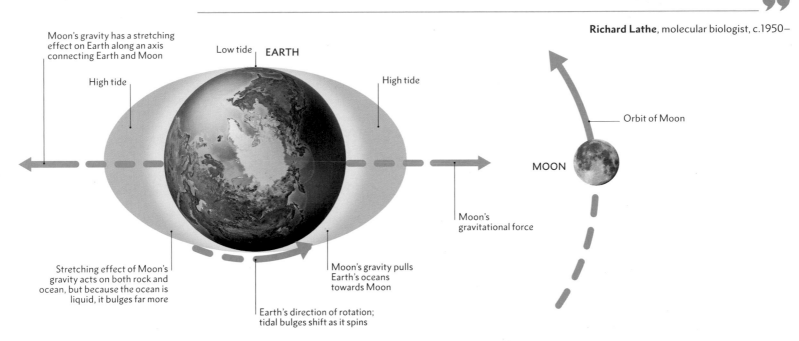

Moon's gravity has a stretching effect on Earth along an axis connecting Earth and Moon

Low tide | **EARTH**

High tide

High tide

MOON

Orbit of Moon

Moon's gravitational force

Stretching effect of Moon's gravity acts on both rock and ocean, but because the ocean is liquid, it bulges far more

Moon's gravity pulls Earth's oceans towards Moon

Earth's direction of rotation; tidal bulges shift as it spins

THE **CONTINENTS** ARE **BORN**

At some time around 4 BYA, Earth's crust began moving, forcing some crust down into the mantle. Magma erupted and cooled into a new, lighter kind of crust – continental crust. It bobbed up higher than the surrounding rock, creating the first land masses. The process continues today, with 30 per cent of our planet's surface now made of continents.

Before continents came cratons – the seedlings from which greater swathes of land would grow. Cratons in turn were made from strings of islands formed from the first continental crust. The process began in the Archean Era (4–2.5 BYA). Although Earth had cooled since the Hadean era, the planet was still much hotter than it is today. Earth's layers had settled, however, and oceans had formed on a solid crust.

Today, Earth's crust is made of both heavy oceanic crust and continental crust, which is lighter and thicker. The primordial crust was uniform, but when currents in Earth's mantle began dragging on its underside (see pp.92–93), it began moving, splitting into plates. When these plates collided, one plate was forced under the other. This triggered a further stage of

Primordial crust initially covered Earth. When two plates of the moving crust met head-on, one was forced underneath. In the mantle, its lighter materials were melted first, and these bubbled to the surface.

First continental crust formed when magma cooled, building a volcanic island of crystalline rock, typically granite

SHALLOW OCEAN

SUBDUCTING CRUST

VOLCANIC ISLAND

PRIMORDIAL CRUST

MANTLE

Crust was forced down, or subducted, into the hot mantle and melted

Melted crust formed magma rich in light elements, such as silicon, oxygen, aluminium, sodium, and potassium

Movements of Earth's crust pushed adjacent islands together and formed progressively larger masses of light rock called cratons. But two more processes were at work: heavy material rose to the surface where cratons split, and new heavy, oceanic crust was also created where plates separated in oceans.

Crust continues to be forced downwards

Island collided with another island, forming a craton

Some cratons rifted (split) and admitted heavier materials from below to fill the gap

Erosion of the craton by oceans, wind, and rain created sediments, such as sandstone

CRATON

Subducting crust continued to be pushed into the hot mantle and then melted

Heavy magma, rich in magnesium and iron, could push upwards into rifts in the craton

The first continents eventually formed from colliding cratons and islands. Because they were light, they stayed on the surface, but became composed of a growing variety of rock. Oceanic crust, being heavier, is continuously subducted, and never gets old and complex. It is replaced by new crust at spreading ridges.

Oceanic crust is destroyed by subduction

Craton pushed into other cratons and islands

Volcanic rock, greenstone, formed from heavy magma

Crust melted at base but stayed solid on top

Sandstone pushed inland by colliding cratons

Basalt from speading oceanic ridge could be incorporated into continent

Granite from original islands was compressed and changed into a banded rock called gneiss

CONTINENT

differentiation, in which some primordial crust melted and created lighter material that bobbed to the surface and solidified, forming islands. Over millions of years, the movement of Earth's crust pushed the islands together to form cratons – small proto-continents. Eventually, these cratons collided and coalesced to create successively larger land masses – the first continents.

THE FIRST SUPERCONTINENT

By the end of the Archean Era, 2.5 BYA, the Earth's surface had 80 per cent of the land mass it does today, largely gathered together into a supercontinent called Vaalbara. Vaalbara was formed by colliding cratons called Kaapvaal and Pilbara. These survive today, but Kaapvaal is now in South Africa and Pilbara is in Australia, and each has

rocks dated to 3.6–2.7 BYA. In fact we now know these land masses have split and rejoined more than once (see pp.158–59), and that the cratons that formed the first continents are now scattered across the modern continents. Even though continents change, cratons remain as their stable cores.

Continent formation is still occurring. Oceanic crust continues to subduct under other oceanic crust, causing magma to push to the surface and cool into arcs of volcanic islands – such as those in the Caribbean.

THE OLDEST CONTINENT
WHOSE ROCKS STILL EXIST TODAY **IS CALLED "UR"** AFTER THE ANCIENT SUMERIAN CITY

◀ **Nishinoshima**
In 2013, a new island was discovered off the coast of Japan. It appeared when lava broke through Earth's crust in a burst of volcanic activity and then cooled, following the same process that created continents 4 BYA.

Plates of crust beneath ocean moved apart

New heavy oceanic crust was created at a spreading ridge, where the old crust was diverging; the new rock formed was heavy, volcanic basalt

Further island chains and cratons were built as the creation of continental crust continued

VOLCANIC ISLAND

VOLCANIC ISLAND

Heavy magma rose to fill the gap left by diverging crust

New oceanic crust continued to be created at oceanic spreading ridges

OCEANIC CRUST

THE **CORES OF CONTINENTS**... MAKE UP THE STABLE LITHOSPHERE. **THEIR FORMATION...** **OCCURED BILLIONS OF YEARS AGO**.

Nicholas Wigginton, *Science* editor, c.1970–

DATING EARTH

The question of Earth's age has only been resolved in the last few decades. As knowledge increased and scientific techniques were honed, estimates of the age of our planet increased from thousands of years to billions. We now know that Earth is around 4.54 billion years old.

It was not always clear Earth had an origin at all. Ancient Greek philosophers including Aristotle believed that our planet was eternal – it has always been here and always will be. Most civilizations had their own origin stories (see pp.18–19), and before the onset of modern science, religious texts were the main sources of ideas about Earth's origins. In 1645, Irish Bishop James Usher famously used the genealogy in the Bible to calculate the date of Earth's creation as 23rd October, 4004 BCE.

EARLY SCIENTIFIC IDEAS

Not everyone believed the idea of a young Earth. Back in the 16th century, French thinker Bernard Palissy argued that if the erosion of rocks was caused by the gradual battering of wind and rain, then Earth must be much older than a few thousand years. French natural historian Benoît de Maillet tried to explain why marine fossils were found at high elevations by wrongly concluding that Earth's sea level must have been much higher in the past. This was long before the discovery of plate tectonics (see pp.90–91). This idea of rates of erosion was revisited by Scottish geologist James Hutton

in the late 18th century as the tide of opinion began to turn towards a greater age for the planet. Hutton argued that Hadrian's Wall, despite being built by Romans in England more than 1,000 years previously, had barely eroded. Therefore, other rocks that had been significantly eroded must have been around much longer. Hutton also noted that layers of rock had not been laid down continuously, but in separate episodes of deposition, leading to "unconforming" layers that would have taken millions, not thousands, of years to form. Victorian geologist Charles Lyell agreed with Hutton, but emphasized the idea of Earth in a state of slow, perpetual change. Rates of change observed in modern times could then be used to estimate rates of change in the past.

THE DEBATE INTENSIFIES

By the middle of the 19th century, attempts to determine Earth's age had picked up steam, and scientists from many different disciplines made estimates. In 1862, physicist William Thompson (later Lord Kelvin), imagined our infant planet as a ball of molten rock and calculated how long it would have taken to cool to its present temperature, concluding 20–400 million years. He did not take into account the effect of radioactivity, a phenomenon that had yet to be discovered. Lyell criticized his ideas for being too conservative and inconsistent with what he had learnt about the deposition of rock layers. Charles Darwin joined the debate, stating in *On the Origin of Species* that Earth must be at least 300 million years old in order for chalk deposits in England to have eroded to their current state. Charles's son, astronomer George Darwin, believed that the Moon was formed from Earth. If so, he reasoned it would have taken at least 56 million years for the Moon to reach its current

distance. By the 20th century, the general consensus for the age of Earth had leapt from thousands of years to tens, if not hundreds, of millions of years.

THE AGE OF RADIOACTIVITY

It was the discovery of radioactivity by Henri Becquerel in 1896 that would enable scientists to find concrete evidence of Earth's age. The decay of radioactive atoms in rocks occurs over millions of years, and the proportion of unstable atoms remaining can be measured to reveal the rock's age (see pp.88–89). Over the next 30 years, many scientists used radiometric dating to analyze rocks from all over the world – arriving at ages between 92 million years and 3 billion years.

By the 1960s, the number of ways to use radioactivity to date rock samples started to rise. The precision of these techniques and the accuracy of the calculated ages steadily increased. We know now that Earth has been around for close to 4.54 billion years, give or take 50 million years. Such figures are supported by the age of meteorites that we think are slightly older than Earth.

▲ Dangerous beliefs
Bernard Palissy (1509–1589) worked as a potter for most of his life, but he was also a scientist. He put forward his then-radical belief that fossils were prehistoric animals, and not from the biblical flood. The French authorities ultimately imprisoned him.

▼ Clues in the rocks
A sketch from 1787 of rock layers at Jedburgh, Scotland, shows horizontal layers of rock that sit on top of vertical layers, each from different periods. This unconformity served as geologist James Hutton's evidence that Earth was very ancient.

FOSSILIZED TREES ON TOP OF A **PREHISTORIC SEA BED** 1,800M (5,900FT) **HIGH IN THE ANDES** CONVINCED CHARLES DARWIN THAT **EARTH WAS VERY OLD**

▼ **History in the rocks**
Rock such as this limestone on a Greek coast, with its apparent long history of deposition, followed by crumpling, followed by erosion, was the sort of evidence that, in the 18th and 19th centuries, set the minds of pioneering geologists thinking about the amount of time needed for geological change.

WITH RESPECT TO HUMAN OBSERVATION, **THIS WORLD** HAS **NEITHER A BEGINNING NOR AN END**.

James Hutton, geologist, 1726–1797

ZIRCON **CRYSTAL**

Some ancient crystals have survived 4.4 billion years on Earth. Their persistence provides an excellent opportunity to probe into our planet's history, and learn more about the origins of life and the first oceans.

The Jack Hills of Western Australia are home to the oldest material ever found on Earth. These tiny zircon crystals are each only the size of a dust mite, yet hold within them the secrets of our planet's turbulent infancy. The oldest crystals date from 4.4 BYA – 100 million years after a giant impact struck Earth and created the Moon – which means that Earth's solid crust, in which they formed, must be at least the same age. Zircon is a mineral that contains the element zirconium. It has a similar hardness to diamond, its more illustrious cousin – which means zircon crystals can survive erosion and other geological processes, making them an excellent record keeper of Earth's history.

Normally zircon crystals are red, but when scientists bombard them with electrons in order to study them, they take on a blue hue. Analysis of these crystals is subverting previous ideas of the conditions on early Earth. It was long thought that our planet's infancy was a hellscape, one much too fierce to support liquid water and life, but opinions are beginning to shift to an Earth that cooled relatively quickly, because the crystals needed those cool conditions to form.

Crystal composition

Radiometric dating analysis uses a device called a mass spectrometer. The rock sample is broken into atoms, then the atoms are ionized (given an electric charge). As the ions pass through the device, magnets sort them according to their mass, because the magnets deflect lighter ions more easily. This allows the sample's different ions to be identified and their precise proportions to be measured so the rock's age can be determined.

Mass spectrometer

▼ How radiometric dating works
Uranium atoms are so large and unstable that they decay – they give off radiation and change into more stable atoms – and they do this at a known rate. Measuring the ratio of uranium in rock to its final decay product (lead) tells us how much radioactive decay has occurred since the rock formed, and therefore how much time has passed.

Uranium atom

Lead atom produced by the radioactive decay of a uranium atom

One-quarter of the original uranium atoms remain

One-eighth of the uranium atoms remain

When the rock formed, the sample contained only uranium as it solidified from molten rock and crystallized.

704 million years later, the uranium atoms have decayed, giving off radiation and changing into lead atoms.

After 1.406 billion years, more uranium atoms have decayed. The more lead found in the rock, the older the sample.

Today, a geologist measures the ratio of uranium to lead remaining in the rock and dates this rock to 2.112 billion years old.

This particular zircon crystal is 4.4 billion years old

Evidence of early oceans

By comparing the ratio of oxygen isotopes found within the Jack Hills zircon crystals, scientists have concluded that oceans of liquid water may have been present on Earth as early as 4.4 billion years ago. Isotopes are versions of an atom with differing atomic weight. The ratio of oxygen-18 to oxygen-16 isotopes found in the crystals indicates the presence of liquid water.

Earth in the Archean Era, 3.5 BYA

Signs of life

Earth was previously thought to be inhospitable until 3.8 billion years ago, but isotope analysis of graphite flecks found inside zircon crystals dating back to 4.1 billion years ago suggests that life was present at this earlier time. Graphite is made of carbon, and the ratio of carbon-12 to carbon-13 isotopes in the graphite is characteristic of the ratio produced by living organisms.

Protecting the crystals

Around 200,000 zircons have been unearthed in the Jack Hills since the 1980s, and 10 per cent of them are more than 3.9 billion years old. The geology of the area is so important that the Australian government has declared the region a geoheritage site, to protect it from future mining activity and preserve its scientific treasures.

Jack Hills, Australia

This zircon crystal is incredibly small — measuring just 0.4mm — and is barely visible to the naked eye

CONTINENTS
DRIFT

The map of our modern world is a familiar image, but this arrangement of continents is a relatively recent development in our planet's history. Entire continents have split and moved apart over hundreds of millions of years. This idea wasn't accepted until the late 20th century.

The fact that Earth's land masses have shifted over time makes sense when looking at a map of the world. Some continents appear to fit together, like puzzle pieces. However, the notion that these vast land masses could move was long considered outrageous to the scientific community. Despite their reservations, the idea has been around for centuries, with the Flemish cartographer Abraham Ortelius widely credited as being the first to express such thoughts at the end of the 16th century.

BRIDGING THE GAP

In the 19th century, Antonio Snider-Pellegrini created two maps showing the ease with which the meandering coastlines of the various continents appear to slot into place to form one giant supercontinent. Further evidence that the far-flung continents had once been conjoined came from the fossil record (see pp.158–59). Scientists were beginning to discover that the fossilized remains of similar animals, and in particular plants, were cropping up

Corner of Africa appears to fit snugly with South America's coastline

▲ **First clues**
Explorers noticed that the east coast of South America and the west coast of Africa appeared to fit together. These maps were drawn by geographer Antonio Snider-Pellegrini in 1858.

in places now separated by vast oceans. This was explained away by the idea that continents were once connected via vast land bridges, which have since been eroded away or submerged deep beneath the sea.

Another thorny issue perplexing geologists was the origin of mountain ranges, such as the Himalayas. The leading idea in the 19th century was that the peaks were formed as wrinkles, as Earth cooled and shrank. If that were true, mountain chains should be spread evenly across the planet's surface – and that is not the case.

Ideas continued to develop at the turn of the 20th century. George Darwin, Charles's son, proposed that the Moon had once formed part of Earth and its absence accounted for the vast, landless Pacific Ocean. His theory suggested that the continents separated as the Moon broke away, explaining their present positions. Another theory was that Earth was

expanding. As the planet got bigger, its land masses were forced to spread out. Both of these ideas gradually lost support as the precise physical mechanisms behind them could not be found.

A NEW IDEA

In 1912, German scientist Alfred Wegener argued in favour of continental drift. He not only showed matching fossil evidence on disparate continents, but also concluded that the types of rock and other geological structures were similar too. He decided that this idea could not co-exist with the theory of now-submerged land bridges, so he suggested that the continents themselves had moved apart. This offered a potential solution to the mountain conundrum. If continents were free to roam, then over time some could collide. If India had smashed into mainland Asia, the Himalayas would be the result of continental crumpling.

Wegener published his findings the same year, suggesting that Earth's land masses ploughed through the sea over time. His work met with a lukewarm reception from the scientific community, in part because

▶ **Bold ideas**
German scientist Alfred Wegener (1880–1930) hoped to collect solid evidence for his continental drift theory on his fourth expedition to Greenland, but he died while collecting supplies for his camp.

◀ **Continent scars**
In 1977, this map, the result of a lifetime's work by oceanographers and cartographers Marie Tharp and Bruce Heezen, revealed the ocean floor in new detail, providing conclusive evidence for plate tectonics.

the idea, arguing that the planet's crust ruptures at plate boundaries, allowing magma to well up from the mantle. As this material solidifies, it forms a ridge, pushing the existing sea floor apart. So it is not that

IT TOOK OVER 300 YEARS FOR THE IDEA OF CONTINENTAL DRIFT FINALLY TO BE ACCEPTED AS FACT

the continents plough through the ocean crust as Wegener had suggested, but rather that the sea floor itself is growing, carrying away the continents, which are part of moving tectonic plates (see pp.92–93).

Today, these ideas are brought together as the theory of plate tectonics. It is supported by observations of Earth from space using geodesy, which maps small changes in Earth's gravity to locate concentrations of mass. Studies of the polarity of Earth's magnetic field, which is known to have flipped frequently over time (north becoming south, and vice versa), also lends weight. This leaves stripes of magnetic

...he could not provide a plausible reason as to why the continents would drift. He incorrectly calculated the rate of their movement and overestimated by a factor of 100 compared to today's accepted value, which did not help his cause.

Wegener's academic background was also a hindrance. Given his training as an astronomer and meteorologist, many in the geological community suggested he did not have the expertise required to be taken seriously. He was not without some support, however – British geologist Arthur Holmes backed his ideas, arguing as early as 1931 that Earth's mantle contained currents that helped move parts of the crust.

CLUES FROM THE SEA FLOOR
It was not until the 1950s that evidence emerged to turn the tide of opinion in Wegener's favour. In 1953, analysis of rocks in India suggested that it was once in the Southern Hemisphere, bolstering Wegener's mountain formation argument. Around the same time, a huge underwater mountain range – the Mid-Ocean Ridge – was discovered. It is Earth's longest mountain

range and extends through all of its oceans. The geologists of the day now had to explain the presence of this ridge, too. It would fall to former US Navy officer turned geologist

Harry Hess to tie all these ideas together. Having used sonar to map the ocean during World War II, by the early 1960s, Hess's research led him to propose that the continents did indeed drift apart thanks to a process called "sea-floor spreading". In 1958, Australian geologist Samuel Carey had suggested that Earth's surface, its crust, was constructed from plates. Hess ran with

I ONCE ASKED ONE OF MY LECTURERS... I WAS TOLD, SNEERINGLY, THAT IF I COULD PROVE THERE WAS A FORCE THAT COULD MOVE CONTINENTS, THEN HE MIGHT THINK ABOUT IT. THE IDEA WAS MOONSHINE.

David Attenborough, natural history broadcaster, 1926–

rock on the ocean floor (see pp.94–95), which allows us to date the bands and show how fast the sea floor is spreading.

Plate tectonics was not widely accepted until the 1970s, when maps of the ocean floor, such as that made by Marie Tharp and Bruce Heezen, left no doubt that the sea floor was spreading, accounting for continental drift.

HOW EARTH'S CRUST MOVES

The surface of our planet is sculpted by extremely slow convection currents in the mantle layer below. Earth's system of plate tectonics sets it apart from the other rocky planets in the Solar System, since its surface is constantly changing and is alive with geological activity.

Earth's surface layer, the crust, is formed of seven major tectonic plates – African, Antarctic, Eurasian, North American, South American, Pacific, and Indo-Australian – along with several smaller ones. These solid plates float on a semi-solid layer called the mantle. Plates move incredibly slowly, typically at about the rate that fingernails or human hair grow. Since Earth's layers stabilized 4 BYA, these plates have been constantly moving.

▼ **Volcanic eruption**
The Eyjafjallajökull volcano in Iceland erupts molten magma, along with black clouds of ash that fall on the ground as added layers atop Earth's crust.

EARTH'S SURFACE MOVES
Convection currents in the mantle are generated by heat in the core that filters into the mantle. Although the mantle is almost solid, it flows slowly, tugging at the base of the crust and moving the plates. The crust is of two kinds: oceanic crust, which is made of dense rock rich in magnesium and iron, and continental crust, made of rock with lighter elements including aluminium. Where the edge of a plate is made of oceanic crust, its greater density makes it subduct, or slip underneath, the lighter crust. It then sinks deep into the hot mantle, causing an upwelling of molten magma that breaks the surface of the crust as a volcano.

TECTONIC PHENOMENA
Where plates meet, a range of tectonic activity may occur, but exactly what depends on the crust material and the direction of movement. There are three main types of plate boundary: transform boundaries, where plates slide or grind past one another; divergent boundaries, where they slide apart, allowing magma to cool into new crust; and convergent boundaries, where two plates collide head on. Parts of the crust sink and melt at subduction zones, but new crust is made elsewhere by volcanoes and at mid-ocean ridges, where oceanic crust diverges.

Earthquakes, sudden movements of Earth's crust, occur at plate boundaries. At divergent and transform boundaries, they tend to be shallow, whereas collisions at convergent boundaries cause the deepest earthquakes.

Where two plates collide, they can push up continental crust to form a mountain range, such as the Himalayas. Those particular mountains were created when the Indian plate slammed into the Eurasian plate around 50 million years ago.

Underwater volcanoes spew molten lava, which cools into new oceanic crust

Convection current causes an upwelling of molten magma

Heat in the core causes convection currents in the mantle that drive the movement of tectonic plates

▶ **Dynamic surface**
Earth's crust is constantly changing as the plates move, buoyed by currents in the mantle below. Depending on how the plates interact, earthquakes can occur and volcanoes and mountain chains can form.

Solid crust

Semi-solid mantle

Liquid outer core

Solid inner core

Divergent plate boundary causes a mid-ocean ridge as magma rises to fill the gap left by the separating plates

MID-OCEAN RIDGE

OCEAN

HOTSPOT ISLANDS

OCEANIC TRENCH

MELTING CRUST

TECTONIC FAULT

VOLCANO

" CONTINENTAL DRIFT... EARTHQUAKES, VOLCANICITY... ARE **UNDOUBTEDLY CONNECTED** ON A GRAND SCALE. "

Alfred Wegener, geologist and meteorologist, 1880–1930

Volcanic islands are a result of magma from the mantle that has risen and cooled through the crust – these areas are called hotspots

Seamounts are hotspots where magma has cooled under water, but has not reached the ocean's surface

Convergent plate boundary causes oceanic crust to be forced underneath (subducted under) lighter continental crust, creating a deep oceanic trench

Volcanoes occur at a convergent boundary because of the upwelling of magma created by the subducting, melting crust erupting at the surface

Fold mountains are wrinkles in the continental crust, pushed upwards due to the pressure of colliding plates

Transform plate boundary causes a fault, or crack, in the crust where the plates are sliding past each other. Pressure builds on the plates until they slip suddenly, causing an earthquake

OCEAN **FLOOR**

In many ways, the ocean floor is a guide to Earth's history – studying it helps us decipher the mysteries of our planet's past. Exploring it has even given scientists clues about how life originated. Mapping the ocean floor reveals a diverse, active landscape full of tectonic phenomena.

The depths of the ocean are cold, dark, and incredibly hostile. At its deepest point there are 1.2 tonnes of water pressing down on every square centimetre (8.4 tons per square inch). Such extremes mean oceanographers resort to imaging the sea bed using sonar from the surface. It is easier for us to get images from Mars than map parts of our own sea bed.

Despite its inaccessibility, the ocean floor holds clues that are vital in understanding the development of Earth's crust, and also life. Deep ocean exploration is sharpening our ideas on plate tectonics (see pp.90–91). The chemically-rich material and heat generated by underwater volcanoes found on the ocean floor have led biologists to believe that these areas are where the first life-forms appeared (see pp.106–07).

The deepest places of the ocean floor are where two oceanic plates meet and form an underwater valley – one plate slips underneath (subducts beneath) the other, creating a V-shaped trench. The deepest ocean trench is the Mariana Trench in the Pacific Ocean: its deepest point is at 10,994m (36,070ft) below sea level. It could accommodate Mount Everest with about 2,000m (6,560ft) of water to spare.

The Puerto Rico Trench in the Atlantic Ocean has depths greater than 8,400m (27,560ft). The underwater boundary between the Caribbean and North

American plates, where the Puerto Rico Trench is found, is a particularly active area of the ocean floor. Its unique plate boundary and unusual phenomena provide a rich resource for scientific research: oceanographers, biologists, seismologists (who study earthquakes), and bathymetrists (who study the underwater terrain of lakes and oceans) all work here, hoping to unlock the secrets of the ocean floor.

How sonar surveys work

Marie Tharp, oceanographer

Multibeam sonar records the time taken for sound to bounce back from the sea floor in order to measure ocean depth. Oceanographers can use this data to create a coloured map of the sea floor, showing its terrain. Side-scan sonar is more accurate in that the intensity of its echoes can reveal whether the ocean floor is rocky (strong) or sandy (weak). Marie Tharp and Bruce Heezen mapped Earth's ocean floor in the 1950s (see pp.90–91).

Caribbean plate is sliding towards the east

Muertos Trough

▲ WEST

CARIBBEAN PLATE

◀ SOUTH

ANTILLES ARC

▶ **Clues on the ocean floor**
Magma from the mantle breaks through the crust and forces tectonic plates apart (see pp.92–93). As the magma cools to form new crust, minerals in the magma orient themselves in line with Earth's magnetic field. For reasons unknown, Earth's north-south polarity reverses from time to time, and over millions of years these reversals are etched into the ocean floor as a series of stripes.

Magnetic field reversals create stripes

Cooling material forces plates apart

Older rock with frozen magnetic alignment

Younger rock with frozen magnetic alignment

Molten material from mantle breaks through crust

The Antilles islands have been formed due to both folding and volcanism at this plate boundary

The island of Puerto Rico rises above the ocean surface

Seamount emerging from ocean surface becomes one of the southernmost islands of the Bahamas

The most negative gravity anomaly on Earth is found in the Puerto Rico Trench; this indicates an active downward force

▼ **Exploring the ocean floor**
A bathymetry map generated by sonar reveals the underwater terrain of the northeastern corner of the Caribbean plate. Differences in relief are represented by colour, highlighting deep sea trenches in purple.

KEY

Above sea level	
Sea level - 0m	0 ft
2,000m	6,562ft
3,000m	9,843ft
4,000m	13,123ft
5,000m	16,404ft
6,000m	19,685ft
7,000m	22,966ft

PUERTO RICO TRENCH

NORTH ▶

VIRGIN ISLANDS TROUGH

NORTH AMERICAN PLATE

ANEGADA TROUGH

EAST ▼

Tectonic activity

The boundary where the Caribbean and North American plates meet looks like a convergent plate boundary due to the presence of an ocean trench, which normally indicates subduction, but here, the plates are mainly sliding against one another instead – forming a transform plate boundary. The Caribbean plate is sliding to the east at a rate of 2cm (0.8in) per year. Since it grinds against the North American plate, earthquakes can occur when the plate jerks and slips. Seismologists study the seismic waves produced by the earthquakes. To the east, the Caribbean plate is pushing against the North American plate, resulting in mountain folds that break the surface as the Antilles island arc.

North American plate is sliding towards the west

Compression of the Caribbean plate's crust from the slightly subducting North American plate creates folds

Exploring the deep

Submersibles are invaluable tools for scientists wanting to explore deep sea ocean trenches, because they are able to withstand deep-sea pressure. Robotically-piloted submersibles, or AUVs, are pre-programmed with instructions on where to explore and what to measure. Some submersibles also allow scientists to visit the ocean floor in order to examine and collect samples of both rocks and life-forms for analysis at the surface.

Example of an AUV

THRESHOLD

LIFE EMERGES

Earth has a privileged position in the Solar System – in a band that's not too cold and not too hot to support liquid water. It is in this vital ingredient that life first emerges. And through a process of natural selection life evolves from simple bacteria to complex vertebrates, shaping our planet and filling it with astounding diversity.

GOLDILOCKS CONDITIONS

Living organisms emerged from non-living complex chemicals. Life-forms could metabolize, meaning they were able to extract energy from their surroundings. They could also copy themselves and adapt to their environment – through the process of natural selection.

Abundant complex chemicals and minerals

Planet with solid crust and liquid water

Stable habitat, possibly in the deep ocean, with a source of heat energy

Complex chemicals
Rocky planets, such as Earth, are made of a rich variety of elements, including oxygen, silicon, iron, nickel, aluminium, nitrogen, hydrogen, and carbon. The last of these, carbon, can build a large range of complex molecules in combination with other elements.

What changed?
Chemical reactions produced ever larger and more complex molecules. Molecules with self-copying abilities became more common. Reactions occured that both provided energy and the means to build more complex molecules. The chemicals of life became packaged inside membranes, forming protocells – the first true living organisms.

Heat from Earth's core
The planet's interior was hot, because of radioactivity and also due to heat left over from its violent formation. The heat energy reached the surface at volcanoes and deep-sea vents.

Mineral catalysts
The reactions that built the large, complex molecules of life needed to be driven by a chemical booster, or catalyst. Minerals bubbling up from Earth's mantle at deep-sea vents are thought to be a possible source of those catalysts.

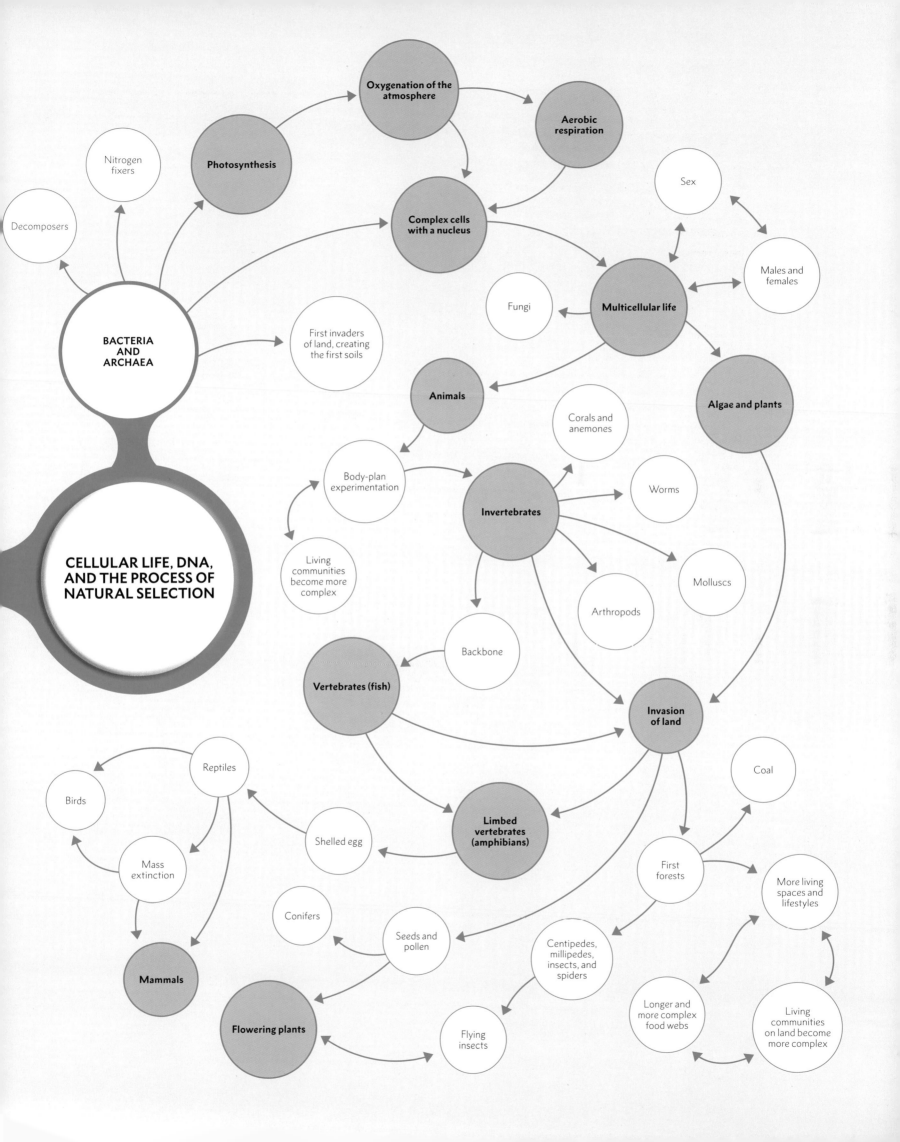

STORY OF LIFE

Life is over 4 billion years old, first emerging when Earth was only one-tenth of its present age. But even at the very beginning, life, although microscopic, was already the most complex thing in the known universe.

The Earth's violent birth left a planet where life was not only possible, but perhaps inevitable. As the land cooled and permanent oceans formed, the first protocells emerged – probably deep under water around chemically-rich fissures in the young ocean floor. Within a few million years, these protocells had become microbes – and for billions of years after that, the world belonged only to them. They evolved ways of getting energy either from sunlight or by eating other microbes, laying the foundations for the rest of life's diversity.

The biggest, most complex of life-forms – multicellular life – evolved only in the last billion years of Earth's history. These are the organisms that evolved into the familiar plants and animals of recent times. It was then that life could emerge from the microscopic and fill the oceans and land with greenery and fast-moving creatures.

PLANTS AND GREEN ALGAE

ANIMALS

The earliest known animal embryos and cnidarians (relatives of jellyfish and anemones) are fossilized, 635 MYA.

Rifting of supercontinents, 650 MYA, creates Iapetus Ocean and may have triggered Ediacaran and Cambrian explosions of evolution.

Sponges, the first animals, evolve 750 MYA, DNA evidence suggests.

Plants appear 934 MYA, according to modern DNA evidence.

3 MULTICELLULAR LIFE

The oldest fossil of a multicellular organism is 1.2 billion years old and belongs to a seaweed, *Bangiomorpha*. The fossil is complete with a possible stalklike "hold-fast" and reproductive organs. This is also the earliest complex organism (eukaryote) that can be attributed to a group still alive today – the red algae.

1 BYA

"Experimental" Ediacaran animals, including *Charnia* (above), appear, 550 MYA.

1 ORIGIN OF LIFE

A carbon trace in Australian rocks 4.1 billion years old could be life's oldest "signature". DNA evidence (from living organisms) leads to a slightly earlier estimate of life's beginnings and predicts that all organisms alive today can trace their ancestry back to a hypothetical microbe called LUCA – our Last Universal Common Ancestor.

Bacteria and archaea split from their common ancestor, LUCA, 4.2 BYA, according to DNA evidence from organisms alive today.

A type of archaea emerges, 3.8 BYA, according to modern DNA evidence, that goes on to form the nucleus of complex cells.

Chloroplasts appear 1.5 BYA, allowing complex cells to collect energy from sunlight.

Eukaryotes (organisms with complex cells) split into plantlike and animal-like groups, 1.6 BYA.

Fossil stromatolite

Mitochondria – the energy-producing factories of complex cells – evolve, 2 BYA.

EARTH

4 BYA

MICROBES

First permanent oceans possibly form, 4.4 BYA, providing the first habitat for life.

The Late Heavy Bombardment – a peak in space impacts 4.1–3.9 BYA – possibly strips away the atmosphere and kills all early life.

Stromatolites, mounds formed by bacterial colonies, provide the earliest fossil evidence of life.

Bacteria invade land 3.18 BYA, according to DNA estimates of the date of origin of landliving bacteria.

Complex cells with a nucleus evolve 2.73 BYA, according to DNA evidence.

2 BYA

3 BYA

Stromatolites – colonies of bacteria – are still forming on today's Australian coastline.

Soils rich in organic matter, 2.9 BYA, provide evidence of early life on land.

Traces of an oxygenated habitat, 2.7 BYA, indicate that photosynthetic organisms have started to fill the air with oxygen.

Fossil soil-surface bacteria are the first trace of life on land, 2.6 BYA.

The Great Oxygenation completes the flooding of Earth's atmosphere with oxygen, 2.4 BYA.

2 COMPLEX CELLS

Eukaryotes have complex cells with a nucleus and include plants, animals, fungi, and many microbes. Traces of steroid-like substances – unique to eukaryotes – have been found in rocks 2.4 billion years old, but direct evidence comes from the fossil *Diskagma* – a possible fungus – from 2.2 BYA.

"THERE ARE **4 MILLION** DIFFERENT KINDS OF ANIMALS AND PLANTS IN THE WORLD – 4 MILLION DIFFERENT **SOLUTIONS** TO THE PROBLEMS OF **STAYING ALIVE**."

David Attenborough, natural history broadcaster, 1926–
Life on Earth, 1979

0 MYA

Apes evolve 25 MYA.

Darwinius

Messel lake pit in Germany preserves a time capsule of mammal evolution, including early primate *Darwinius*, 47 MYA.

Primates first appear in the fossil record 56 MYA.

Asteroid impact, 65 MYA, causes extinction of dinosaurs, pterosaurs, and large marine reptiles, allowing the explosive evolution of large mammals and birds.

100 MYA

600 MYA

Ediacaran fossil, possibly a jellyfish

Ground cover on land was provided by the first plants with strong transport tissues 420 MYA. Towering above them was the enigmatic, funguslike *Prototaxites*, such as *Cooksonia*.

Flowering plants, including *Archaefructus*, and *Montsechia*, appear 120 MYA.

Fossil Archaeopteryx shows that birds have developed flight 150 MYA.

Animal trackways show evidence from 530 MYA of unidentified arthropods on land; oldest known fish are fossilized: *Myllokunmingia* and *Haikouichthys*.

Bonelike tissue is fossilized 510 MYA: dentine in a fish.

Experimental animal body plans fossilized 505 MYA in Canada's Burgess Shale.

Trace of fossil fur proves mammals have evolved fur 165 MYA.

Seed-bearing plants diversify 190 MYA.

500 MYA

DNA evidence suggests insects evolve 483 MYA.

Spores of land plants, fossilized 470 MYA, prove mosslike plants have invaded land.

200 MYA

Milk production evolves in mammals 210 MYA.

Earliest fossil dinosaur, 231 MYA, heralds the age of giant reptiles.

Mammals, such as *Adelobasileus*, evolve from their reptilian cynodont ancestors 225 MYA.

Air breathing and internal fertilization – advances vital for animals living on land – are shown in a fossil millipede, 428 MYA.

Jaws first preserved as a fossil 436 MYA, in a placoderm fish.

Fossil trees are preserved 380 MYA and provide evidence of forests.

Fossil tetrapod (limbed vertebrate) shows that vertebrates are invading land 375 MYA.

Fossil seeds, 372 MYA, prove plants have become free of watery habitats and can complete their life-cycle on dry land.

Fossil reptile, 318 MYA, shows some vertebrates were breaking free of watery habitats.

Mammal-like reptile, or synapsid, is fossilized 312 MYA.

Fossil cynodont, 260 MYA, shows diverse teeth, a muscular jaw structure, and a large braincase – all features that will characterize its descendants: mammals.

The Great Dying kills all trilobites and more than 70 per cent of known animal and plant species at the end of the Permian period, 250 MYA.

400 MYA

300 MYA

Fossil cones show that plants 305 MYA have evolved structures that protect their seeds.

LIFE'S
INGREDIENTS FORM

Earth's crust is made of dozens of chemical elements, but only some – including carbon, hydrogen, oxygen, and nitrogen – are the stuff of living things. Their atoms lock together into complex molecules and it was this kind of chemical assembly that precipitated the origin of life.

Earth has an iron core surrounded by mostly silicon-based rocks. Carbon is comparatively scarce, but all known life is carbon-based. Both silicon and carbon atoms bond prolifically with others, but while silicon's affinity is mainly with oxygen (making up the silicon dioxide that dominates Earth's rocks), carbon is versatile. It bonds with other elements, such as hydrogen, nitrogen, and phosphorus.

Complex life needs complex molecules. Earth – with its rocks still cooling in the wake of its violent birth, and liquid water condensing into the first oceans – provided just the right conditions for them to form.

Earth's first atmosphere was thick with unbreathable gases, such as carbon dioxide, hydrogen, nitrogen, and water vapour – but these were sources of life's elements. In a world without oxygen gas to react with it,

hydrogen joined to other elements, making methane (CH_4) and ammonia (NH_3). In 1953, American chemists Stanley Miller and Harold Urey simulated early Earth in the lab with electrical sparks to imitate lightning. They showed that with enough heat and energy, the chemicals in Earth's atmosphere could make simple organic molecules – life-giving, carbon-based chemicals.

EVEN BIGGER MOLECULES

But life needed more – proteins, which are long chains of amino acids, and DNA. Today, pools rich with protein would be cleared by hungry organisms. But early Earth was energized by warmth and full of minerals that acted as catalysts, boosting specific chemical reactions. Giant molecules could persist long enough to get trapped in membranes – precursors of the first cells.

Atmosphere was heavy with carbon dioxide, so atmospheric pressure was higher than today, allowing water to stay liquid way above its modern-day boiling point

Clouds of water droplets would have filled the sky, as they do today

Liquid water – in which the first life formed – would have first persisted as oceans at some time between 4.4 and 4.2 BYA

▶ Recipe for life
Small molecules of less than half a dozen atoms were abundant on newly-formed Earth. They reacted to form bigger organic molecules with a "skeleton" of bonded carbon atoms – which, in turn, linked to form long-chain molecules.

SIMPLE INGREDIENTS

Oxygen   Nitrogen

Carbon

Hydrogen

Water   Ammonia   Methane

SIMPLE ORGANIC MOLECULES

Range of different amino acids

LARGE ORGANIC MOLECULE

Groups specific to each kind of amino acid (in full colour) stick out

Standard amino acid repeating units, in faded colours, form the backbone

Chain of amino acids – the beginnings of a protein

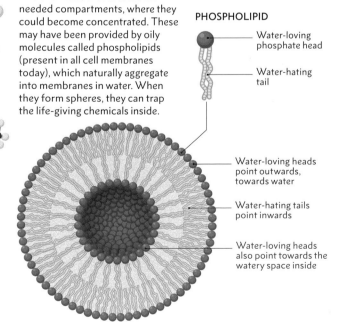

▼ Life wrapped up
The chemicals that created life needed compartments, where they could become concentrated. These may have been provided by oily molecules called phospholipids (present in all cell membranes today), which naturally aggregate into membranes in water. When they form spheres, they can trap the life-giving chemicals inside.

PHOSPHOLIPID

Water-loving phosphate head

Water-hating tail

Water-loving heads point outwards, towards water

Water-hating tails point inwards

Water-loving heads also point towards the watery space inside

MEMBRANE FORMING A SPHERE

◄ **Hellish origins**
Earth in the Hadean eon (4.6–4.0 BYA) was unrecognizable. Exposed land was unprotected from the Sun's burning radiation and would remain lifeless for another billion years – by which time erosion had started to make the first soils. Conditions suitable for life may have existed, however, in the deep ocean or shallow seas.

Dry land was formed by crater rims made by asteroid impacts, not by tectonic movements, which create mountains today

Lava could fill craters as asteroid impacts triggered volcanic activity

Cooling seas, cut off from the violence elsewhere, may have provided the conditions needed for newly-formed complex organic molecules to persist

Earth's crust was mostly too hot and unstable to nurture life. The greater internal heat of the young Earth, and the frequent impacts from space, caused volcanic activity on an unimaginable scale

Volcanoes spewed minerals that may have acted as catalysts, helping to drive the formation of bigger organic molecules at calmer locations

4.1 BYA | FIRST TRACE
OF POSSIBLE LIFE

2.4 BYA | OXYGEN
FILLS THE AIR

936 MYA | ESTIMATED ORIGIN OF
ALGAE AND PLANTS

THE **GENETIC** CODE

A living organism is the most precisely ordered thing in the known universe. The assembly and upkeep of a living body need direction and control. The entire operation is guided by self-replicating molecules of nucleic acid (DNA and its ancestors) that were present at the dawn of life.

Until the discovery of DNA's precise shape in 1953, it was a mystery how life-forms passed on genetic information to the next generation. Once revealed, the double-stranded structure of DNA hinted at how information was inherited whenever one cell splits into two. In the next years, experiments confirmed not only that

acids, possibly a type called RNA, were probably capable of boosting their own replication reactions. Their chains could have acted as templates guiding the assembly of new parallel chains. Copying from a template is also used by DNA in living organisms today, but it happens only when the two chains of the double helix separate

▶ **Reading the code**
In a living cell's nucleus, DNA's double helix is unzipped so that genes can be used to make RNA, and then protein. Here, a strand of RNA is being built by matching bases (chemical components), copying the sequence. This RNA strand will go on to make a specific protein useful to the life-form. The sequence of RNA bases is the code for a specific sequence of chemical components that makes just the right protein.

> **DNA** IS LIKE A **COMPUTER PROGRAM** BUT FAR, FAR **MORE ADVANCED** THAN ANY SOFTWARE **EVER CREATED.**

Bill Gates, technology pioneer and philanthropist, 1955–

DNA carried units of heredity (called genes), but also that it exerted its influence in an astonishingly intricate way.

INFORMATION CARRIERS
DNA is a giant long-chain molecule – just like protein, cellulose, and many other biological molecules. But whereas cellulose is a monotonous fibre of identical subunits, those of DNA – and protein – come in different kinds. Different subunits follow in an information-carrying sequence – just as letters form a word. DNA belongs to a class of long-chain information-carriers called nucleic acids. The sugars and other components of their structure would have been among life's primordial ingredients. The first nucleic

in preparation for cell splitting. Otherwise, one chain is fixed to another like the sides of a ladder. The copying results in two double helices, each with identical information destined for a new daughter cell. In this way, genetic information is copied and inherited.

USING THE INFORMATION
DNA cannot carry out any tasks alone. It instructs other molecules – the proteins – to do the work of maintaining and developing a living organism. A single DNA molecule carries hundreds of sections – genes – each carrying instructions to make a specific protein. In a living cell, sections of DNA are continually being unwound and wound – as genes are exposed for protein manufacture.

The rungs that connect DNA's backbones are chemical components called nucleobases, or bases for short. Each base is a unit of digital information

Bases coloured yellow are adenine. There are three other types: guanine (green), cytosine (blue), and thymine (orange). Each binds only to one other type of base

▼ **They were simpler times...**
Today, DNA needs protein to replicate and RNA to make protein to carry out all its other functions. At the origin of life, there was no such complexity. The earliest replicating molecules, possibly RNA, had the ability both to carry data and multiply unaided.

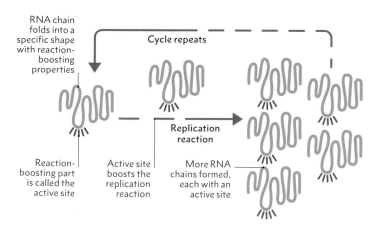

RNA chain folds into a specific shape with reaction-boosting properties

Cycle repeats

Reaction-boosting part is called the active site

Active site boosts the replication reaction

Replication reaction

More RNA chains formed, each with an active site

A second, identical, DNA chain binds to the specific pattern of bases on its partner, forming the famous double helix structure

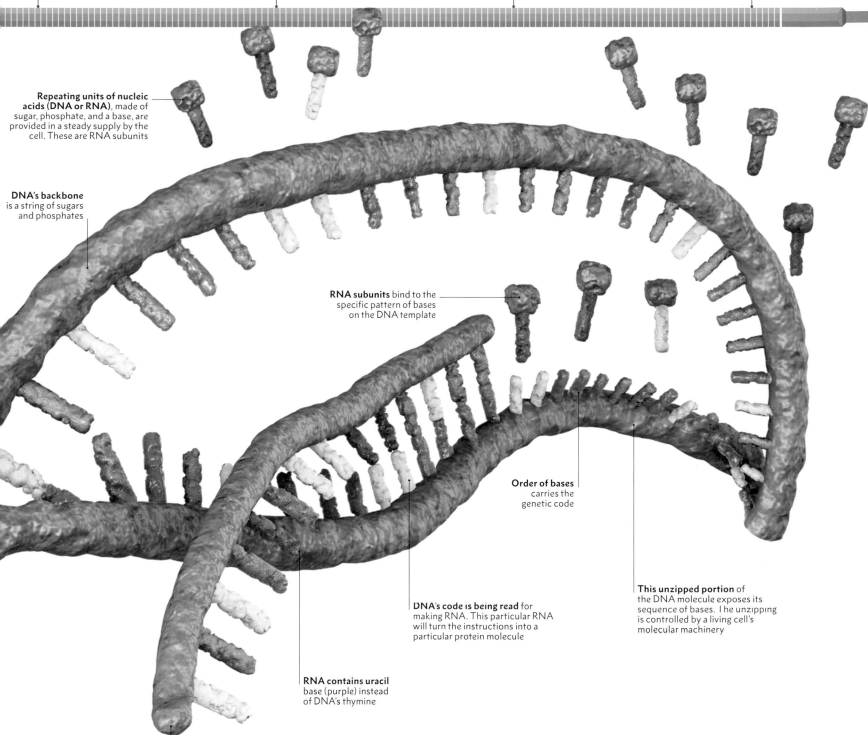

Repeating units of nucleic acids (DNA or RNA), made of sugar, phosphate, and a base, are provided in a steady supply by the cell. These are RNA subunits

DNA's backbone is a string of sugars and phosphates

RNA subunits bind to the specific pattern of bases on the DNA template

Order of bases carries the genetic code

This unzipped portion of the DNA molecule exposes its sequence of bases. The unzipping is controlled by a living cell's molecular machinery

DNA's code is being read for making RNA. This particular RNA will turn the instructions into a particular protein molecule

RNA contains uracil base (purple) instead of DNA's thymine

RNA backbone has a different sugar to DNA

DNA IS AMONG THE **LONGEST OF MOLECULES** – CHAINS IN HUMANS ARE **UP TO 8.4CM** (3.3IN) **LONG** AND CONTAIN **249 MILLION** BASE PAIRS

◄ **Discovering DNA**
In 1953 in Cambridge University, scientists made a breakthrough. American biologist James Watson (far left) and British biologist Francis Crick deduced that DNA (deoxyribonucleic acid) had a regular double-helical shape and properties that would allow it to pass on genetic information.

LIFE **BEGINS**

Life arose from non-living matter by processes of gathering complexity. As self-replicating molecules mixed with catalysts – substances that drive chemical reactions – self-assembly snowballed into the first cells: organisms with familiar characteristics of life.

All life consists of cells with the chemicals of life contained inside a membrane. A living organism is continually dynamic, resisting collapse into disorder and death. How such a system emerged from the non-living Earth is a mystery, but scientists apply what they know about biochemistry and conditions on early Earth to deduce what might have happened. The transition demands a special setting, and conditions may have been just right around 4 BYA.

PAID TO EAT A FREE MEAL

Deep-sea volcanic vents were rich in chemicals and were warm, but not so hot as to break apart big molecules. Billions of years ago, they were also a safe haven from bombarding asteroids and fierce solar rays. Vents today get encrusted with metal sulphides as the water cools. These minerals boost, or catalyze, reactions – some of which convert carbon dioxide into acetate. Acetate has a pivotal position in the metabolism of all life today. What is more, one sort of acetate-forming reaction can even generate energy. This combination of food manufacture and payment in energy – all trapped within the catalytic encrustation – could have been a "hatchery" for life.

> **TODAY'S DNA**, STRUNG THROUGH ALL THE **CELLS OF THE EARTH**, IS ... AN EXTENSION AND **ELABORATION** OF THE **FIRST MOLECULE**.
>
> **Lewis Thomas**, physician, writer, and educator, 1913–1993

ESCAPING THE CHIMNEYS

The first "protocells" formed when oily membranes encapsulated chemicals that were generated in the chimneys. Sea water helped protocells disperse from the chimneys, and the catalytic minerals in it helped maintain their primitive metabolism.

The versatility of the element carbon – which forms the skeleton of acetate – means that its atoms can assemble into a wide range of molecules. Some of the molecules generated by mineral-catalysis may have developed catalytic abilities of their own – and could even drive their own assembly. It is possible that these molecules may have been related to RNA – a material found in all cells today. RNA – or molecules like it – marked the emergence of biological information, too. Such molecules could control how cells maintained the emerging qualities of life.

▲ Hot habitat
As water emerges from a deep-sea vent, encrusting minerals build up "chimneys", some of which appear to smoke with dark iron sulphide. These habitats support bizarre life-forms today – entirely dependent on the mineral effluent.

▶ The origin of life
A chemical reaction boosted by minerals inside a deep-sea chimney, and contained inside a membrane, may have been the basis for the first life – a "protocell". More complex protocells later started to make their own catalysts, which drove their reactions. To begin with, these catalysts may have been RNA. But eventually, protocells developed protein catalysts called enzymes. RNA (and eventually DNA) took over the job of controlling the entire assembly.

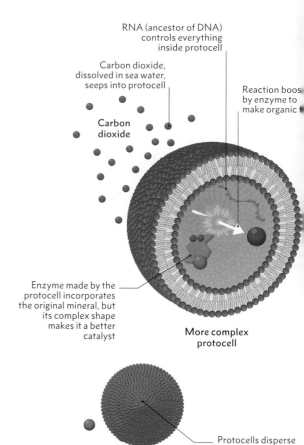

RNA (ancestor of DNA) controls everything inside protocell

Carbon dioxide, dissolved in sea water, seeps into protocell

Carbon dioxide

Reaction boos by enzyme to make organic

Enzyme made by the protocell incorporates the original mineral, but its complex shape makes it a better catalyst

More complex protocell

Protocells disperse into the surrounding sea water

Minerals

Chimney formed from encrustations of minerals spewing from the vent

Carbon dioxide seeps into protocell

Energy released when carbon dioxide forms organic food

Minerals catalyze (boost) the reaction

Organic food such as sugar or acetate, produced

Chimney of a deep-sea vent

Protocell

LIFE BEGINS GRADUALLY AS PROTOCELLS

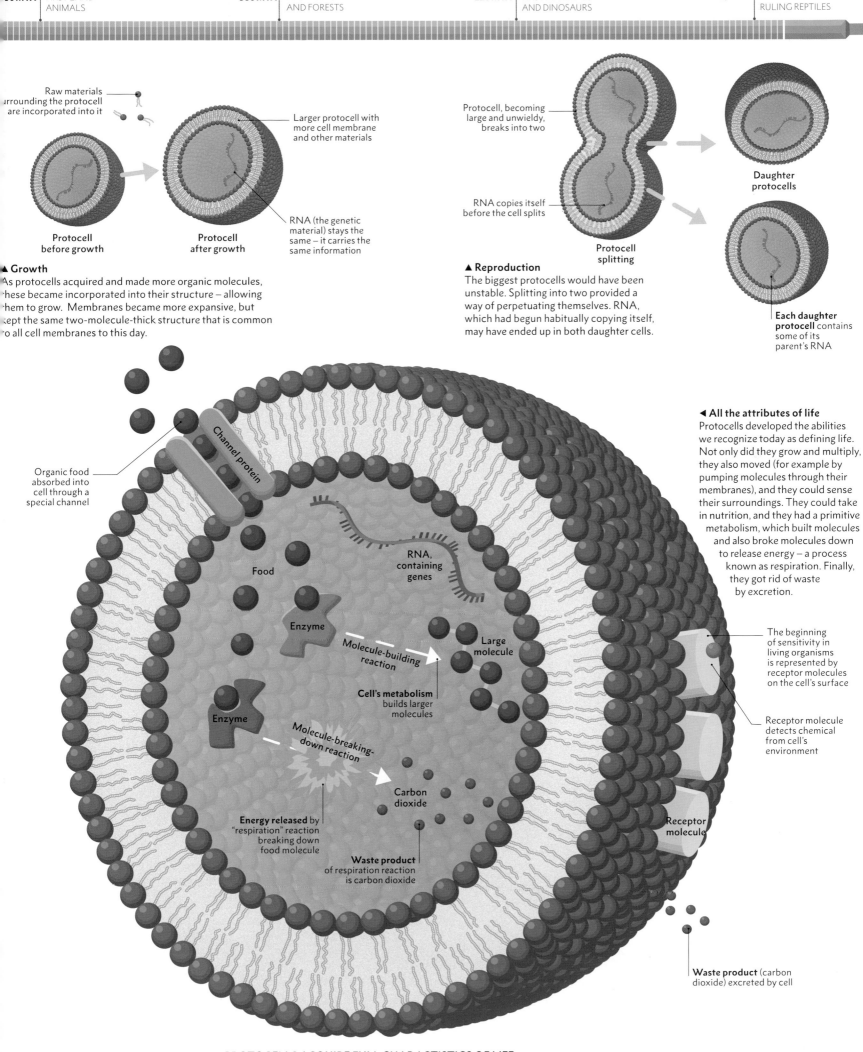

▲ Growth

As protocells acquired and made more organic molecules, these became incorporated into their structure – allowing them to grow. Membranes became more expansive, but kept the same two-molecule-thick structure that is common to all cell membranes to this day.

Raw materials surrounding the protocell are incorporated into it

Larger protocell with more cell membrane and other materials

RNA (the genetic material) stays the same – it carries the same information

Protocell before growth

Protocell after growth

▲ Reproduction

The biggest protocells would have been unstable. Splitting into two provided a way of perpetuating themselves. RNA, which had begun habitually copying itself, may have ended up in both daughter cells.

Protocell, becoming large and unwieldy, breaks into two

RNA copies itself before the cell splits

Protocell splitting

Daughter protocells

Each daughter protocell contains some of its parent's RNA

◄ All the attributes of life

Protocells developed the abilities we recognize today as defining life. Not only did they grow and multiply, they also moved (for example by pumping molecules through their membranes), and they could sense their surroundings. They could take in nutrition, and they had a primitive metabolism, which built molecules and also broke molecules down to release energy – a process known as respiration. Finally, they got rid of waste by excretion.

Channel protein

Organic food absorbed into cell through a special channel

Food

RNA, containing genes

Enzyme

Molecule-building reaction

Large molecule

Cell's metabolism builds larger molecules

Enzyme

Molecule-breaking-down reaction

The beginning of sensitivity in living organisms is represented by receptor molecules on the cell's surface

Receptor molecule detects chemical from cell's environment

Energy released by "respiration" reaction breaking down food molecule

Carbon dioxide

Waste product of respiration reaction is carbon dioxide

Receptor molecule

Waste product (carbon dioxide) excreted by cell

PROTOCELLS ACQUIRE FULL CHARACTISTICS OF LIFE

HOW **LIFE EVOLVES**

Even at the dawn of life, the process of evolution was under way. Life was changing, and at the root of every novelty was mutation – imperfections in DNA's copy-making process. The mistakes produced variety, and on a changeable planet some variations succeeded, while others failed.

All organisms change during their lifetime. But a grander scale of change, at the level of populations, happens through generations. When an organism reproduces, it copies its entire DNA, which ranges from under a million to many billions of digital "bits" of information. The enterprise represents a monumental turnover of molecular data. Even with natural system-checks in place, copying errors, called mutations, happen.

beneficial mutations are selected – they proliferate and pass on their "good genes" to at least some of their offspring. Those with mutations that harm their survival or ability to reproduce will diminish and may die out.

The changing environment, and a life-form's habitat and survival strategy within it, determine whether its mutations are helpful or harmful. Deep-sea fish have big eyes and glowing devices that allow them to

> **EVOLUTION** HAS **NO LONG-TERM GOAL**. THERE IS NO LONG-DISTANCE TARGET, **NO FINAL PERFECTION** TO SERVE AS A CRITERION FOR SELECTION.
>
> **Richard Dawkins**, evolutionary biologist, 1941–

Mutation produces the raw material of variation. Some mutations have scarcely any effect, but others can abort development, while a few are beneficial.

SELECTION BY THE ENVIRONMENT

While mutation is haphazard, evolution is far from random. The mutations are subject to a selection process. Life-forms with

hunt in the dark, while desert cacti have water stores defended with spines. Cactus spines and luminous lures need genetic diversity to appear, but it is the environment that selects them for the right places. Chance can play a role in spreading mutations, especially in small populations, but only natural selection can explain adaptation – the fitting of an organism to its environment.

NEW SPECIES

Although some mutations can produce sudden, distinct novelties, evolutionary change is generally slow and gradual. Selection typically works on sets of genes that work together to control broad features such as size or shape. But living diversity is not continuous – it occurs in discrete units called species. New species arise when two populations can no longer interbreed. They cannot exchange genes, and their evolutionary paths drift apart. This divergence might happen across an emerging barrier – such as a river or mountain range. But mutations themselves, such as those involving whole chromosomes, especially among plants, can prevent interbreeding and isolate populations.

There are millions of species living today, but all – including countless more that lived in the past – are products of evolutionary change shaped by the environment.

▶ **Reaching the limit**
A few microbes, that today stand out as bright colours at the edges of hot acidic pools, are a testament of the extent to which genetic variation and adaptation allows life to live in extremes.

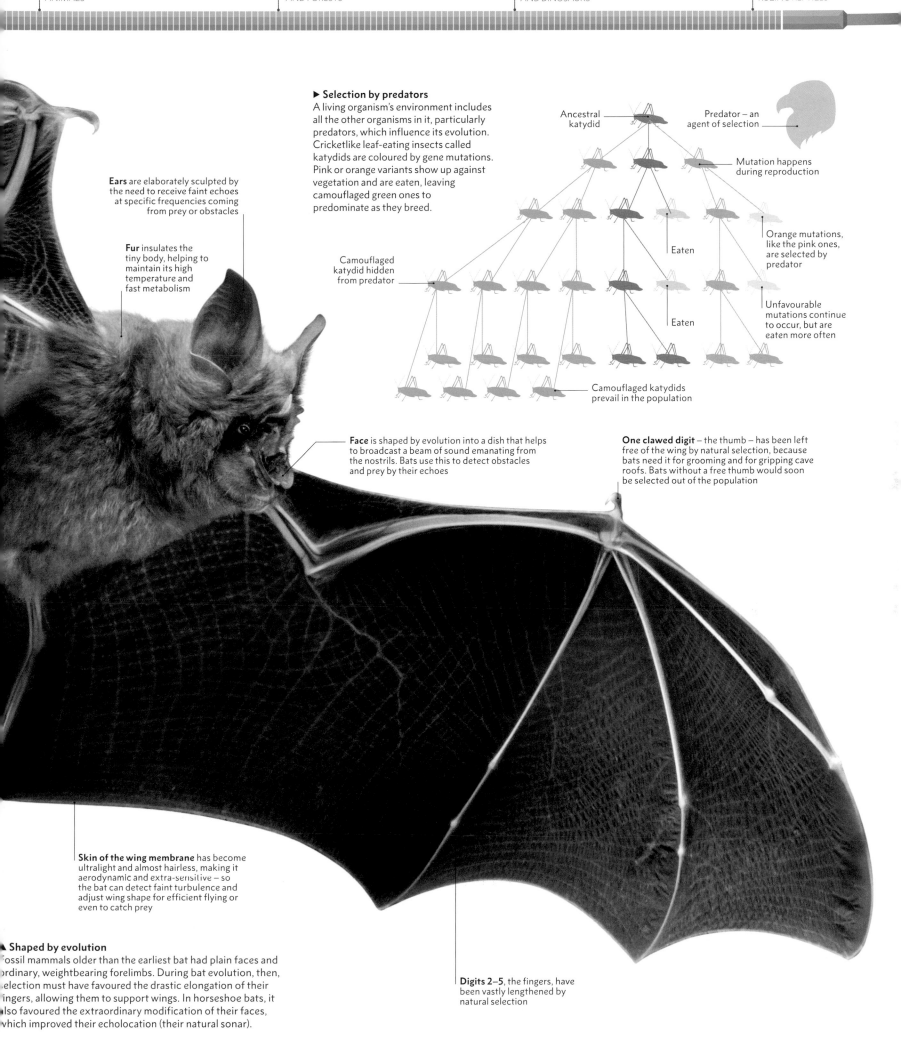

▶ Selection by predators
A living organism's environment includes all the other organisms in it, particularly predators, which influence its evolution. Cricketlike leaf-eating insects called katydids are coloured by gene mutations. Pink or orange variants show up against vegetation and are eaten, leaving camouflaged green ones to predominate as they breed.

Ancestral katydid

Predator – an agent of selection

Mutation happens during reproduction

Camouflaged katydid hidden from predator

Eaten

Eaten

Orange mutations, like the pink ones, are selected by predator

Unfavourable mutations continue to occur, but are eaten more often

Camouflaged katydids prevail in the population

Ears are elaborately sculpted by the need to receive faint echoes at specific frequencies coming from prey or obstacles

Fur insulates the tiny body, helping to maintain its high temperature and fast metabolism

Face is shaped by evolution into a dish that helps to broadcast a beam of sound emanating from the nostrils. Bats use this to detect obstacles and prey by their echoes

One clawed digit – the thumb – has been left free of the wing by natural selection, because bats need it for grooming and for gripping cave roofs. Bats without a free thumb would soon be selected out of the population

Skin of the wing membrane has become ultralight and almost hairless, making it aerodynamic and extra-sensitive – so the bat can detect faint turbulence and adjust wing shape for efficient flying or even to catch prey

◀ Shaped by evolution
Fossil mammals older than the earliest bat had plain faces and ordinary, weightbearing forelimbs. During bat evolution, then, selection must have favoured the drastic elongation of their fingers, allowing them to support wings. In horseshoe bats, it also favoured the extraordinary modification of their faces, which improved their echolocation (their natural sonar).

Digits 2–5, the fingers, have been vastly lengthened by natural selection

► **Galápagos finches**
These finches were collected from the Galápagos islands and Darwin noticed that slight differences in the size and shape of their beaks might have arisen from a common ancestor.

L ife changes over the course of thousands, and millions, of years. From one form of life another will arise, modified in some way by the environment in which it lives. The second form of life is more adapted to survive in its environment, and it retains some aspects of its previous form. This is evolution by natural selection, and we can track its progress through the fossil record.

HISTORY OF
EVOLUTION

Some have called it the biggest idea of all time: that everything that has ever lived on Earth – dodos and diatoms, cabbages and kings – has descended from a single common ancestor. The possibility of life's evolution occupied some of the greatest minds, but it took one gentleman's lifetime pursuit of "the species problem" to explain how it could happen.

EARLY CLUES

Philosophers of antiquity had anticipated evolutionary thought: some considered the possibility that all life could be ranked in a hierarchy – with humans at the top.

In the 17th and 18th centuries, western naturalists explored the world and filled museums with fossils. Those that named these extinct animals did so from a religious point of view. Animals were assumed to have been created in their current form by God. Every species on Earth had always been there, and they could not be changed. Fossils could be explained away as animals that had died during the Great Flood. Scientists who compared the anatomy of various animals saw plenty of parallels between species. These similarities supported the idea of an affinity between certain groups of animals. For instance, African baboons were undoubtedly closer to Asian macaques than they were to diminutive American marmosets. Likewise, chimpanzees seemed close to humans. What did this closeness mean, if anything?

ALTERNATIVE WORLD VIEW

For Charles Darwin – born into a reverent society – these anatomical affinities caught his attention. He was recommended for a five-year voyage aboard the HMS *Beagle*. During his journey, he collected specimens from across the globe.

Darwin pondered on the unexpected regional similarities in his specimens. Similarities between species that lived thousands of miles away from each other seemed to go against the idea of a single, spontaneous Creation event. Animals on

The Galápagos Islands resembled those in nearby South America, and the unusual wildlife in Australia seemed to belong to a different Creation altogether. Upon Darwin's return to England, ornithologist John Gould examined his collection of Galápagos birds. Darwin assumed they belonged to multiple families, but Gould showed how they were in fact species of closely related finches within one family. Darwin's experiences were persuading him that not only were these new species modified from a former generalized species, but perhaps that was the case with all forms of life – that there is one common ancestor for all. Darwin ruminated on his theory that evolution happened by infinitesimally small changes over many, many years and animals with traits that aided survival were more likely to breed and pass these "favourable" characteristics on to the next generation.

In 1858, English naturalist Alfred Russell Wallace wrote to Darwin with the same idea. A year later, Darwin published his ideas in a book, his famous *On the Origin of Species* in 1859, which caused a stir in the scientific community. He faced outrage, since it essentially challenged Biblical Creation as fact. Nevertheless, Darwin's theories gained respectable supporters, including the English naturalist Thomas Henry Huxley, a friend of Darwin's who championed his cause in the scientific community. Within a few years, evolution by natural selection was being lauded in textbooks. In his *Principles of Biology*, the philosopher Herbert Spencer coined an expression that became synonymous with Darwin's ideas: "survival of the fittest".

A UNIFIED THEORY

Darwin's *On the Origin of Species* was exhaustive in its catalogue of evidence, but the mystery of inheritance remained. Darwin understood that life changed over time, but how exactly did these changes occur? The popular view was that hereditary qualities blended from two parents – akin to mixing paints of different colours. No one knew if these qualities physically existed. In reality, this blending led to a dilution of varieties, not the emergence of new ones, and so was not a sufficient explanation.

 CHARLES DARWIN WAITED **23 YEARS** BEFORE PRESENTING HIS IDEAS TO THE PUBLIC, **DUE TO THEIR CONTROVERSY**

The breakthrough came from an unlikely source: an Augustinian friar in Austria. In the 1860s Gregor Mendel's experiments in breeding different varieties of pea plants allowed him to deduce that inheritance was due to particles, later called genes. Sexual reproduction remixed genes to produce unique combinations, some of which may express themselves in later generations. This explained two mysteries: the appearance of characteristics that skip generations, and the perpetuation of characteristics that aided survival (natural selection). When he bred yellow and green peas together, Mendel saw that the next generation of peas were uniformly yellow. Therefore, some traits were more likely to express themselves than others. When this generation was interbred, the result were a group of peas with mixed colours, indicating that traits could also skip generations.

Mendel's discoveries not only augmented Darwin's, despite each having no knowledge of the other's work, but also debunked popular rival theories – such as "Lamarckism". The French naturalist Jean-Baptiste Lamarck had proposed that features acquired through life, such as larger and stronger muscles, could be transmitted to offspring. Mendelism was finally rediscovered in 1900 and more scientists began thinking about evolution with genetic inheritance in mind. With genetics as the exciting new discipline of natural science, it became clear that new varieties of genes arise by a process of spontaneous mutation. Natural selection acts upon these varieties by choosing, and keeping, the most useful. By the 1940s German-American biologist

Ernst Mayr showed that if populations fragmented, evolution could take different courses away from a single ancestor – and create new species.

Fossils record evolution in progress: fish fins morphing into amphibious limbs, limbs into wings, mammalian limbs back into fin-like flippers, and so on. Today, DNA analysis proves beyond doubt that even the lowliest and loftiest life-forms share the same origins.

MICROBES APPEAR

Bacteria have been around far longer than any other kind of organism. They were the first to photosynthesize, the first to consume food – and are still the only living things capable of making their food in the absence of light. Billions of years ago, they were pioneers of both oceans and land.

Bacteria are the simplest cellular organisms, but also by far the most abundant and widespread. They are far smaller than the cells of plants and animals – most are about one-tenth the size of a human skin cell. They are called prokaryotic ("pro" meaning before, and "karyon" meaning kernel), because their cells lack the dense nucleus that contains DNA in more complex cells.

Bacteria seem uniform in structure, but this belies remarkable chemical diversity. In 1977, biologists recognized some kinds of prokaryotes as an entirely new life-form,

BACTERIA ARE SO **WIDESPREAD**, SOME LIVE 3KM (2 MILES) **DEEP IN EARTH'S CRUST**, LIVING ON ENERGY FROM **RADIOACTIVE URANIUM**

▼ Bacteria inside animals
Many food-eating bacteria live inside the guts of animals – such as these on the lining of a human colon. Most maintain a cooperative relationship with their host by exchanging nutrients –in humans, they are esential to digestion. But a few cause disease.

called archaea. These archaea – mostly living in hostile environments, such as salt lakes or hot acidic pools – had unique, ether-based membranes unlike any other living thing. Some performed bizarre chemical processes, spewing out methane.

BANKS OF DEFENCES

Early bacterial evolution happened in a world teeming with other microbes – and many of these early life-forms produced

▼ Bacillus
The shapes of bacteria vary from spherical to spiral-shaped, but this rod-shaped type, called a bacillus, is very common. It shows a range of features present in some modern bacteria. Most early bacteria would not have had the outer capsule layer, nor the hairlike pili.

Plasmid – one of many short loops of DNA

Main genome – a long, twisted, closed loop of DNA, containing a few thousand genes, loosely bound to the centre of the cell

repelling substances, so-called antibiotics, as they competed for food and space. Bacteria, therefore, have layers of defences. Outside their thin cell membrane, which is common to all life, they have a tough cell wall, and most types also have a second membrane that helps stop antibiotics from penetrating – and still today, bacteria with a wall sandwiched between inner and outer membranes are most resistant to antibiotics.

CHEMICAL DIVERSITY

Bacterial nutrition spans the full range of types seen in plants and animals – and more besides. Many have retained the food-making capability of life's earliest ancestors, deriving energy from minerals.

Some of these bacteria invaded soils and became critical for other life by recycling elements such as nitrogen. Others – the cyanobacteria – evolved photosynthesis, making food from sunlight, and were the first organisms to pour oxygen into the atmosphere. But as microbial communities evolved to be more complex, many became food-eaters – absorbing nourishment from their surroundings. It was bacteria like these that – billions of years later – would invade the dead and living bodies of plants and animals, becoming decomposers or disease-causing parasites.

Last Universal Common Ancestor, or "LUCA"

BACTERIA

ARCHAEA

FUNGI

LAND PLANTS

ANIMALS

EUKARYOTES

◄ **Tree of life**
This tree shows the branching relationships among all forms of life, according to DNA analysis. The analysis suggests that all cellular life alive today has a common origin – it evolved just once, from an unknown ancestor dubbed "LUCA", and that it has three main branches, or domains: bacteria, archaea, and eukaryotes.

KEY

Bacteria are prokaryotes – all simple, single-celled microbes.

Archaea are prokaryotes, like bacteria. They resemble bacteria, but at a chemical level they are utterly different, and only distantly related.

Eukaryotes are much more complex (see pp.118–19), but most branches are also microbes. The plants, animals, and fungi are just small twigs within the eukaryote limb of the tree of life.

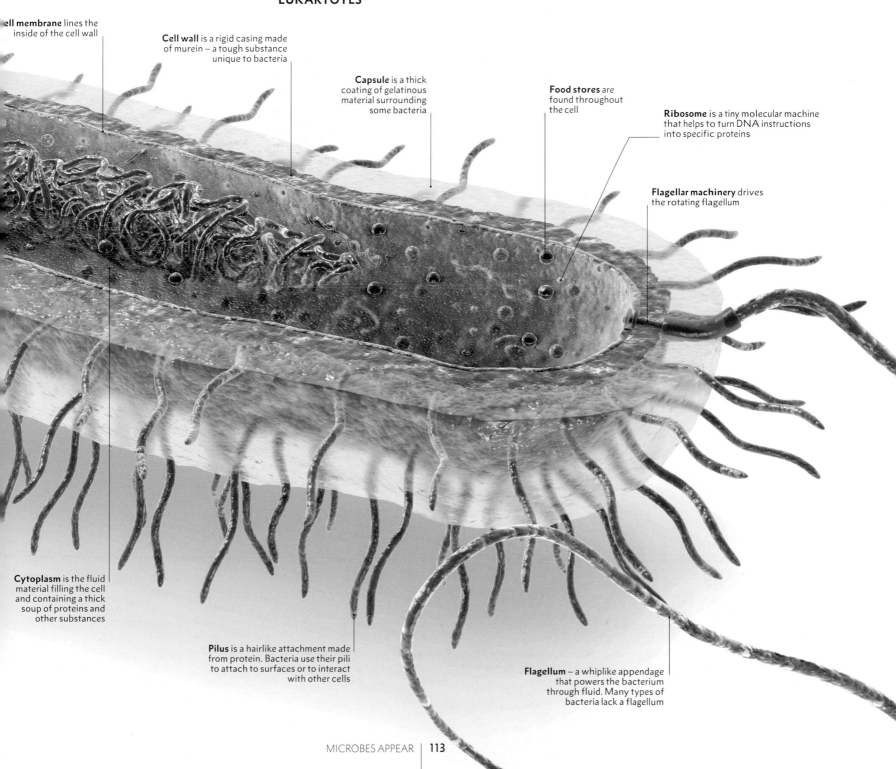

Cell membrane lines the inside of the cell wall

Cell wall is a rigid casing made of murein – a tough substance unique to bacteria

Capsule is a thick coating of gelatinous material surrounding some bacteria

Food stores are found throughout the cell

Ribosome is a tiny molecular machine that helps to turn DNA instructions into specific proteins

Flagellar machinery drives the rotating flagellum

Cytoplasm is the fluid material filling the cell and containing a thick soup of proteins and other substances

Pilus is a hairlike attachment made from protein. Bacteria use their pili to attach to surfaces or to interact with other cells

Flagellum – a whiplike appendage that powers the bacterium through fluid. Many types of bacteria lack a flagellum

LIFE DISCOVERS SUNLIGHT

Life needs energy, and the first living things drew it from minerals and made their food in the darkness of the deep ocean. Those that followed found energy in other places – and, as ancestors of plants and animals, they captured sunlight in the shallows or ate food made by other cells.

Every living thing – from a microbe to the tallest tree – consumes energy that changes small molecules into big ones, pumps life-giving matter into cells, and resists decay. The immediate energy source for this is food. Energy-rich substances, such as sugars and fats, go through a kind of controlled combustion inside cells – in the same way that chemical fuel can be burned to power any machine. But instead of ignition, cells use molecular catalysts (called enzymes) to tease the energy from their nutritive fuel in a safe and manageable way. The process is called respiration.

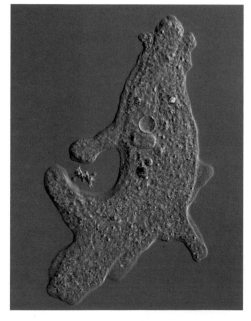

▶ **Predator in miniature**
Amoebas get food by engulfing smaller organisms, such as algae, and breaking them down using digestive enzymes. It means amoebas can live in darkness but need prey to stay alive.

The most self-sufficient strategy for nutrition is to make food, such as sugar, fat, and protein, from non-food materials. Carbon dioxide in air or dissolved in water provides the carbon and some of the oxygen. Water can provide the hydrogen – and minerals such as nitrates, phosphates, and sulphates deliver nitrogen, phosphorus, and sulphur. Today the world is covered in plants that use the Sun's energy to do just that – but the full scope of food-making life is far greater.

MAKING FOOD

Plants are not the only food producers. The most self-sufficient organisms of all can live without light and survive on nothing but water dosed with minerals. These life-forms – all of them bacteria or archaea – can extract energy from chemical processes involving these minerals – and use it to manufacture their food. Organisms that perform this chemical nutrition were among the first life-forms to thrive in the deep, mineral-rich oceans. Some are now the unseen recyclers of nature, their mineral-changing abilities helping to return the nitrogen in dead plants and animals to other living things.

A significant shift in the abilities of prehistoric microbes came when they invaded sunlit shallow waters. These new bacteria used sunlight to make food – in the process of photosynthesis. They could only get nourishment in daylight – but the reward for doing so far outweighed that of making

▲ **Energy from sunlight**
A thin mat of cyanobacteria on a living stromatolite uses green chlorophyll to trap sunlight. The energy is used to make organic food from carbon dioxide and water, and oxygen bubbles off as a by-product.

food in darkness: sunlight contains much more energy than minerals. These microbes therefore thrived as they basked in coastal seas. They reorganized and reinvented chemical processes, changing energy-giving reactions into new ones that used solar radiation. They did it with pigments, such as chlorophyll, that absorbed and trapped the light energy. The first photosynthesizers converted carbon dioxide to sugar by adding the hydrogen from hydrogen sulphide. Scientists know this due to the yellow deposits of sulphur this process left behind in rock. But a later refinement to photosynthesis helped life-forms get hydrogen from water instead. The substance left over this time – oxygen – eventually filled the atmosphere (see pp.116–17), and later helped cells burn

BY BLENDING **WATER AND MINERALS** FROM **BELOW** WITH **SUNLIGHT** AND CARBON DIOXIDE FROM **ABOVE**, GREEN PLANTS **LINK THE EARTH TO THE SKY**.

Fritjof Capra, physicist (1939–)

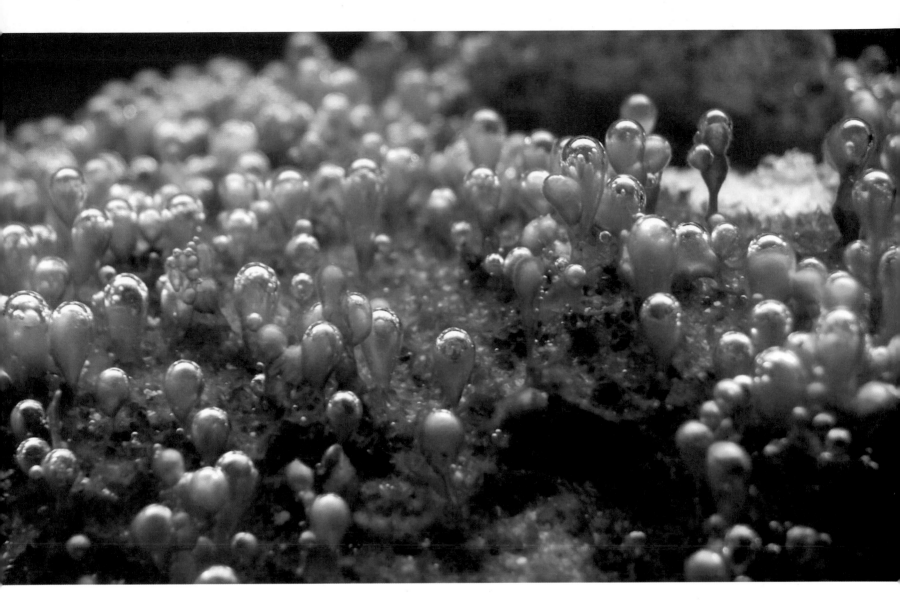

their food in respiration more efficiently. These pioneers were probably like today's cyanobacteria. They grew into sticky films of cells that trapped sediment. Over thousands of years, these colonies formed rocky mounds called stromatolites ("stroma", bed; "lithos", rock). Stromatolites still live in a few warm coastal seas, where extra-salty conditions suppress grazing animals – but they are abundant in the fossil record.

CONSUMING FOOD

As soon as some life-forms started producing food, the opportunity for a shortcut existed. Instead of being producers, organisms could evolve a new strategy – they could eat food produced by others. These organisms abandoned food-making and became consumers – collecting their nourishment in ready-made form. Those that consume organic food in this way are represented by animals, fungi, and a whole range of microbes. The earliest food-eaters probably acquired dissolved food – such as sugars – simply by absorbing it from the vicinity. Decomposers, such as fungi, still get nourishment this way – producing digestive juices to break down any organic materials that are close by so they become more absorbable. Active hunting, in which one organism eats and digests another, became an obvious next step, and complex cells, such as amoebas, evolved the means to engulf tinier organisms. It was the appearance of this predatory behaviour that marked the start of microscopic food chains.

Today, producers and consumers are linked by the transfer of energy along bigger food chains. Ocean and land life starts with the solar-powered algae and plants that now provide almost all of the world's food. Herbivores and predators are voracious in the scale of their consumption, while all these living things are, in turn, dependent on the fungi and bacteria that – in their various ways – recycle dead matter.

▼ **Where photosynthesis is happening**
Photosynthesis is the principal food-making process for modern life. Plants and algae are the producers of food chains that support animals on land and in oceans.

Marine algae are concentrated in seasonally recycled, nutrient-rich waters far from the equator or near to coasts

Tropical rainforests have especially high productivity on land

KEY

Chlorophyll density in the ocean

Minimum   Maximum

Vegetation density on land

Minimum   Maximum

OXYGEN FILLS THE AIR

Nearly two and a half billion years ago, Earth's air underwent a dramatic change: it became oxygenated. This momentous event was caused by new kinds of microbes, and it was incredibly important for the future of all life.

These microbes, bubbling away in the ocean's sunlit shallows, produced oxygen, and ensured that the organisms that followed would never be the same again.

Oxygen is a remarkable element. It causes fire, which turns organic material to cinder – but it is also a component of complex molecules, such as DNA. Most living things need it to breathe and stay alive. Today, oxygen gas makes up about one-fifth of the atmosphere's chemical composition, but for the first half of Earth's history, there was practically no gaseous oxygen at all. Instead, all oxygen lay chemically bound in water and rocks. Photosynthesizing microbes were the first organisms to release oxygen by splitting it away from water as they made their food (see pp.114–15).

POISON TURNED PROFIT

Early life was so unaccustomed to growing levels of oxygen that the response was cataclysmic. The same oxygen that can corrode metal to rust wreaked havoc on the delicate machinery of cells ill-protected from it. Much of early life, having evolved in habitats devoid of oxygen, died in the new poisonous oxygen onslaught. A few microbes had the means to survive – they had enzymes that locked the oxygen away inside their molecules where it could do no damage. But one kind of life-form went a stage further by exploiting the fact that oxidation can be productive as well as destructive.

The eagerness with which oxygen reacts means that oxidation releases energy. So much energy is released during combustion that the reaction grows hot. For billions of years, cells had been honing ways of capturing energy to drive the processes of life. The presence of oxygen opened up a new avenue of metabolism – aerobic respiration – by reacting oxygen with organic molecules (see pp.102–03) and harnessing the energy that was released. It was such an efficient mechanism for creating energy that within another billion years, virtually all life on Earth was breathing oxygen.

Layer of chert

Rich iron layer

◄ Bands of evidence
Excavation of rocks dating back to before the Great Oxygenation Event reveals bands of red iron ore. They formed in the seas in which oxygen was being released.

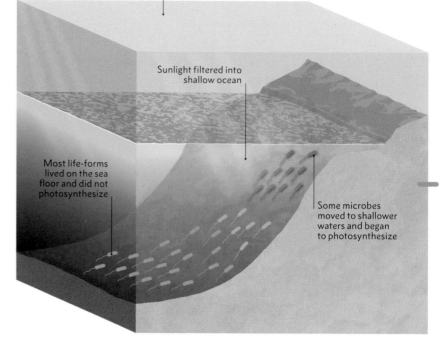

Early atmosphere was composed of relatively unreactive gases, such as nitrogen and carbon dioxide, and the sky was red

Sunlight filtered into shallow ocean

Most life-forms lived on the sea floor and did not photosynthesize

Some microbes moved to shallower waters and began to photosynthesize

Life probably originated in the deep ocean, beyond the reach of sunlight. As early life-forms dispersed into new habitats, those in the sunlit shallows found a new source of energy for making food: light energy from the Sun.

Oxygen was released into the air from an oxygen-saturated ocean

Carbon dioxide-rich atmosphere slowly became richer in oxygen

Bands of iron oxide formed deeper layers as new sediment layers were laid down above

For hundreds of millions of years, oxygen produced by photosynthesis was soaked up by the ocean's iron and laid down in rusty bands that today comprise an important part of the world's reserves of iron ore. When the ocean's dissolved iron ran out around 2.4 BYA, oxygen saturated the water, then started to fill the atmosphere.

Stromatolites were formed by layers of minerals laid down by microbes hungry for the Sun's energy

Oxygen was released into the ocean by photosynthesizing microbes

Tail-like flagellum used to swim

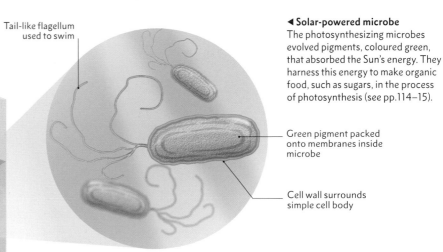

◀ **Solar-powered microbe**
The photosynthesizing microbes evolved pigments, coloured green, that absorbed the Sun's energy. They harness this energy to make organic food, such as sugars, in the process of photosynthesis (see pp.114–15).

Green pigment packed onto membranes inside microbe

Cell wall surrounds simple cell body

Bacterial mats formed

Iron oxide formed a red, rusty layer on the sea bed

Microbes in shallow seas began photosynthesizing between 3.8 and 3.2 BYA. They formed colonies, collecting as bacterial mats and building stromatolites. By extracting hydrogen from water, they released oxygen, but it did not escape into the atmosphere. It reacted with the ocean's dissolved iron, turning it to iron oxide on the sea bed.

> ❝
>
> IT IS THIS CONDITION THAT MAY HAVE **SET THE ENVIRONMENTAL STAGE** AND ULTIMATELY THE CLOCK **FOR THE ADVANCE OF**... ANIMALS.
>
> ❞

Timothy Lyons, biogeochemist professor, c.1960–

Atmosphere was oxygen-rich, and the sky was blue

Earlier microbes died off

Stromatolites died off

After 2.4 BYA, the ocean's water was full of oxygen and the atmosphere was oxygen-rich. Since organisms had evolved in habitats low in oxygen, these new conditions poisoned most of them. Only a few had the means to detoxify the oxygen, and so could survive.

New organisms evolved that can use oxygen for energy

Stromatolites fossilized, turning to rock

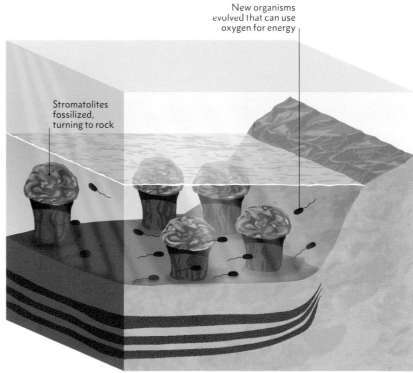

New microbes evolved and could now use oxygen to extract more energy from food and went on to be the dominant life-forms in the new oxygen-rich habitat. A few oxygen-hating microbes persisted where oxygen could not reach them – such as in thick muds.

COMPLEX **CELLS EVOLVE**

In a world 2.7 BYA, teeming with microbes, life found a way to move forward. Simple bacteria were joined by bigger cells to form microscopic cooperatives, merging and collaborating to form complex new cells. Such cells would become the living units of plants and animals.

The abilities of bacteria are limited by their simple structure. Although they can perform chemical tricks impossible in more complex life, they are restricted in how they move and socialize. Greater possibilities opened up when bigger microbes swallowed smaller ones – and kept them alive inside them.

CELLULAR COMPARTMENTS

Plant and animal cells are eukaryotic ("eu", true; "karyon", kernel), meaning they have a central compartment called the nucleus. This, together with many other membrane-bound chambers, distinguishes these complex cells from bacteria. The chambers are called organelles, because their uses in a cell are comparable to the functions of organs in a larger body. Some, notably chloroplasts and mitochondria, are reminiscent of some free-living bacteria. It suggests they came to be when microbes in prehistoric communities engulfed smaller cells for food, but instead of eating them, held them captive, preserving their life processes. In this way, some photosynthetic bacteria of yesterday became the chloroplasts of today. And mitochondria, which respire using oxygen, came from oxygen-breathing bacteria. Even the nucleus may have begun like this, although little remains to hint at its probable archaea ancestors. In each case, the prisoners were "cultivated" and passed down whenever their hosts reproduced. Over millions of years, host and organelle became entirely codependent.

Eukaryotes expanded more than bacteria ever could. Some used their photosynthesizing chloroplasts to become algae and plants. The food-eaters became amoebas, fungi, and animals. A few, such as *Euglena*, could even switch between photosynthesis in sunshine and absorbing food in darkness. But it was cell-to-cell interaction that continued to be the driving force in escalating complexity – so, in time, eukaryotes evolved into the largest and most elaborate organisms on the planet.

Ridged surface, or pellicle, is tough enough to protect the organism but flexible enough to let *Euglena* engulf prey

Golgi body is a cluster of sacs that help refine and sort proteins and other cellular products

Photosynthetic membranes, arranged just like those in cyanobacteria alive today, are packed with chlorophyll, which absorbs light energy

Chloroplast creates sugar by photosynthesis. The ancestors of chloroplasts were probably ancient cyanobacteria. Like mitochondria, chloroplasts have their own DNA, with around 100 genes

Outer membrane is permeable to organic molecules needed for aerobic respration

Outer membrane is in three layers – a relic of the chloroplast's origin as a cyanobacterium inside a host cell

CHLOROPLAST

MITOCHONDRION

Inner membrane folded to fit in lots of enzymes that perform aerobic respiration – the process that uses oxygen to break down food for energy

Mitochondrion is rod-shaped like a bacillus and is a descendant of free-living bacteria. It even retains some DNA, containing more than 30 genes, from its time as a free-living organism

Food particles engulfed by the cell are digested inside by enzymes

Endoplasmic reticulum is a stack of membranous envelopes. Most are studded with protein-making granules called ribosomes; others help make oily substances

Nucleus contains DNA inside its double membrane. Nuclei may have originated as free-living archaea – microbes that survived in hot acidic pools

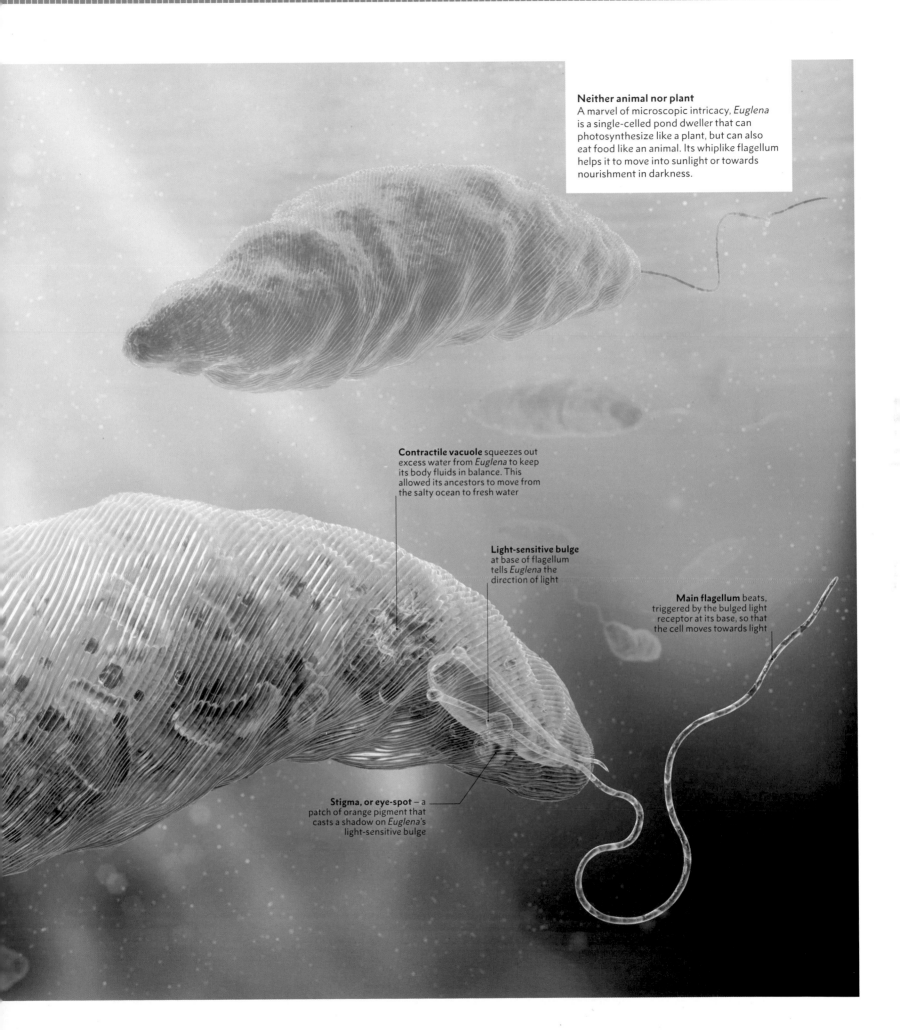

Neither animal nor plant
A marvel of microscopic intricacy, *Euglena* is a single-celled pond dweller that can photosynthesize like a plant, but can also eat food like an animal. Its whiplike flagellum helps it to move into sunlight or towards nourishment in darkness.

Contractile vacuole squeezes out excess water from *Euglena* to keep its body fluids in balance. This allowed its ancestors to move from the salty ocean to fresh water

Light-sensitive bulge at base of flagellum tells *Euglena* the direction of light

Main flagellum beats, triggered by the bulged light receptor at its base, so that the cell moves towards light

Stigma, or eye-spot – a patch of orange pigment that casts a shadow on *Euglena*'s light-sensitive bulge

SEX MIXES GENES

Mistakes in the copying of genetic material, known as mutations, create new genes and characteristics – but it is the sexual behaviour of life that mixes them up, creating unique individuals. Sexuality is a basic property of all known life and it is likely that it emerged very early on in evolution.

Some organisms reproduce without sex, so offspring carry exact copies of their parent's genes. The only way they can change over generations is when mutation produces variety. But most organisms, because of their sexuality, can vary much more. Sex mixes up DNA, enriching a population with new combinations. A plant species might have genetically-determined white or purple flowers, as well as tall or dwarf statures. These variants are produced by mutations (see pp.108–09), but sex mixes them up, so both tall or dwarf plants can produce flowers of either colour.

The simplest kind of sex happens when bacteria exchange bits of DNA. When they separate, each partner is genetically changed, but no new cells are made. So bacteria have evolved sex, but not sexual reproduction.

HOW TO SHUFFLE A HUGE GENOME
Complex, or eukaryotic, cells (see pp.118–19), including those of all plants, fungi, and animals, cannot exchange their genes as bacteria do: their long, unwieldy chains of DNA prevent it. Instead, they rely on first making special sex cells containing only half their DNA, and then fuse, or fertilize, them with half the DNA of another individual.

To achieve the halving and fertilization, they need two "doses" of each kind of gene. The halving process, called meiosis,

> THERE ARE **8 MILLION** GENETIC COMBINATIONS POSSIBLE IN THE **SPERM OR EGGS** PRODUCED BY **EVERY HUMAN**

separates the doses into sex cells (usually sperm and eggs), and fertilization restores the double dose. This ensures that each gene gets inherited and no information is lost.

VARIETY IN SPERM AND EGGS
Fertilization mixes genes from different individuals, but meiosis ensures that all the sex cells coming from a single parent are different, too. As a prelude to meiosis, DNA is shuffled around in the cells of the sex organs, so that all the sperm or egg cells made by one parent are genetically different.

Plants, animals, and other complex organisms evolved sexual lifecycles that were moulded by their capabilities. Fungi – which grow as microscopic threads – adopted a method reminiscent of bacteria: their threads fuse in places without producing true sperm or eggs. Plants – rooted to the ground – evolved cycles that used dispersive spores or pollen. But in all these organisms, sex served to multiply the raw material for natural selection – variation.

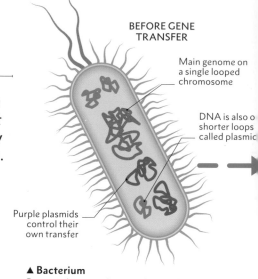

Main genome on a single looped chromosome

DNA is also o shorter loops called plasmic

Purple plasmids control their own transfer

▲ Bacterium
Bacteria have sex by transferring DNA to another individual. Some of the genes that control the exchange are actually on the DNA that is moved, so the DNA strand controls its own transfer, a little like an independent life-form.

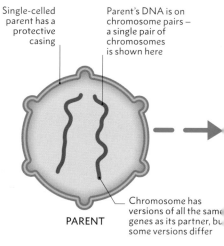

Single-celled parent has a protective casing

Parent's DNA is on chromosome pairs – a single pair of chromosomes is shown here

Chromosome has versions of all the same genes as its partner, bu some versions differ

PARENT

▲ Complex microbe
Chlamydomonas is a single-celled microbe, but as a complex cell (eukaryote), it has a double-dose of DNA divided into pairs of equivalent chromosomes Each member of a chromosome pair has equivalent genes to its partner, but these genes may differ, due to mutations accumulated over millions of years.

▼ Spawning
Production of sex cells can be prolific. Corals release millions of sperm and eggs simultaneously – increasing the chance of fertilization in the open ocean water.

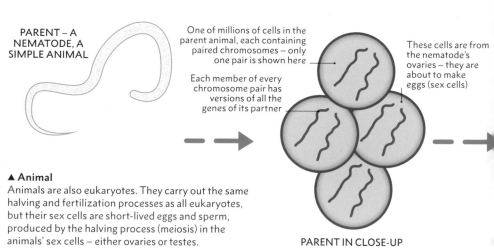

PARENT – A NEMATODE, A SIMPLE ANIMAL

One of millions of cells in the parent animal, each containing paired chromosomes – only one pair is shown here

These cells are from the nematode's ovaries – they are about to make eggs (sex cells)

Each member of every chromosome pair has versions of all the genes of its partner

▲ Animal
Animals are also eukaryotes. They carry out the same halving and fertilization processes as all eukaryotes, but their sex cells are short-lived eggs and sperm, produced by the halving process (meiosis) in the animals' sex cells – either ovaries or testes.

PARENT IN CLOSE-UP

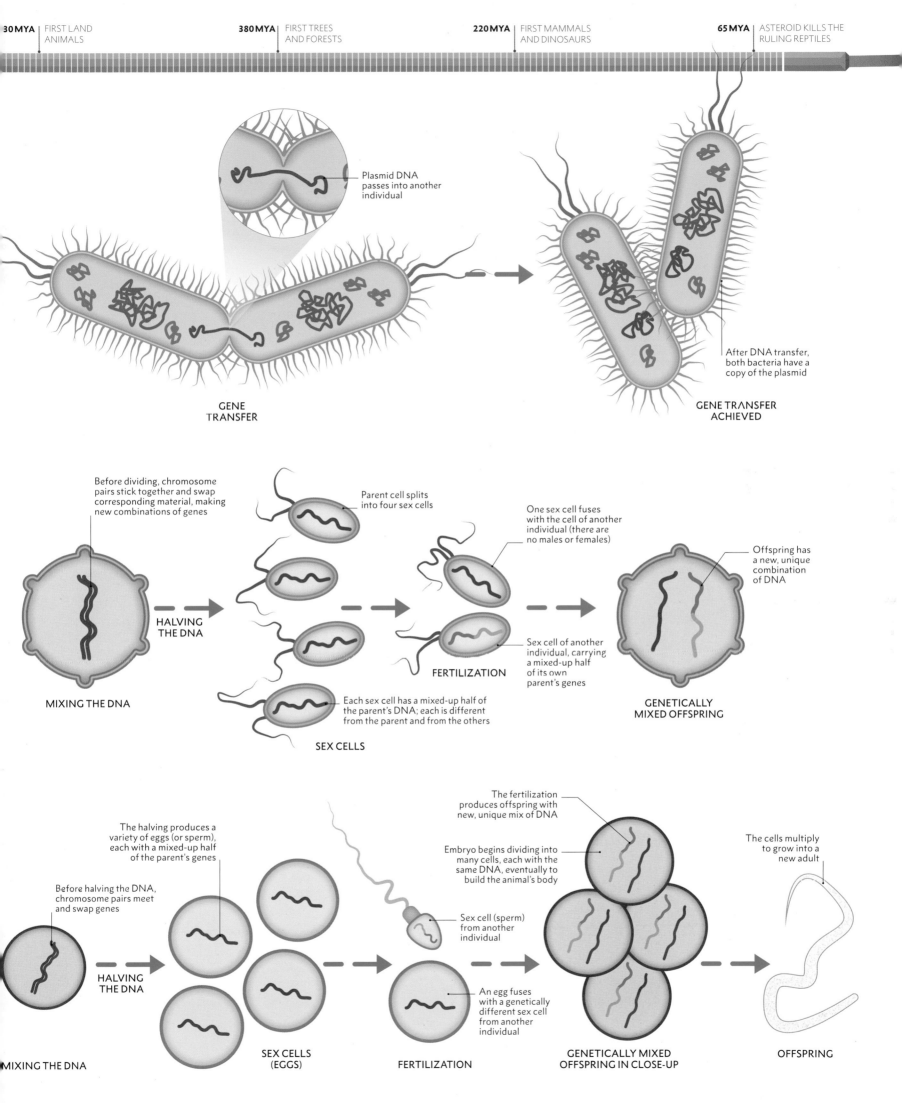

Plasmid DNA passes into another individual

GENE TRANSFER

After DNA transfer, both bacteria have a copy of the plasmid

GENE TRANSFER ACHIEVED

Before dividing, chromosome pairs stick together and swap corresponding material, making new combinations of genes

Parent cell splits into four sex cells

One sex cell fuses with the cell of another individual (there are no males or females)

Offspring has a new, unique combination of DNA

HALVING THE DNA

MIXING THE DNA

Each sex cell has a mixed-up half of the parent's DNA; each is different from the parent and from the others

SEX CELLS

FERTILIZATION

Sex cell of another individual, carrying a mixed-up half of its own parent's genes

GENETICALLY MIXED OFFSPRING

The halving produces a variety of eggs (or sperm), each with a mixed-up half of the parent's genes

The fertilization produces offspring with new, unique mix of DNA

Embryo begins dividing into many cells, each with the same DNA, eventually to build the animal's body

The cells multiply to grow into a new adult

Before halving the DNA, chromosome pairs meet and swap genes

Sex cell (sperm) from another individual

HALVING THE DNA

MIXING THE DNA

SEX CELLS (EGGS)

An egg fuses with a genetically different sex cell from another individual

FERTILIZATION

GENETICALLY MIXED OFFSPRING IN CLOSE-UP

OFFSPRING

4.1 BYA | FIRST TRACE
OF POSSIBLE LIFE

2.4 BYA | OXYGEN
FILLS THE AIR

936 MYA | ESTIMATED ORIGIN OF
ALGAE AND PLANTS

CELLS BEGIN TO **BUILD BODIES**

The step from microscopic, single-celled microbes to organisms such as plants and animals, with up to trillions of cells, was another quantum leap in the complexity of life. Maintaining order in a multicellular organism demands that cells not only stick together in the right way, but also communicate so that the entire body develops properly.

There are limits to the capabilities of a single-celled microbe. Cells cannot grow beyond a certain size without becoming unmanageable – using diffusion, materials for life pass in and out of their bodies only over microscopic distances, and the oily cell membrane breaks up if a cell gets too big. Cells divide when they reach a certain stage, so microbes stay microscopic.

▲ **Temporary body**
Slime moulds are on the cusp of multicellularity. They are usually solitary, amoeba-like single cells, but in times of stress, they band together and form multicellular fruiting bodies such as these.

Bigger organisms with cooperating working parts can evolve new ways to live, but they must become multicellular to do so. Some microbes refuse to separate after division, so their cells remain attached in a colony. The simplicity of this arrangement – division without segregation – suggests that multicellularity in itself is not such a monumental achievement – but getting body parts (and therefore cells) focused on different tasks is another matter.

DIVISION OF CELLULAR LABOUR
True multicellularity happens when a colony's cells work together and specialize, relying on chemical cues from their neighbours to do so. All cells in a colony carry copies of DNA made by replication during each cellular division. Although they keep identical genetic blueprints, cells switch off selected genes as they forego certain

functions to concentrate on specific jobs – and increasingly rely on other cells around them to supply their deficiencies.

In the Precambrian oceans, filter-feeding sponges were among the first multicellular animals, although they are just a step away from being a loose colony. A sponge passed through a sieve can sprout new individuals from each separated cell, and the same is true of some simple algae. Later, more complex, animals and plants had cells more committed to their specific roles. Their fate – to become skin, muscle, or another tissue – is set by their location in the early embryo. Cooperating tissues then become organs, such as solar-powered leaves or beating hearts, and their cells no longer survive alone.

Multicellularity might make cells forever dependent, but it reaps enormous benefits for the bigger body. It allowed life to evolve working parts, such as stinging tentacles and sex organs. The variety of body sizes now possible multiplied the complexity of natural communities, leading to elaborate food webs and habitats built from the bodies of larger organisms, from corals to trees.

Cleft suggests this is an embryo that has just made its first cell division, from one to two cells

TWO-CELL STAGE

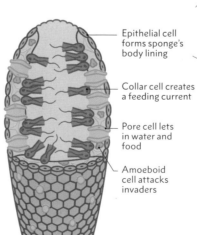

16-CELL STAGE

SPONGE

- Epithelial cell forms sponge's body lining
- Collar cell creates a feeding current
- Pore cell lets in water and food
- Amoeboid cell attacks invaders

CHOANOFLAGELLATE COLONY

- Collar
- Flagellum beats to create a current that carries food to the cell

◄ **Creature or colony?**
The distinction between colonies of cells and true multicellular life is not always clear. Single-celled microbes called choanoflagellates form stalked colonies. Many cells in a sponge look and behave in much the same way. What makes the animal more than a colony are its different, specialized cell types, which must cooperate in an integrated way to survive.

One of four cells in this fossil, suggesting it is an embryo that has divided twice

FOUR-CELL STAGE

Granular texture is due to the mineralization process of fossilization

A membrane encloses the cells, just as it would in an animal embryo

EIGHT-CELL STAGE

Cells in this "embryo" are more rounded – perhaps due to loss of its enveloping membrane

32-CELL STAGE

This membrane encloses what looks like a ball of cells – called a blastula in animal embryos

BLASTULA STAGE

66

THE **ANCESTORS** OF THE **HIGHER ANIMALS** MUST BE ... **ONE-CELLED BEINGS**, SIMILAR TO THE **AMOEBAE** WHICH ... OCCUR IN OUR RIVERS, POOLS, AND LAKES.

99

Ernst Haeckel, evolutionary biologist, 1834–1919
The History of Creation

▲ **Arrested development**
Astonishing fossils from the Doushantuo Formation of China appear to show embryos frozen in time at their very earliest stages of cell division, as they change from a single egg cell to form first two, then four, and eight cells, and so on. This act of cell division without separating is at the root of multicellularity; it may be that these fossils represent very early multicellular animals beginning life around 635 million years ago.

Showing off
Many males use colour to impress females in species that have good daytime vision – such as big-eyed jumping spiders. This male peacock jumping spider combines colour with choreography in his courtship display.

MALES AND FEMALES DIVERGE

As well as evolving complex, multicellular bodies, plants and animals also diverged into two sexes. In each species of animal, half became females and – through yolky eggs or pregnancy – focused on nourishing their offspring. The other half – the males – became fighters and show-offs.

Contrast between the sexes can be very pronounced indeed. A female elephant seal can be five times smaller than her mate – and an anglerfish female 40 times bigger. All sexual organisms have a shared genetic investment in producing offspring, but males and females have dissimilar – although complementary – interests in the way they help create the next generation.

investment in the next generation makes a female choosy when it comes to selecting mates and passing on her genes.

The cost of sperm production is far lower. In the drive to pass on their genes, males invest more in beating other males to fertilize eggs, either in competition, such as a race or fight, or by wowing females with advertisement displays. This has resulted

> WE CAN HARDLY BELIEVE THAT ... THE **FEMALE** ... IS NOT **INFLUENCED** BY THE **GORGEOUS COLOURS** OR OTHER ORNAMENTS WITH WHICH THE **MALE ... IS DECORATED**.
>
> **Charles Darwin**, biologist, 1809–82, *The Descent of Man and Selection in Relation to Sex*

MATING TYPES AND SEXES
The lowliest of organisms manages to be sexual without having males and females at all. Many microbes and fungi have multiple, but identical-looking, "mating types". Subtle chemical differences dictate whether they can fuse to mix their genes.

Mating types have equal reproductive responsibilities. But the evolution of different sexes changes this. Although each sex contributes the same amount of genetic information, the female sex supplies hers as an egg provided with nourishing yolk, while males make lightweight sperm devoted to racing to fuse with that egg. The battle of the sexes began when sperm started swimming towards food-packed eggs.

CHOOSY FEMALES, SHOWY MALES
Some females – such as many insects and fish – deposit tiny amounts of yolk in each egg so can still afford to produce hundreds. Others make fewer, yolkier eggs or give birth to young after a costly pregnancy. Either way, high bodily

in extravagant male features, from the giant jaws of stag beetles to a bird-of-paradise's plumes. Fossil evidence – such as the crests of male pterosaurs – suggests that this is nothing new. But male displays relying on colour, voice, or behaviour leave no trace; today these attributes provide some of the most dazzling natural spectacles – as males fight, dance, or sing their way to mating success.

◀ **Size contrast**
An egg's package of cytoplasm and yolk makes it one of the biggest kinds of cells. A sperm – one of the smallest – has a whiplike flagellum that helps it swim, powered by a single mitochondrion.

ANIMALS GET A BRAIN

All animals have a nervous system that detects and responds to change. But only some evolved more complex behaviour. The animals that did are those that started swimming or crawling forwards. They developed a battery of sense organs and a decision-making brain to lead the way.

Some of the first animals, such as jellyfish, moved with tentacles radiating from the body in all directions. Their body had a top and bottom, but no front or back – so no head and tail. It was enough to respond to food and danger, and they had a nervous system for that, made up of long, interconnecting nerve cells. A stimulus, which can be any prompt from the environment, triggered their system to fire electrical impulses along the nerve cells' fibres – and when the signal reached a muscle, the muscle contracted to pull on a part of the body. But complex behaviour was impossible: they had no brain to analyze sensory input and make decisions.

A HEAD FOR THINKING

More than 600 MYA, forward-moving animals introduced a key innovation. If they moved in one direction consistently, one part of the body – the front end – always encountered new territory first. Animals concentrated sense organs at this end and developed a corresponding mass of nerve cells that processed all the incoming data: they evolved the first heads with the first brains. A central conduit – a nerve chord – carried impulses through the body, allowing communication between brain, muscles, and sense organs. It meant a fundamental rearrangement. Two sides of the newly elongated body developed as mirror images of each other, giving the new kind of animal a single line of symmetry down the midline of its body. This body plan came to dominate animals from the simplest flatworms to the most complex vertebrates.

Brain power allows complex behaviour, so spiders, for instance, can spin webs to catch prey. But as long as behaviour has a fixed pattern, it can still be "hard-wired" and determined by genes. Genuine versatility would come where traces of the brain's electrical activity left memories that affected behaviour. Big-brained animals, such as mammals and birds, can learn from experience. And among them, a few gained foresight – the ultimate expression of brain power that foreshadowed human creativity.

Nerve net extends into each tentacle

Nerve fibre, the long, thin part of a nerve cell, carries electrical impulses

Nodes are points where nerve fibres meet and communicate

▲ **Nerve net**
An anemone does not have any nerve cells concentrated in a brain. Instead, they are arranged into a net, with sensory ones collecting information and deeper ones communicating with muscles. Behaviour is in its simplest stimulus-response form.

▼ **Fossil brain**
Soft tissues, such as the brain, rarely fossilize, but the fossil head of a Cambrian shrimplike animal called *Fuxianhuia* shows a detailed brain impression. The large optic lobes suggest the animal relied on vision.

Nerve chord – a thick bundle of nerve fibres – is one of a pair running down the ventral (belly) side of the animal

Auricle is a projection on the side of the head that is sensitive to chemicals and is used to find food

Eye-spot, or ocellus, responds to light but doesn't produce detailed images

Brain is simply a concentration of the biggest ganglia at the head end of the body

Snout is the first part of the body to encounter new things and is touch-sensitive

> PARTS OF THE BRAINS OF DIFFERENT ANIMALS HAVE **EXPANDED AND PROSPERED IN IMPORTANCE**... ALL IN ACCORDANCE WITH THE DEMANDS OF THE **LIFESTYLE OF THE SPECIES**.

Susan Greenfield, neuroscientist, 1950–

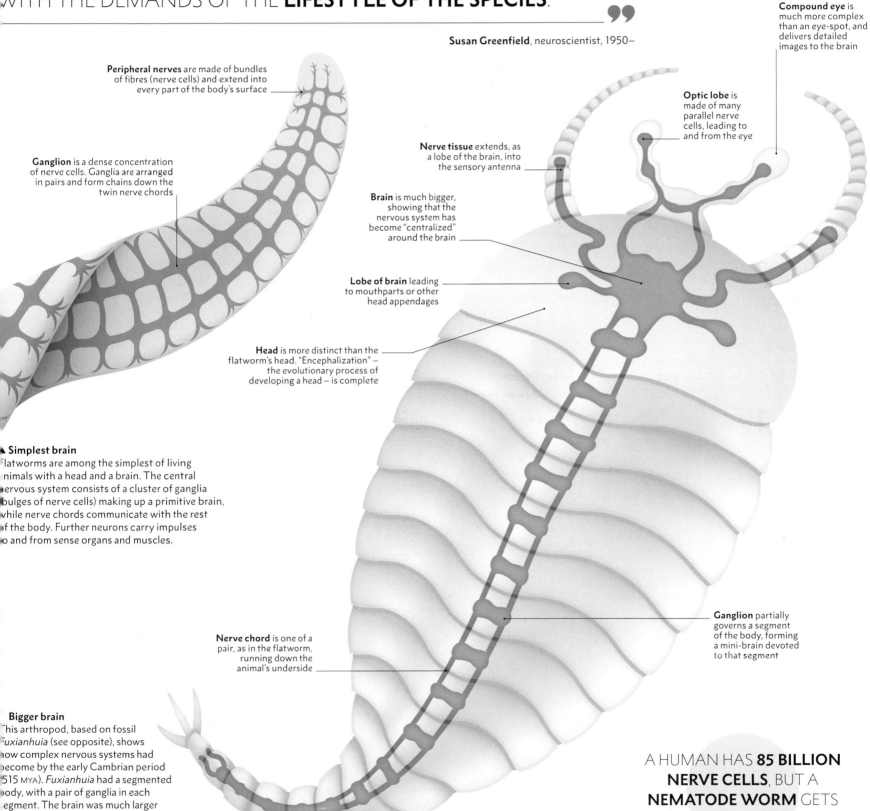

Peripheral nerves are made of bundles of fibres (nerve cells) and extend into every part of the body's surface

Ganglion is a dense concentration of nerve cells. Ganglia are arranged in pairs and form chains down the twin nerve chords

Compound eye is much more complex than an eye-spot, and delivers detailed images to the brain

Optic lobe is made of many parallel nerve cells, leading to and from the eye

Nerve tissue extends, as a lobe of the brain, into the sensory antenna

Brain is much bigger, showing that the nervous system has become "centralized" around the brain

Lobe of brain leading to mouthparts or other head appendages

Head is more distinct than the flatworm's head. "Encephalization" – the evolutionary process of developing a head – is complete

Simplest brain
Flatworms are among the simplest of living animals with a head and a brain. The central nervous system consists of a cluster of ganglia (bulges of nerve cells) making up a primitive brain, while nerve chords communicate with the rest of the body. Further neurons carry impulses to and from sense organs and muscles.

Nerve chord is one of a pair, as in the flatworm, running down the animal's underside

Ganglion partially governs a segment of the body, forming a mini-brain devoted to that segment

Bigger brain
This arthropod, based on fossil *Fuxianhuia* (see opposite), shows how complex nervous systems had become by the early Cambrian period (515 MYA). *Fuxianhuia* had a segmented body, with a pair of ganglia in each segment. The brain was much larger and features fat superhighways of nerve cells extending into the head's appendages and sense organs.

A HUMAN HAS **85 BILLION NERVE CELLS**, BUT A **NEMATODE WORM** GETS BY WITH **302**

ANIMAL LIFE
EXPLODES

The first big explosion of animal life occurred just over 600 MYA – in oceans already alive with algae and microbes. From modest beginnings as creepers and grazers on the sea bed, animals quickly evolved into all the main groups alive today.

▼ Colonizing the ocean floor
The earliest animals hugged the ocean floor, but their diversity and ecology escalated as some of them dug deeper into the mud and others grew upwards into the water, discovering new survival strategies and building complex communities.

The oldest full-body fossils seem to appear so suddenly in the geological record that the first chapter in the evolution of animals has been called an "explosion". A fuller picture actually reveals what might be a series of explosions. An early wave of evolution left behind fossils worldwide, but notably in Newfoundland, Canada, and in Australia's Ediacara Hills, which gave their name to this period, the Ediacaran (635–541 MYA). The animals preserved are unrecognizable – some are disc-shaped, others frondlike – and scientists cannot place them in any modern groups. These were not the first animals. DNA evidence points to an even earlier pre-Cambrian origin, but the earliest forms left little more than tracks and traces. Those fossil traces can be a rich source of data themselves, however, telling us about animal lifestyles and communities.

EARLY RECYCLERS

Animals evolved from single-celled organisms. The pre-Cambrian track marks show that the lives of these first animals were tied to sediments on the ocean bed. Some crawled over the surface or grew into spongelike mats. Animals had evolved muscle systems, which distinguish them from other multicellular life. Their muscles helped them play an active role in shaping their environment. In their search for

FROM THE **BEGINNING** TO THE **END** OF THE CAMBRIAN PERIOD, ANIMAL **BURROWING DEPTH INCREASED** FROM 1 CM (½ IN) TO **1 M** (39 IN)

dissolved food, some of these pioneers of the sediment evolved into burrowers and began churning the sediment in ways that had never happened before. This swirled materials between the ocean water and the bottom muds – adding oxygen to the sediment and exchanging organic matter and minerals between the two habitats.

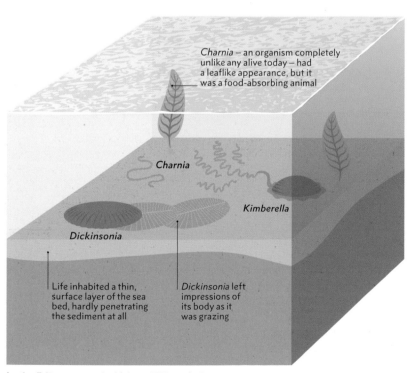

Charnia – an organism completely unlike any alive today – had a leaflike appearance, but it was a food-absorbing animal

Charnia

Kimberella

Dickinsonia

Life inhabited a thin, surface layer of the sea bed, hardly penetrating the sediment at all

Dickinsonia left impressions of its body as it was grazing

In the Ediacaran period (about 560 MYA), the sea bed was colonized by surface mats of algae, microbes, and possibly sponges. Scratch marks were made by early animals, possibly including *Kimberella*, as they grazed the algae.

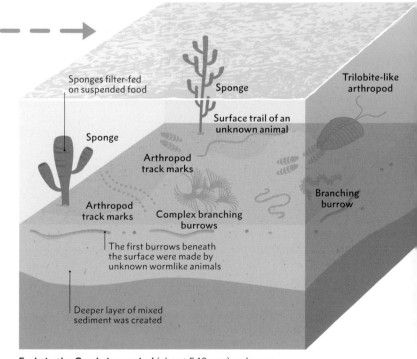

Sponges filter-fed on suspended food

Sponge

Trilobite-like arthropod

Sponge

Surface trail of an unknown animal

Arthropod track marks

Arthropod track marks

Complex branching burrows

Branching burrow

The first burrows beneath the surface were made by unknown wormlike animals

Deeper layer of mixed sediment was created

Early in the Cambrian period (about 540 MYA), a deeper layer of mixed, recycled sediment was created by animals burrowing and digging. The earliest known arthropods, probably resembling trilobites, left tracks – long before the first trilobite body was fossilized.

EA-BED COMMUNITIES

y the early Cambrian, animal communities ere flourishing on and around the sea ed. The fossil record of this time is less ncomplete, as many animals had chalky xoskeletons – protection from others but lso able to support taller bodies and olonies. As plankton became richer with igger organisms, their dead bodies and aste were more likely to sink. For the first me, life-forms in the water column were rongly linked to those on the ocean floor y a primitive food chain. Deposit-feeders ame to depend on this rain of food.

Now was the time of the full Cambrian xplosion, documented most famously by Canada's Burgess Shale fossil assemblage 05 MYA). All the major kinds of living nimals – flatworms, molluscs, and rthropods included – had evolved. But ther, less familiar, types evolved alongside em. Some fossils suggest the existence of nimals very unlike anything alive today, nd many scientists have described this eriod as a time of experimentation in ody shaping. Many of these ancient ypes disappeared without leaving lasting escendants, but others went on to fill e planet with animal life.

◄ **Experimental body**
Opabinia is an example of an experimental body plan from the Burgess Shale. This creature is not related to any animal alive today, and some experts regard it as a failed body-plan experiment that soon died out.

> "
> SOME **15–20 BURGESS SPECIES** CANNOT BE ALLIED WITH ANY **KNOWN GROUP**. MAGNIFY SOME OF THEM... AND YOU ARE ON THE SET OF A **SCIENCE-FICTION FILM**.
> "
>
> **Stephen Jay Gould**, palaeontologist and evolutionary biologist, 1941–2002
> *Wonderful Life: The Burgess Shale and the Nature of History*

Arthopods

Fanworm

Burrowing anemone

U-shaped burrow

Vertical worm burrows

A range of worms and anemones held out tendrils or felt with a proboscis for food

ater in the Cambrian (529 MYA), deposit-feeders subsisted on he "rain" of detritus from plankton above. They included animals ith food-grabbing tentacles, including burrowers similar to the anworms of today, and a diversity of trilobite-like arthropods, hich left different types of tracks as they patrolled the sea bed.

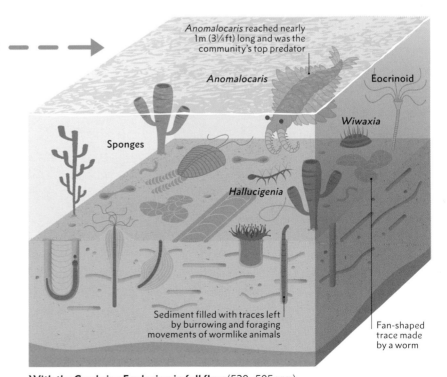

Anomalocaris reached nearly 1m (3¼ft) long and was the community's top predator

Anomalocaris

Eocrinoid

Wiwaxia

Sponges

Hallucigenia

Sediment filled with traces left by burrowing and foraging movements of wormlike animals

Fan-shaped trace made by a worm

With the Cambrian Explosion in full flow (520–505 MYA), new lifestyles and experimental body plans really took off. Unique animals such as *Anomalocaris*, *Wiwaxia*, and *Hallucigenia* evolved, but left no successful descendants.

ANIMALS GAIN A **BACKBONE**

Backboned animals – from fish to mammals – have a history stretching back to small larva-like filter-feeders emerging in the evolutionary explosion of the Cambrian period. The internal skeleton they evolved went on to support animal bodies far larger than was possible before.

Vertebrates (animals with a spine, or vertebral column) emerged from small muscular swimmers in the Cambrian seas, before 500 MYA. They had a rubbery rod – a notochord – running through the back of a tapering body and blocks of flexing muscle that curved the rod from side to side. Fish use the same technique to swim today – but in most, the rod grows only in the embryo and is replaced with a harder backbone by adulthood. The Cambrian rod-backs were modest filter-feeders, but a backbone gave their descendants dramatically new ways to live their lives.

CARTILAGINOUS BEGINNINGS

The earliest elements of a skeleton were made from cartilage: tough, but flexible, tissue packed with collagen. Cartilage grew in the head of the first fish, such as *Haikouichthys*, and protected the brain and supported arches between their gill slits. In later animals, cartilage grew over the notochord and protected the spinal cord too, becoming the first true vertebral column. The column allowed stronger swimming, while fins – with cartilaginous supports of their own – improved control and stability.

Bodies with supporting cartilage could get bigger and more agile – but demanded more food and oxygen, too. The earliest fish got both by straining water through their gills – but feeding functions were later taken over by the mouth and throat, leaving the gills free to become better at extracting oxygen. This happened in bottom-living, armoured, jawless fish called ostracoderms, which used throat muscles to suck food in from mud. But ostracoderms were also pioneers for another reason: they had the first bone.

BONY BODIES

Bone has its collagen hardened with at least 70 per cent mineral. It may have evolved as a reservoir for the extra calcium and phosphate needed to trigger fast-acting muscles and nerves. But it had obvious mechanical benefits, too. Ostracoderms ("ostrakon", shell; "derma", skin) used bone as outer armour, packed with so much mineral it excluded living cells. Later fish permeated their bone with life-supporting microscopic channels, meaning it could grow from within to make an internal skeleton. Most vertebrates alive today have a bony skeleton, with cartilage largely around joints. A few – such as sharks and rays – reverted to a more lightweight cartilaginous skeleton, but bony fish diversified more, counteracting their heavier bone with a buoyant gas-filled swim bladder. And a bony skeleton was critical for the evolution of the land vertebrates that followed. Only giant bones could bear the weight of the biggest dinosaurs.

▼ Step by step
Fossils show that the evolution of a spine happened during the Cambrian period, 541–485 MYA. The story began with a back stiffened by a notochord (a rubbery rod) and passed through stages where vertebrae were made first from cartilage then mineralized as a true backbone.

Cranium, or braincase, surrounds the brain. In early vertebrates, this formed an open-topped cage, but this later closed over, giving better protection

Mandible is actually a former set of gill arches, reshaped by evolution into a jaw

Brain

Nerve chord

Notochord – a stiff supportive rod

Gill slit – used for filter feeding

Chordate – a proto-fish with only a notochord

Cranium (braincase) of cartilage

Cartilage gill arch stiffens gill, helping to hold it open for feeding

Craniate – protofish with a braincase

Rods of cartilage support the dorsal fin. They grow under the skin as part of the dermal (skin) skeleton, unconnected to the internal skeleton

◀ **Modern vertebrate**
A body reinforced by an internal jointed skeleton has enormous evolutionary promise. The great white shark is a highpoint of this potential: one of the most formidable top predators in the world today. Its skeletal elements are made from cartilage reinforced with mineral deposits. Sharks share the main skeletal elements of most other living vertebrates, except that they lack ribs.

Vertebrae surround and protect the spinal chord. They make up the vertebral column, or spine

Gill arches are elements of the skeleton between the gill slits that support feathery gills, holding them open to absorb oxygen from the water

The pectoral fins' skeleton is part of the internal skeleton. Later, this allowed other vertebrates to adapt these and the rear paired fins into limbs and to invade land (see pp.140–41)

GREAT WHITE SHARK

Bony plates covering head – fish first evolved bone as external armour

Vertebrae made of cartilage, making a chain called a vertebal column, or spine

Notochord still present in some early fish

Cartilage gill arch

Vertebrate – a jawless fish with cartilage internal skeleton and bony armour

Cranium made of bone

First gill arch transformed into primitive hinged jaws

Backbone made of vertebrae turned to bone by adding calcium minerals

Swim bladder – added because it gives fish the buoyancy it needs in the presence of its heavy, mineralized skeleton

Gill now used for extracting oxgygen from the water

Vertebrate – fish with bony internal skeleton

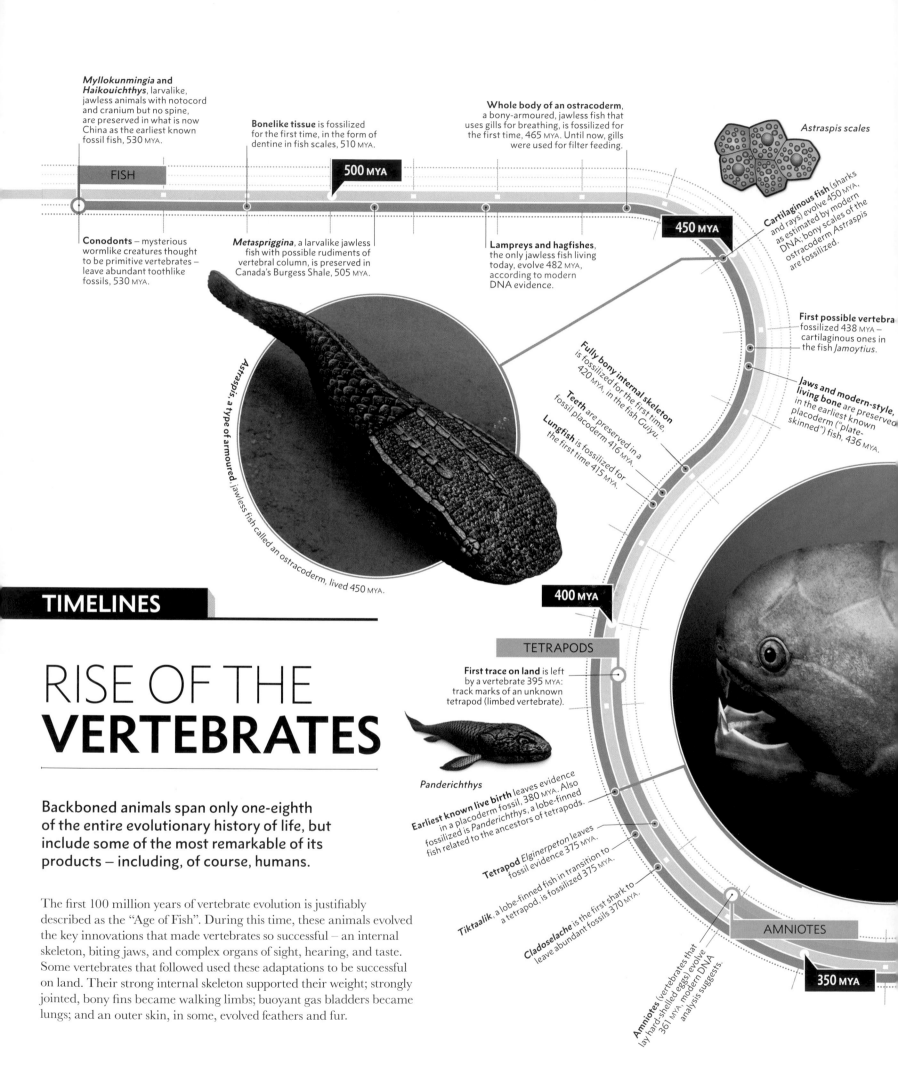

Myllokunmingia and Haikouichthys, larvalike, jawless animals with notocord and cranium but no spine, are preserved in what is now China as the earliest known fossil fish, 530 MYA.

Bonelike tissue is fossilized for the first time, in the form of dentine in fish scales, 510 MYA.

Whole body of an ostracoderm, a bony-armoured, jawless fish that uses gills for breathing, is fossilized for the first time, 465 MYA. Until now, gills were used for filter feeding.

Astraspis scales

FISH

500 MYA

Conodonts – mysterious wormlike creatures thought to be primitive vertebrates – leave abundant toothlike fossils, 530 MYA.

Metaspriggina, a larvalike jawless fish with possible rudiments of vertebral column, is preserved in Canada's Burgess Shale, 505 MYA.

Lampreys and hagfishes, the only jawless fish living today, evolve 482 MYA, according to modern DNA evidence.

450 MYA

Cartilaginous fish (sharks and rays) evolve 450 MYA, as estimated by modern DNA; bony scales of the ostracoderm *Astraspis* are fossilized.

Astraspis, a type of armoured, jawless fish called an ostracoderm, lived 450 MYA.

First possible vertebra fossilized 438 MYA – cartilaginous ones in the fish *Jamoytius*.

Jaws and modern-style, living bone are preserved in the earliest known placoderm ("plate-skinned") fish, 436 MYA.

Fully bony internal skeleton is fossilized for the first time, 420 MYA, in the fish *Guiyu*.

Teeth are preserved in a fossil placoderm 416 MYA.

Lungfish is fossilized for the first time 415 MYA.

400 MYA

TIMELINES

RISE OF THE
VERTEBRATES

Backboned animals span only one-eighth of the entire evolutionary history of life, but include some of the most remarkable of its products – including, of course, humans.

The first 100 million years of vertebrate evolution is justifiably described as the "Age of Fish". During this time, these animals evolved the key innovations that made vertebrates so successful – an internal skeleton, biting jaws, and complex organs of sight, hearing, and taste. Some vertebrates that followed used these adaptations to be successful on land. Their strong internal skeleton supported their weight; strongly jointed, bony fins became walking limbs; buoyant gas bladders became lungs; and an outer skin, in some, evolved feathers and fur.

TETRAPODS

First trace on land is left by a vertebrate 395 MYA: track marks of an unknown tetrapod (limbed vertebrate).

Panderichthys

Earliest known live birth leaves evidence in a placoderm fossil, 380 MYA. Also fossilized is *Panderichthys*, a lobe-finned fish related to the ancestors of tetrapods.

Tetrapod *Elginerpeton* leaves fossil evidence 375 MYA.

Tiktaalik, a lobe-finned fish in transition to a tetrapod, is fossilized 375 MYA.

Cladoselache is the first shark to leave abundant fossils 370 MYA.

AMNIOTES

Amniotes (vertebrates that lay hard-shelled eggs) evolve 361 MYA, modern DNA analysis suggests.

350 MYA

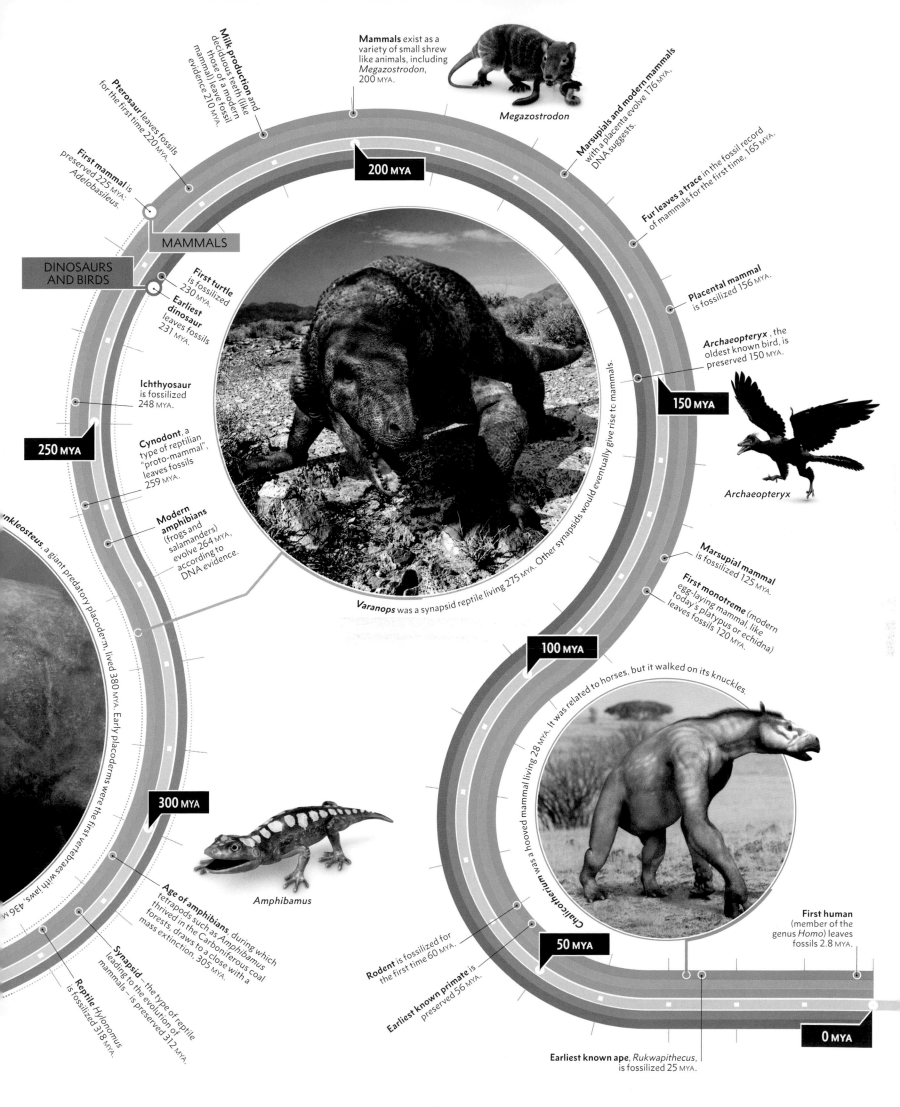

Milk production and deciduous teeth (like those of a modern mammal) leave fossil evidence 210 MYA.

Pterosaur leaves fossils for the first time 220 MYA.

First mammal is preserved 225 MYA: *Adelobasileus*.

Mammals exist as a variety of small shrew-like animals, including *Megazostrodon*, 200 MYA.

Megazostrodon

Marsupials and modern mammals, with a placenta evolve 176 MYA, DNA suggests.

Fur leaves a trace in the fossil record of mammals for the first time, 165 MYA.

Placental mammal is fossilized 156 MYA.

Archaeopteryx, the oldest known bird, is preserved 150 MYA.

200 MYA

150 MYA

Archaeopteryx

MAMMALS

DINOSAURS AND BIRDS

First turtle is fossilized 230 MYA.

Earliest dinosaur leaves fossils 231 MYA.

Ichthyosaur is fossilized 248 MYA.

Cynodont, a type of reptilian "proto-mammal", leaves fossils 259 MYA.

Modern amphibians (frogs and salamanders) evolve 264 MYA, according to DNA evidence.

250 MYA

Other synapsids would eventually give rise to mammals.

Varanops was a synapsid reptile living 275 MYA.

Marsupial mammal is fossilized 125 MYA.

First monotreme (modern egg-laying mammal, like today's platypus or echidna) leaves fossils 120 MYA.

...kleosteus, a giant predatory placoderm, lived 380 MYA. Early placoderms were the first vertebrates with jaws, 436 M...

300 MYA

Amphibamus

Age of amphibians during which tetrapods such as *Amphibamus* thrived in the Carboniferous coal forests, draws to a close with a mass extinction, 305 MYA.

Synapsid — the type of reptile leading to the evolution of mammals — is preserved 312 MYA.

Reptile *Hylonomus* is fossilized 318 MYA.

100 MYA

Chalicotherium was a hooved mammal living 28 MYA. It was related to horses, but it walked on its knuckles.

Rodent is fossilized for the first time 60 MYA.

Earliest known primate is preserved 56 MYA.

50 MYA

First human (member of the genus *Homo*) leaves fossils 2.8 MYA.

0 MYA

Earliest known ape, *Rukwapithecus*, is fossilized 25 MYA.

Neck joint between the shield-like bones of the thorax and skull was not a true neck, but, unusually in fishes, it was flexible here

Jaw muscles pulled the head back here, aided by the flexible joint at the back of the head, to help open up the jaws for a wider bite.

▼ **Terror of the Devonian seas**
Dunkleosteus was among the first predators to catch fast-moving prey with snapping jaws. Studies of its fossilized skull suggest it could have had one of the strongest bites in the history of vertebrate life.

Jagged edge of jaw bone could slice through prey – 100 million years before sharks evolved their bladed teeth

Joint connecting upper and lower jaws was powered by strong, fast-acting muscles to pull the jaws closed and give a formidable bite

Thoracic shield was a plate of bone that anchored muscles that pulled on the lower jaw to rapidly open the mouth

JAWS CREATE TOP PREDATORS

Predators have been a part of the natural world ever since organisms evolved the ability to eat one another. However, backboned animals started as filter-feeders that sucked mud from the ocean floor. It was not until they evolved jaws that they could sit at the top of long food chains.

Many invertebrates – such as predatory worms, sea scorpions, and centipedes – have evolved sharp-edged jaws that can grab prey. But vertebrates, using cartilage and bone, made their jaws bigger and more muscular. The first jawed vertebrates did so through an evolutionary rearrangement of the arches that support the gills. Over generations, the front arches were shifted forwards into the roof and floor of the mouth and met towards the back of the skull, forming a hinged joint.

SUPER-PREDATORS

Reshaping the gill arches into moveable jaws may have helped to fill the gills with more oxygen, but the development of stronger muscles allowed the jaws to bite, too. This helped fish both to catch prey and also to kill and dismember it. Natural selection would have favoured the evolution of bigger fish with more powerful jaws – opening up more ambitious avenues of predation.

The earliest-known jawed vertebrates were placoderms: mostly armour-plated fish that flourished during the Devonian period (419–359 MYA). One of the largest known was *Dunkleosteus*, whose fossil remains are found

throughout the world – evidence of its success. Growing twice the length of a car, *Dunkleosteus* was the biggest predator of its time – and its jaws could easily puncture the armour of its contemporaries. Its size and

strength meant that it could prey on bigger animals, including other predators. Devonian oceans had an extra link to their food chains: a top predator.

DIETARY DIVERSITY

Despite their apparent supremacy, the placoderms did not last. They disappeared in the Late Devonian mass extinction – an event that was probably triggered by a drop in oxygen levels. But other jawed

vertebrates – notably the sharks – had evolved in the meantime, and they survived. Although their jaws were built from flexible cartilage, they had blade-edged teeth that could be serially replaced – something

that placoderms probably could never do. But it was bony vertebrates that took jaws and their especially hard, enamel-coated teeth to a new level. Crocodiles, dinosaurs, and mammals developed deeply-rooted teeth that could better resist struggling prey. Dentition was also modified in animals lower in the food chain. Grazing mammals developed grinding teeth, and their biting jaws became chewing jaws – extending the ecological range of vertebrates more than ever.

>
> THE **VERTEBRATES** THAT CAME **STORMING THROUGH**... SWEEPING MOST OF THE [JAWLESS FISH] ASIDE **DURING THE DEVONIAN**, WERE **THE ONES WITH JAWS**.
>
> **Colin Tudge**, biologist and writer, 1943–

▼ **Top of the food chain**
The evolution of bigger jawed vertebrates broadened the size range of their potential prey – to include other smaller predators. As a result, food chains lengthened. In this food chain, arrows show the flow of energy from prey to predator.

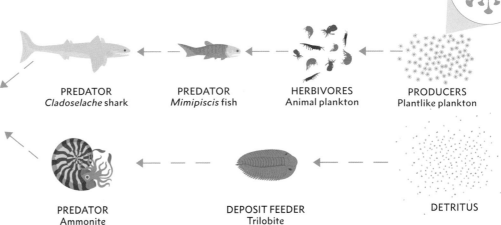

TOP PREDATOR
Dunkleosteus

PREDATOR
Cladoselache shark

PREDATOR
Mimipiscis fish

HERBIVORES
Animal plankton

PRODUCERS
Plantlike plankton

PREDATOR
Ammonite

DEPOSIT FEEDER
Trilobite

DETRITUS

Plant pores

A scanning electron micrograph (SEM) of a pine leaf clearly shows rows of stomata. These open and close, allowing the plant to control the passage of gases – a useful adaptation to life on land.

PLANTS MOVE ONTO LAND

The first sign that the land was turning green probably came when algae crept above the tidal zone along ocean shores. However, the move to permanently drier environments further inland required plants with roots anchored in soil, and shoots that could grow upright in dry air.

Vegetation grew in water long before it invaded the land. Algae had evolved broad fronds that intercepted the Sun's light energy and a "holdfast" that stuck the body to rock. These seaweeds still live in the ocean today. Many survive periodic exposure at low tide, but they are too flimsy to last long on dry land.

WATERPROOFING THE LEAVES

Water screens out some of the Sun's energy. On land, although plants bask in stronger radiation, they risk drying out. Land plants because of the evolution of a complex substance called lignin. By coating their microscopic transport vessels, lignin helped to form water-tight tubes that could deliver water and minerals up the stem. Lignified vessels were also physically strong, so these new plants grew and branched vertically. Tough vessels also grew downwards as stronger, branching roots penetrated the soil to anchor the weight and absorb dissolved minerals. Many of these taller plants were already better suited to life on

> ...THE **FIRST ZOOLOGICAL LANDFALL** WAS CONTINGENT ON THE **GREENING OF THE TERRESTRIAL LANDSCAPE** BY **PLANT LIFE**...WHICH WAS... MORE AN INVASION OF AIR.
>
> **Karl Niklas**, professor of plant science, 1945–

evolved a waxy waterproof coating on their epidermis – the surface "skin" of cells. Pores in the epidermis called stomata helped to keep gases moving for processes such as photosynthesis (see pp.114–15) and respiration. The earliest land plants, like the mosses and liverworts of today, could only hug the land with creeping stems. They clung there with rhizoids – microscopic hairs that scarcely penetrated the ground to function as primitive roots.

STANDING TALL

Strength is required to stand upright. Plant cells are surrounded by a scaffolding of tough fibrous cellulose, and the thickening of this wall in places helps stems bear some weight. Although mosses can do this, they can rise no more than a few centimetres. Other plants managed to grow taller

land by producing seeds. But thickened lignified tissue, called wood, helped trunks get thicker and trees became taller still.

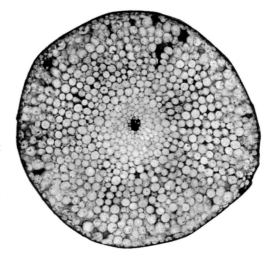

◄ Rigid stem
A cross-section of a fossilized plant (*Rhynia gwynne-vaughanii*) from the Devonian period about 410 MYA reveals water-tight tubes that conducted water and nutrients.

WENLOCK
LIMESTONE

Few organisms leave any kind of fossilized trace, but in some locations conditions have preserved extraordinary snapshots of entire communities. Their wonderful fossils – rich in species and finely detailed – offer rare insights into the ways groups of animals and plants lived and died.

Wenlock Edge – an outcrop of limestone on the Welsh-English border – holds an example of such a fossil assemblage, or Lagerstätte. It is packed with animals of a tropical reef from more than 420 MYA. At this time, the site straddled the coastline of the ancient Iapetus Ocean, where many of Earth's animals had evolved. The fossils show that corals, sponges, trilobites, and brachiopods flourished in the warm shallows.

Lagerstätten form under certain conditions that favour preservation. The Wenlock assemblage includes hard-shelled animals that have been broken or uprooted – suggesting that crashing waves left debris in mud at the bottom of a slope. It means a single Wenlock slab could contain animals

from scattered localities. Other Lagerstätten may preserve communities intact. The Burgess Shale in the Canadian Rockies has soft-body impressions of animals that were smothered in mudslides 508 MYA. Although their orientation is chaotic, the postures suggest they were killed instantly. But not all Lagerstätten result from violent slaughter. North America's Green River formation comprises 50 million-year-old sediments left in lake basins that contain fish, leaves, insects, and even small birds complete with feathers. The oxygen-poor conditions in the lakebed muds slowed bacterial decomposition and allowed fragile parts to fossilize intact. The same process happened in Germany's Messel lake at a similar time.

Rugose coral was as solitary horn-shaped extinct relative of the corals that live today

Clam was a free-swimming filter-feeder like today's scallops

Giant flying ant with iridescent colours intact

Identifying extinct animals

An abundance of fossils from the same age not only helps to reconstruct the interacting lives of prehistoric animals, but helps to resolve their diversity too. Species are described on the basis of specimens – but fossil specimens are frequently incomplete. When so many individuals are preserved together, biologists have a better, more representative, view of anatomy – helping them to divide one species from another.

Bird complete with fossilized feathers

Frog, including an outline of soft body parts

◀ **Messel lake pit**
The site of Messel, Germany, shows very fine preservation of a community living 47 MYA. Its special conditions included poisonous gas emanating from the lake, which not only killed animals instantly, but also ensured no living scavengers ate the fallen remains before they were mineralized.

A piece of colonial coral has been ripped from its position on the reef, like many other attached Wenlock animals

Fenestella, of which this is just a fragment, was a fan-shaped colony of tiny filter-feeding animals called bryozoans

Crinoids, or feather stars (relatives of starfish), have left many broken fragments of their branched arms

Top part of a cystoid – an extinct relative of starfish

How was the community suddenly buried?

Scientists studying taphonomy – the history of a fossil – note that this slab has an abundance of lightweight animals – such as brachiopods, crinoids, and bryozoans, but most of their shells and cases are broken. Taphonomists believe wave-smashed fragments of the living reef were washed away on currents and collected in calmer spots, where their remains were buried. Other Wenlock fossils show trilobites that are partially enrolled – suggesting that they were buried alive.

Trilobite in defensive rolled posture

Where did the animals live?

This slab shows a death assemblage, meaning it includes animals that died together. Palaeoecologists (scientists who study ancient ecology) need further fossils to build a picture of where the organisms lived. From remains of the animals fossilized as in life, they have found that on the ancient reef, harder-shelled brachiopods – more resistant to wave action – lived higher on the shoreline, whereas free-swimming animals lived in deeper waters.

Brachiopods had two shells connected by a hinge, just like a clam, but they are not related to clams

Supporting stems of crinoids were easily broken by strong currents and are abundant in some limestone rocks

Restoring the past

To reconstruct prehistoric life-forms, palaeontologists use all the fossil evidence to put forward a hypothesis about how they looked and behaved, although they can never be certain about their conclusions. The Wenlock fauna consisted of attached animals – such as crinoids and honeycomb corals – that formed a reef habitat, which also contained bottom-feeding trilobites and predatory *Orthoceras* – a shelled relative of squid.

Restoration of *Orthoceras* in Ordovician seas

Brachiopod with both shells open in death

Brachiopod

ANIMALS INVADE LAND

For billions of years, much of life was confined to oceans, lakes, and rivers. Such an ancient aquatic heritage meant that the first complex organisms also lived only in water. Dry land offered so many new opportunities that terrestrial colonization happened not just once, but many times.

It is likely that the first microbes were invading land within a billion years of life's origin. For these bacteria, the wet coastal rocks and moist sediments where oceans lapped the shore were a natural extension of their range. As erosion and detritus formed the first soil over 3 BYA, bacteria began to live between its particles. The earliest burrowing organisms would have churned coastal sediment and added more organic material that served as food for fungi and other decomposers. Soils were becoming so enriched, that by 470 MYA, land was becoming an inviting place for plants, too.

LIVING ON LAND

Above ground, colonization was less straightforward. All living cells, whether of single- or multicellular organisms, must be surrounded by moisture. Land plants survived by evolving a thick, waxy outer layer (cuticle) that both retained water and let gases in and out (see pp.136–37).

The first land animals had a cuticle, too, that served the same water-retaining function, but there were other challenges to overcome in just getting around. In the Cambrian period (541–485 MYA), marine

◀ **First air-breather**
This modern millipede has armoured segments similar to those of *Pneumodesmu* a millipede that lived 428 MYA. *Pneumodesmus* is the earliest body fossil of an animal known to walk on land and breathe air. Fragments of its exoskeleton show that it had spiracles, or breathing holes.

animals had evolved into some gigantic forms, but size was a liability on land. A body is buoyed in water, effectively weighing less, but on land, the same animal may be too heavy to move. Early land animals needed stronger muscles and supporting skeletons, and compensated for this extra baggage by getting smaller. At first, wormlike land animals probably survived underground or in rocky crevices, where, in moist microhabitats, these small animals might have used their skin to breathe air.

The early terrestrial colonists also included jointed-limbed arthropods. Prehistoric arthropods, relatives of today's crabs and spiders, were already thriving in the oceans. Their jointed limbs and armour gave them the potential to succeed on land. Fossil and DNA evidence indicates that millipedes and centipedes were part of the first big wave of land colonists, possibly more than 500 MYA. Their articulated, armoured bodies helped them crawl over land without dehydrating and they evolved breathing holes in this armour, called spiracles, and got oxygen straight from the air. Millipedes would have been among the first grazers of land plants and centipedes the first predator of the terrestrial ecosystem.

FILLING THE FORESTS

Fossil evidence shows that by 380 MYA, the land was already supporting its first trees. By the beginning of the Carboniferous period (359 MYA), Earth was home to rich, swampy forests teeming with life. Plants could grow taller because of the evolution of tougher

> " THE **TETRAPODS**, WITH THEIR LIMBS AND FINGERS AND TOES, INCLUDE OURSELVES AS HUMANS, SO THAT THIS **DISTANT DEVONIAN EVENT** IS PROFOUNDLY **SIGNIFICANT FOR HUMANS** AS WELL AS **FOR THE PLANET**. "
>
> **Jennifer Clack**, palaeontologist, 1947–
> *Gaining Ground: the Origin and Evolution of Tetrapods*

Track between the footprints suggests the creature dragged its abdomen

Small, thin prints suggest at least eight pairs of legs

◀ **Life's first steps**
These fossilized marks made in sand dunes in the early Cambrian period, 530 MYA, represent the oldest trace of animals on land that we have discovered. They were made by an arthropod that divided its time between land and sea.

supporting materials, such as woody lignin. Forests gave height to the land ecosystems – providing new niches for tree-climbing and flying animals. In particular, they encouraged the biggest radiation of land animals of them all: the insects. The evolution of life on land was producing entirely new kinds of animals with new ecological interactions: web-spinning predatory spiders, browsing insects, and grazing snails. In terms of diversity and abundance, the organisms roaming the land were rivalling anything swimming in the water of the oceans.

OUR ANCESTORS REACH LAND

When invertebrate life conquered land, vertebrates were still confined to water habitats. As with invertebrates, when vertebrates started to move on to land 395–375 MYA during the Devonian period, their bodies needed to change.

Fishes use their paired fins for stabilizing their swimming and although a few use them secondarily to "walk" on the sea bed, for most of them, fins are not strong enough to fashion into legs. One group, however – the "lobe-fins" – had an advantage. A few,

TIKTAALIK ROSAE LIVED **375 MYA**; **THE FIRST FOSSILS** WERE DISCOVERED IN **2004** IN THE **CANADIAN ARCTIC**

such as lungfishes and coelacanths, are still alive today, but in the Devonian, there were many different forms. They differed from all other fishes in having a stronger bony support for each of their paired fins. Their flexible joints allowed these fins to be used to walk under water and later helped them emerge from the water and crawl across land. Lobe-finned fishes may have done this in times of drought, just as lungfishes do today. As lobe-fins wandered further ashore, their fins evolved into limbs with fingers and toes.

Fishes had other features that prepared them for a terrestrial life. Most species have a gas-filled bag – the swim bladder – used for controlling buoyancy. Modifications of this swim bladder in some modern fishes mean that the sac can communicate directly with air, helping the fish to breathe and supplement the supply of oxygen it extracts from the water with its gills. In early

lobe-fins, this new kind of breathing mechanism, later powered by chest muscles such as the diaphragm, evolved to become the first air-breathing lungs.

The first vertebrates with lungs are often called amphibians, but these long-extinct creatures are only distantly related to today's frogs and newts. They were the first four-legged vertebrates, or "tetrapods", and ancestors of all reptiles, birds, and

mammals, as well as modern amphibians. An astonishingly complete fossil record documents the transition from fish to tetrapod, via intermediate forms sometimes called "fishapods".

The four-legged, air-breathing plan was a major evolutionary step. Although some legs have since been lost or turned to arms or wings, it is the basis for most land-based vertebrates today.

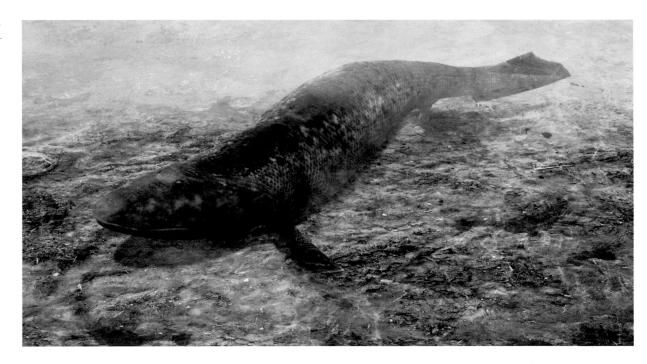

▲ **Transitional fossil** *Tiktaalik rosae* is an evolutionary wonder. Although it resembled a fish, its neck was more flexible than that of true fishes and its fins, although small, had strong joints that may have supported its weight on land.

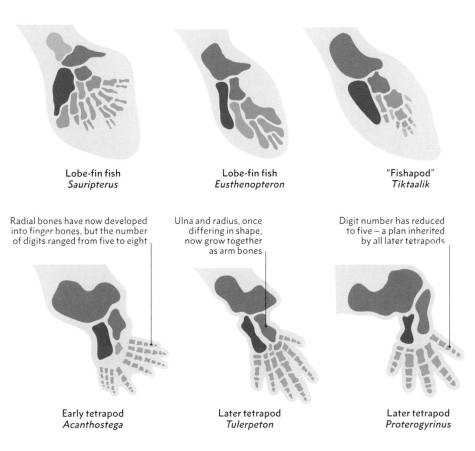

Lobe-fin fish *Sauripterus* | Lobe-fin fish *Eusthenopteron* | "Fishapod" *Tiktaalik*

Radial bones have now developed into finger bones, but the number of digits ranged from five to eight | Ulna and radius, once differing in shape, now grow together as arm bones | Digit number has reduced to five – a plan inherited by all later tetrapods

Early tetrapod *Acanthostega* | Later tetrapod *Tulerpeton* | Later tetrapod *Proterogyrinus*

◄ **Fins to limbs** Dozens of fossilized species show the evolution of fishes to four-legged amphibians. Over time, the same bones mould into different shapes, and a few are lost altogether.

KEY
- Humerus
- Radius
- Ulna
- Ulnare
- Intermedium
- Radials
- Bones missing from the fossil record

REINVENTING **THE WING**

Often, the similarities seen in life are the result of a common ancestor, but not always. For instance, flapping wings required for flight evolved independently in at least four groups of animals at separate points in time, allowing them to take to the air.

Organisms evolve adaptations that make them better suited to their lifestyles. Sometimes, natural selection can produce the same innovation in separate, unrelated groups. This is convergent evolution.

SHARING CHARACTERISTICS

All plants that produce seeds share a common ancestor – in the same way that the stingers of jellyfish and coral are related too. But sometimes, natural selection can produce a similar adaptation in unrelated groups – such as the flippers of swimming ichthyosaurs (reptiles) and dolphins (mammals).

When different forms of life, living in separate environments or even time periods, share an anatomical or behavioural similarity, it is often because they live in similar environments that demand certain adaptations. Despite living millions of years apart, both ichthyosaurs and dolphins needed to be fast swimmers in order to escape predators and catch fast prey, and therefore evolved flippers.

EVOLVING FLIGHT

Insects were the first animals to fly, and they are the only fliers to evolve wings that were not commandeered from existing limbs. Vertebrates became fliers by refashioning their existing limbs. Their forelimbs and hands, over time, evolved into different types of wings. Pterosaurs probably achieved this first and became the most well-known of the reptilian fliers, before becoming extinct along with the dinosaurs. Birds evolved from bipedal dinosaurs and fared better. They survived the same extinction event, possibly due to their warm-bloodedness, to thrive alongside mammals and diversify into a wide range of species. Mammals later evolved one of the more specialized groups of flying animals – bats – most of which take to the air at night and use sonar, or echolocation, to navigate and hunt in darkness.

Birds were the first warm-blooded animals to fly. This lanner falcon shows birds' ability to turn their wings into airbrakes by spreading their feathers.

Pterosaurs, cousins of the dinosaurs, were the first vertebrates to evolve wing-flapping flight. Rhamphorhynchus is an early example from the Jurassic (166–145 MYA).

Bats are the only mammals to have mastered true flight. "Flying" squirrels merely glide.

▼ **Taking to the skies**
The history of flying animals spans hundreds of millions of years of evolution. At four separate points in time, a different group of animals evolved powered flight.

Oldest-known flying insect, a mayfly or stonefly, is fossilized in North America, 314 MYA

400 MYA

300 MYA

ARTHROPODS

REPTILES

Stretched wing membrane attaches to body

Long fifth digit

Pterosaur wings were relatively rudimentary compared to a bird's or a bat's. Wing membranes were supported mainly by a single finger. Pterosaurs did not have the musculature for coordinated flight, and probably relied on soaring on air drafts to get around.

◄ **Anatomy of a wing**
The wings of a pterosaur, bird, and bat each use bones of the arm and hand, but evolution has moulded the bones differently in each case. The shape of pterosaur and bat wings depends on how the bones hold out the flight membrane, made of skin. A bird's flight surface is made of feathers and its shape depends on the form of its feathers.

KEY
- Humerus
- Radius and ulna
- Wrist bones
- Finger bones
- Thumb bones

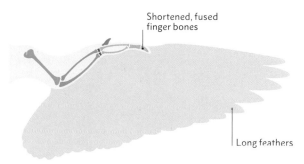

Shortened, fused finger bones

Long feathers

Birds have shorter arm and finger bones that bring the wing under better control. More powerful muscles also mean that the wing, equipped with long flight feathers, can be flapped at wider angles, providing birds with stronger flight than pterosaurs.

Thumb-bone free of wing

Long fingers support wing membrane

Bats have more finger bones than other flying vertebrates. Their wings are supported by four fingers. This makes their shape more flexible than the wings of birds, helping them move in ways that improve manoeuvrability and save energy.

Insect wings, like those of a modern dragonfly, may have evolved when a peak in atmospheric oxygen triggered more active lifestyles.

How did wings evolve?
The earliest proto-wings were flaps on insects' bodies that previously served as gills, or as oars allowing them to skim over water. Climbing insects may have used them to parachute through air before evolving flapping wings, which gave them better aerial control. Pterosaurs, birds, and finally bats became airborne not by growing new appendages, but by adapting existing ones.

Oldest modern bird, *Vegavis*, is fossilized in Antarctica, 66 MYA

Lithornis, the oldest known ratite (a type of flightless bird including kiwis and ostriches) is fossilized in North America, 57 MYA

BIRDS

Oldest known pterosaur, *Faxinalipterus*, is fossilized in Brazil, 220 MYA

Oldest known bird, *Archaeopteryx*, is fossilized in Germany, 150 MYA

At the end of their reign, 68–66 MYA, some pterosaurs reach enormous sizes, with some exceeding 10m (33ft) in wingspan

Oldest known bats are fossilized 56 MYA: *Archaeonycteris* in Portugal and *Marnenycteris* in France

200 MYA

100 MYA

0

MAMMALS

" THE **COMPLETELY PROTECTED EMBRYO** WITHIN **THE SEED** GIVES... A GREAT **ADVANTAGE**. "

Douglas Houghton Campbell, American botanist, 1859–1953

The presence of fossilized seeds indicates that the tree had been pollinated and so successfully fertilized

Woody cone has turned to stone during fossilization

Monkey puzzle
This fossilized cone is 160 million years old but remarkably similar to the cones produced by trees today. This species, *Araucaria araucana*, known as the monkey puzzle and still thrives in Argentina and Chile.

Scales in the cone are modified leaves that protect the seed

THE **FIRST SEEDS**

About 370 million years ago, a new kind of plant evolved. It produced seeds, which are the ultimate embryo survival kit – packed with nutrients and enveloped in a protective casing. Seeds would shape the history of life and play a key part in our own prehistory.

The first algae-like plants completed their entire life cycle – alternating between spores and gametes (eggs or sperm) – under water. As their descendants, mosses and ferns, crept further inland, more resilient spores could be dispersed into the air. However, their sperm still needed water droplets to swim to the egg: no matter how much their deep roots and tough leaves helped them survive droughts, plants still needed periodic rainfall in order to reproduce.

A new kind of plant broke this restrictive link with water by relocating its fertilization into reproductive shoots away from the ground. Female shoots retained their spores,

> *MEDULLOSA* – A **PRIMITIVE SEED PLANT** THAT LIVED 350–250 MYA – HAD **SEEDS THE SIZE OF EGGS**

which grew into eggs. Spores from male shoots became pollen grains that were blown inland to land on female shoots. In the most primitive seed plants, sperm then burst from the pollen grains and swam through the shoot to the egg – something still seen in cycads of today. But in most seed plants, sperm became redundant. Instead, each pollen grain sprouted a tiny thread – a pollen tube – that conveyed a naked male

cell nucleus straight to the egg, dispensing with swimming altogether. Pollen allowed plants to spread further inland than their water-reliant relatives. What is more, these plants completed their break from water by keeping embryos of their next generation in drought-resistant cases – seeds.

HOW SEEDS WORK
Eggs develop inside a thin-walled sac called an ovule. After pollen fertilizes an ovule, its walls thicken, and it becomes a seed. At first, ovules grew exposed on foliage or the scales of cones – reproductive shoots composed of hard scales connected at their base, just like the cones produced by cycads and conifers today. Eventually, most seed plants buried their ovules deeper inside the shoot, beneath a flower (see pp.160–61). When these ovules turn into seeds, the succulent tissue around them becomes fruit. Seed plants had now evolved a method of enticing animals, a different form of complex life, to become part of their life strategy (see pp.164–65).

SEEDS, THEIR SUCCESS, AND US
The pollen method of fertilization and the seed method of dispersal have both been so successful that seed plants now form the basis of all land-based ecosystems and food webs worldwide, including those with humans at the top. Non-seed plants – mosses, ferns, and liverworts – although widespread, no longer dominate any land habitats.

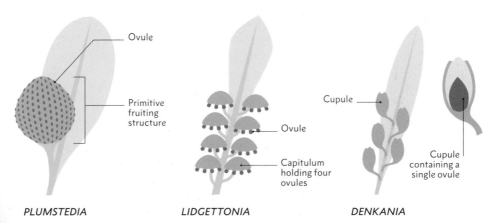

Ovule
Primitive fruiting structure

PLUMSTEDIA

Ovule
Capitulum holding four ovules

LIDGETTONIA

Cupule
Cupule containing a single ovule

DENKANIA

◄ **Primitive seed plants**
The first seed plants are called seed ferns, because of the shape of their leaves, although they are unrelated to the ferns we know today. They grew their ovules in packages attached to the leaves. Cones and flowers eventually evolved in later types of plants.

4.1 BYA | FIRST TRACE
OF POSSIBLE LIFE

2.4 BYA | OXYGEN
FILLS THE AIR

936 MYA | ESTIMATED ORIGIN OF
ALGAE AND PLANTS

▼ **Life in a shell**
Prehistoric reptiles – including dinosaurs – were
pioneers of the shelled egg. The embryo could
develop inside, safe from dehydration. Its parents
may have guarded the egg from predators, just
like many reptiles and birds do today.

The shell is composed of a chalky material
based on calcium carbonate that is hard
enough to withstand damage, permeable to
allow the exchange of respiratory gases,
and sufficiently brittle so the infant can
break free upon hatching

**White shell membranes conceal the
chorion** – a transparent embryonic
membrane that completely encloses the
embryo, amnion, yolk sac, and allantois

The expansive allantois
absorbs oxygen that seeps
through the shell from the
egg's surroundings and
releases carbon dioxide

Some blood vessels in the allantois carry
oxygen into the embryo; others take waste
carbon dioxide away from it. Nitrogen-
containing waste products also build up
in the allantois as deposits of uric acid.

The embryo has already
developed all the major body
parts it will need upon hatching

SHELLED EGGS
ARE BORN

The first backboned animals to live on land could walk, since they had legs, and could breathe air. These early amphibians were still tied to water, however, because they needed a wet place to breed. Reptiles broke this link by producing hard-shelled eggs that could develop on dry land.

The yolk sac is filled with foods, such as protein and fat, that nourish the developing embryo; it shrinks as the embryo grows bigger and uses up its contents

The amnion is a thin transparent membrane that encloses the amniotic fluid, which surrounds the embryo and cushions it from physical harm

Backboned animals originated in water, where fish and amphibians laid their soft eggs encased in nothing but a protective jelly coat. Reptiles not only evolved hard, scaly water-proof skin as protection from dehydration, but transformed their breeding habits too. They covered their eggs in a shell hard enough to protect and contain the embryo on land, yet permeable enough for it to breathe.

EMBRYO SURVIVAL KIT
The shelled eggs produced by most reptiles and all birds are amazing structures that contain all their embryos need to develop. Until the invention of these eggs, all living embryos developed surrounded by fluid. To reproduce those fluid conditions on land, it was a small and manageable evolutionary step to enclose the fluid within a membrane. The membrane is called the amnion, giving the first animals to possess it the name "amniotes" as well as the more familiar "reptiles". Within the egg, the embryo also has its own larder, the yolk sac, just as fish and amphibians do. But it also has an allantois – a waste-disposal pouch absent in its ancestors. The yolk sac grows smaller and the allantois enlarges as it absorbs oxygen and accumulates waste products while the embryo grows. A final membrane – the chorion – serves to contain the entire embryo "survival kit".

By the time they hatch, reptiles are ready to lead independent lives; on the other hand, most bird chicks need parental care for a

time. But, in both cases, hatchlings are ready to eat and breathe as soon as they emerge from the egg.

PREPARED FOR LAND
The shelled egg and its life supporting membranes enabled the amniotes to complete their life cycle on land. They mated on land and laid eggs in a dry nest. A few living reptiles have abandoned their egg-laying ways and give birth to live young.

THE EARLIEST ANIMAL THOUGHT TO LAY SHELLED EGGS IS *PALEOTHYRIS*, AN AMNIOTE LIVING **330** MYA

But one group of amniotes, the mammals, turned live birth into a major asset. They commandeered two membranes – the allantois and chorion – into a placenta, which draws oxygen and nourishment straight from the mother's blood. By nurturing the embryo in the mother's body, mammals improved their offspring's chances of survival beyond those of their larvae-producing ancestors.

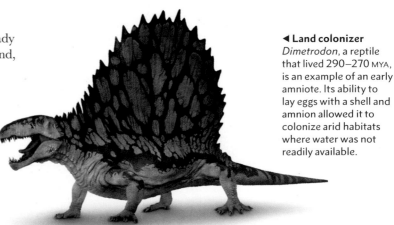

◄ **Land colonizer**
Dimetrodon, a reptile that lived 290–270 MYA, is an example of an early amniote. Its ability to lay eggs with a shell and amnion allowed it to colonize arid habitats where water was not readily available.

HOW **COAL** FORMED

The trees that formed Earth's first forests were giant fernlike plants that resisted decay. Their dead bodies built up, trapping carbon and energy under ground. These were the coal forests – and 300 million years later, their compacted remains would fuel an industrial revolution.

The Carboniferous period (359–299 MYA) was a time when life on land prospered more than ever before. Trees grew from mosslike ancestors, insects took to the air in a world already crawling with invertebrates, and giant amphibians were evolving into reptiles. This time in Earth's history would have huge implications for our own history.

THE FIRST FORESTS

For the first time, terrestrial life could live in the trees, imbuing habitats with an extra richness. The first big invasions of land animals, involving millipedes, insects, and arachnids, had already taken place, but now these groups exploded into a multitude of species, including predators, such as spiders, scorpions, and centipedes. Carboniferous trees could grow tall because they had evolved a tough supporting material called lignin that formed a protective layer. It would also eventually become the carbon-

rich store of energy that formed coal. The trees concentrated lignin in their tissues to more than 10 times the quantity found in today's trees. This not only helped to deter herbivores, but it also resisted decay, because few microbes could digest it. As trees died, their fallen trunks lingered. The lignin, along with the carbon it contained, would be converted to carbon dioxide (CO_2) if it decayed, but it sank into the swampy Earth, locking away its chemical energy. As CO_2 in the atmosphere diminished, oxygen increased, since it would normally be consumed by the same processes of decomposition, which were now suppressed. Oxygen built up in the air to become more than one-third of it by volume. Today, oxygen accounts for only one-fifth of the gas in the atmosphere. The effects of such high oxygen levels would have been bizarre. Ignition would have happened more readily, sparking wildfires. Animals that relied on

passive breathing through their skin or body surface became enormous. The biggest insects that ever lived evolved during the Carboniferous, and amphibians grew to the size of crocodiles.

THE ORIGINS OF COAL

Much of the bulk of the Carboniferous trees sank intact beneath the swampy waters, forming layer upon layer of a deposit called

> *LEPIDODENDRON* TREES GREW **UP TO 40M (130FT) TALL** IN THE **CARBONIFEROUS** PERIOD

peat. In the peat, oxygen was low and acidity high, and instead of decomposing, the carbon-rich remains built up. The peat became compacted under its own weight, squeezing out water and gases, turning first into a form of rock called lignite, and finally

▶ Coal formation
Coal began as undecomposed matter from dead trees. The dead matter was buried as new dead material accumulated on top, and it became compacted under high pressure. Over millions of years of increasing pressure and temperature, the material turned first to the rock lignite, then eventually to coal.

Prehistoric trees and other plants topple and die

Dead matter in swampy soil partially decays to form peat

Pressure of sediment layers squeezes out water and air

Pressure of sediment layers builds

Pressure solidifies and compacts layers of peat into a rock called lignite, which is combustible

As pressures and temperatures rise, deposits lose water and gas, concentrating their carbon levels

Rock is now coal, a more combustible rock with maximum carbon

◀ **Prehistoric energy**
Layers of coal can be seen clearly as dark bands packed between the rock at this coal mine in the Lower Rhine region, Germany.

o a harder, denser rock with an especially high concentration of carbon: coal. Coal deposits are found in rocks that date back to before the evolution of land plants – and these probably came from algae. But coal deposits are especially abundant from the Carboniferous period, where conditions were just right for them to form.

Human civilizations, perhaps as far back as 1000 BCE, recognized the potential of using coal as fuel because of its resemblance to charcoal. Both could be burned to release a great deal of heat. The carbon that had been locked away in coal for millions of years was finally released as carbon dioxide. The emergence of large-scale mining

> "
> **COAL**, OIL AND GAS ARE... **FOSSIL FUELS**, BECAUSE THEY ARE MOSTLY MADE OF... FOSSIL REMAINS... THE **CHEMICAL ENERGY** WITHIN THEM IS A KIND OF **STORED SUNLIGHT ORIGINALLY ACCUMULATED** BY **ANCIENT PLANTS**.
> "
>
> **Carl Sagan**, astronomer and science author, 1934–1996

(see pp.306–07) could tap deposits in seams far below the surface. Since then, the demand for burning fossil fuels has released so much carbon dioxide in such a short amount of time that it is sparking

concerns for humanity. Energy is required for a growing population – however, burning fossils fuels has increased the amount of greenhouse gases and contributed to global warming. Today's civilization must deal with an environmental issue of its own making – and one that affects the entire world.

Ingredient of coal
The fossilized trunk of the plant *Lepidodendron*, an abundant tree during the Carboniferous period. Its tall trunk lacked true bark but was thickened by a layer of tough lignin.

Each diamond-shaped scar marks the point where a leaf has broken away from the trunk

LIZARD IN AMBER

Traces – or fossils – that have been left behind in the rocks and stones of Earth are evidence that extinct species were not the same as those living today. Scientists must turn detectives to work out how they once lived.

More than 99 per cent of species that have ever lived on Earth are now extinct. This means that what we know about the history of life is critically dependent on fossil evidence.

Fossils can form in different ways. If dead organisms are buried quickly in sediment before being eaten, they and the sediment turn to rock. When continents shift position over millions of years, rocks that contain these fossils may buckle and rise – exposing the fossils, as the surrounding rock is eroded.

The fossilization process is never perfect, and preservation quality varies greatly. Older, soft-bodied species leave frailer traces than younger, harder ones. Hard parts of the body, such as the skeleton, are most likely to be fossilized. Footprints, eggs, and faeces can also be fossils. Under the right conditions, the most delicate features, such as skin, feathers, leaves, or even single cells, can be fossilized. Some fossils can be found in amber, such as this lizard. Amber is the solidified resin of trees that has hardened, and animals that get smothered and trapped within it can be exquisitely preserved.

Palaeontologists must consider how a fossil formed when interpreting fossil evidence. Clues are studied from multiple disciplines, such as geography and anatomy, to assemble a picture of how different kinds of organisms lived in the past.

Story of the dead body

The study of taphonomy concerns processes that change a dead animal's body as it decays or fossilizes. Tree resin is organic too, so also decays. This lump of resin fossilized well because it was packed under sediment soon after forming. As a result, *Yantarogekko* was preserved perfectly, sealed away from scavengers and erosion.

Prehistoric spider also trapped in amber

Botanical clue

Analysis of this Baltic amber shows that it was produced by a species of conifer, suggesting that *Yantarogekko*'s habitat was coniferous forest. The presence of the fossilized amber indicates that, by this time, these conifer trees had evolved resin (sticky droplets that seal wounds and deter herbivores), perhaps in response to a prehistoric species of herbivore that fed on them.

Coniferous forest, Poland

▼ **How fossils form**
It takes millions of years for the bodies of living organisms to fossilize. Organic remains decay and harden.

Dead fish settles at the bottom of seabed

Layers of sediment settle over fish's body

Sediment layers compact and turn to rock

Plate tectonics push fossil to surface

Dead animals left uneaten will decay. Left undisturbed the fish's scales settle and are preserved as an outline of its fossilized skeleton.

Buried under sediment, which screens the fish from scavengers, minerals from the water filter into the bones, causing them to crystallize and harden.

Pressure from layers of sediment and rock accumulates over millions of years and the organic parts of the body are entirely replaced by minerals.

Discovery of the fossil may occur when continental drift pushes it to the surface, and erosion may start to wear away at the rock – exposing the fossil.

Locating the habitat

The place where a fossil is found today may differ a great deal from its original habitat. For instance, this amber-entombed lizard was found on the brackish Baltic Sea coastline. When this lizard died 54 MYA, its natural habitat may have been a forest further inland. The evidence suggests that a river washed lumps of amber from the warm coniferous forest downstream to the coast.

Comparing anatomy

The structure of a fossil's body, or the traces the body leaves behind, can be compared with those of related fossils and species alive today. Only the head, front end of the body, and right forelimb of this lizard are preserved in amber, yet this is enough for palaeontologists to recognize it as a species of gecko. This specimen reveals well-developed toe pads and lack of eyelids – features that are preserved in amber but would be lost in a fossilized skeleton preserved in rock.

Banded gecko

Insects entombed with *Yantarogekko* may have been prey

Fixed, transparent scales covering each eye, similar to modern gecko species

▶ **Pangaea**
The continents were merged into one over Earth's southern hemisphere between 300–175 MYA. Inland, forests turned to deserts, while diminished coastlines drove many marine species to extinction.

Shallow seas encircled the coastlines of Pangaea

Vast swathes of arid land spread across what would become North America and Europe during the Permian period (299–252 MYA)

Where continents merged, coastlines disappeared – probably resulting in the extinction of marine life

Pangaea's climate was hot and dry, since land in the centre would not benefit from temperate climatic effects normally provided by nearby oceans and seas

Glaciers had formed around the South Pole during the Carboniferous (359–299 MYA), but gradually receded as the Permian (299–252 MYA) got warmer and drier

THE LAND
DRIES OUT

After terrestrial life flourished in the swampy coal forests, a global drought that lasted 50 million years changed the direction of life's evolution. As vegetation grew tougher leaves and swamps dried up, some moist-skinned amphibians gave rise to the first scaly reptiles.

Shores of the coastline basked in a moist, tropical climate, and so were probably among the last refuges of the Carboniferous swamp forests as the rest of Pangaea dried out

Around 300 million years ago, all of Earth's landmasses collided to form a single supercontinent called Pangaea. This caused a dramatic change in terrestrial life. Climate change had already triggered a collapse in the great swampy forests of the Carboniferous period (see pp.148–49), but

Dimetrodon reached the size of a car, and others became the first big herbivores. Later synapsids also included small reptilian ancestors of mammals.

The Permian closed with violence – a mass extinction so severe that it wiped out more than 70 per cent of animal life. With

MANY OF THE PERMIAN **REPTILES** POSSESS **FOSSIL CHARACTERISTICS** WHICH **FORESHADOW** THE HEAD AND TEETH OF **MAMMALS**.

R. Will Burnett, biologist, 1945–

now, at the dawn of the Permian period, much of the landscape of the new supercontinent was about to turn to desert.

NEW SKIN, LARGER SIZES
Reptiles had evolved in the forests, but now spread across the new parched world. These new vertebrates were better adapted for land than their amphibian ancestors. By evolving hard scales, made from a tough fibrous protein called keratin, they reduced dehydration. Mammals and birds would later use the keratin for their hairs and feathers. The first reptiles to lay hard-shelled eggs (see pp.146–47) also did not need water to breed – unlike their amphibian ancestors. This helped to push vertebrate land colonization like never before.

Two main reptile groups diverged at the start of their reign. One, the diapsids, later went on to produce dinosaurs, birds, and modern lizards. At the time of the Permian it was the second group, the synapsids, that came to rule the arid land. Some evolved to become the biggest land animals of the day. The sail-backed, carnivorous

extraordinary volcanic activity releasing noxious gases, the biggest extinction event ever saw many reptiles disappear. But enough descendants of both groups, the synapsids and diapsids, survived to repopulate the land – first with dinosaurs and mammals, and then with birds.

◄ *Moschops*
With its stocky body, this survivor of the dry Permian world ate tough desert vegetation. It was one of many synapsids – strong-jawed reptiles that would eventually give rise to mammals.

The Palaeo-Tethys Ocean was at its largest during Devonian and Carboniferous periods (419–300 MYA), but then started to close up with movement of land masses in the Permian

REPTILES **DIVERSIFY**

The coming and going of species define the chapters in the history of life. In the wake of a drying supercontinent, the Age of the Reptiles produced some of Earth's most spectacular animals. Reptilian diversity reached its peak, as giant reptiles conquered sky, land, and oceans.

Pteranodon

The great Age of Reptiles spanned more than 200 million years. It began on the parched landscape of Pangaea (see pp.152–53) and ended with an asteroid strike, but even after the demise of the dinosaurs, reptiles prevailed, albeit in a smaller form. Today, lizards and snakes account for nearly one-third of land vertebrate species.

MESOZOIC MONSTERS

During the Mesozoic Era, the stretch of time divided into Triassic, Jurassic, and Cretaceous periods, a group of small, lizard-like reptiles – diapsids – diversified with spectacular results. Some diapsids returned to the ocean habitats of their

it is possible for a land animal to get. As herbivores evolved into giants, so did their predators. Theropods, the bipedal sprinters of the dinosaur family, were nearly all carnivores. The biggest of these, such as *Tyrannosaurus*, were among the most formidable predators ever to walk on land. Evolution also favoured miniaturization among dinosaurs: one group of diminutive theropods grew feathers, turned warm-blooded, and eventually evolved into birds.

MASS EXTINCTION

The reign of the giant reptiles ended with the Cretaceous mass extinction – almost certainly caused by an asteroid or comet

Velociraptor

> ## CREATURES FAR SURPASSING THE LARGEST OF EXISTING REPTILES... DEEMED SUFFICIENT GROUND FOR ESTABLISHING A DISTINCT TRIBE... *DINOSAURIA*.

Richard Owen, palaeontologist, 1804-1892

distant ancestors: the ichthyosaurs and plesiosaurs, such as *Albertonectes*, evolved flippers from limbs and became expert swimmers and hunters of fish.

The most famous diapsids took body size to new extremes. These reptiles – the archosaurs – became crocodilians, flying pterosaurs, dinosaurs, and ultimately birds. They had strong limb muscles that allowed them to walk tall – improving on the lumbering, belly-dragging gait of earlier reptiles.

GIANTS AND MINIATURES

The most successful and diverse archosaurs of the time, dinosaurs evolved into a multitude of predators, grazers, and scavengers. The gigantic, long-necked, herbivorous sauropods, such as *Brachiosaurus*, became about as large as

striking Earth. Catastrophic conditions followed, including wildfires, acid rain, and a global cloud of debris that blocked the Sun's light and brought much of life's food-providing photosynthesis to a temporary halt.

Unable to adapt quickly enough to the rapidly changing conditions, all the giant reptiles – including plesiosaurs, pterosaurs, dinosaurs, mosasaurs, and the giant ancestral crocodilians – became extinct. But lizards, snakes, turtles, and modern crocodiles survived. Surviving along with them were the descendants that would ultimately succeed the reptiles in global domination: birds and mammals.

Edmontosaurus

◄ Diversification
The dinosaurs formed one of many reptile groups that dominated Earth for millions of years. Living alongside them, pterosaurs soared in the skies and plesiosaurs and mosasaurs swam in the oceans. In addition, turtles, lizards, snakes, and crocodilians all appeared for the first time.

Placerias

Deinosuchus

Diphydontosaurus

Titanoboa

Tyrannosaurus

Citipati

Iguanodon

Rahonavis

Plateosaurus

Psittacosaurus

Parasaurolophus

Stegosaurus

Euoplocephalus

Triceratops

Mosasaurus

Albertonectes

Archelon

BIRDS TAKE TO THE AIR

Birds are the most varied of the flying vertebrates, and today there are more than 10,000 species. Their origins lie with the dinosaurs, and scientists have been studying fossils for 150 years to better understand this evolutionary transition.

The story of how birds evolved from reptiles provides biologists with a deeper understanding of how evolution works. From one form of life another can arise so inherently different that at first glance it appears that there is no relationship between the two. Closer inspection of anatomy, the fossil record, and molecular analysis of genomes can lead to surprising connections between seemingly unrelated species.

Superficially, reptiles and birds differ to a large degree. Modern birds look conspicuously distinct from living reptiles, even though they had reptilian ancestors – a group of bipedal, mainly predatory dinosaurs called theropods. Theropods, however, had already evolved to become very unlike the reptiles we know today. Some were not only feathered, but may have been warm-blooded, too.

PREPARING FOR FLIGHT

In some ways, theropods were primed for flying, even if their reasons for doing so are not certain. They walked upright on their hind legs, which meant their front legs were free to become wings. Some small species had hollow bones, which were already lightweight. In some gliding species, long fingers supporting broad, feathered hands provided the lift to sail short distances over ground or from branch to branch. However, genuine wing-flapping flight required at least two more modifications: flight feathers made into stiff blades and stronger muscles capable of sustained flapping.

As birds evolved over time, their breastbones developed a bony protrusion called a keel to which more massive flight muscles attached. Big-keeled birds packed more breast muscle to power their wings. These masters of flight flourished in the forests, grasslands, and wetlands of the post-dinosaur world. They evolved new and better ways to get food, as they caught insects, crushed seeds, or lapped nectar. Others returned to the meat-eating habits of their ancestors and a few, such as ostriches, have abandoned flight altogether and sprint across the ground instead.

Long, asymmetrical flight feathers gave *Confuciusornis* a long, narrow wing

150 MYA

Archaeopteryx
This species retained many reptilian features, including a long, bony tail, teeth, and claws on its feathered wings. It lacked the musculature for strong flight, so may have relied heavily on gliding.

125–120 MYA

Confuciusornis
The first bird known to have a toothless beak, it also had a more birdlike tail and a keel on its breastbone. Like *Archaeopteryx*, its shoulder joint was angled lower than in modern birds, and this restricted the depth of its "flap".

0 MYA

Erithacus
The keeled breastbone of modern birds, such as the European robin, supports massive flight muscles (up to 10 per cent of the bird's body weight), making flight stronger.

◄ **Prehistoric flier**
This crow-sized primitive bird, *Confuciusornis*, lived alongside the dinosaurs 125–120 MYA, during the Cretaceous period. Its fossilized remains have been found in abundance, with many fossils preserving its skeleton and feathers in exquisite detail.

A toothless beak sets *Confuciusornis* apart from its dinosaur ancestors and from *Archaeopteryx*, which had teeth like a dinosaur

Large claw was probably used to climb trees

Wrist bones helped the hand swivel sideways – perhaps to help catch prey

DEINONYCHUS

Strong, bulky claws could grab moving prey

The tail vertebrae ended in a bony stump called a pygostyle, typical of all modern birds; like modern birds, if it had a long tail, it was formed of feathers

Wrist joint's movement was confined to the swivelling motion that became part of the bird's flight stroke

Slender finger bones made wing more light-weight

ARCHAEOPTERYX

KEY

	Humerus		Wrist bones
	Radius and ulna		Finger bones

Backward-facing back toe (hallux) allowed *Confuciusornis* to perch firmly on branches, like many modern birds

▲ **Prehistoric hands**
Hand and wrist bones of *Deinonychus*, a theropod dinosaur, and *Archaeopteryx*, the earliest known bird, show remarkable similarity in anatomy. However, only *Archaeopteryx* could fly.

> "
> **AVIAN FLIGHT** IS THE **MOST VARIED** AND **SUCCESSFUL** OF ALL FORMS OF VERTEBRATE FLIGHT.
> "

John Ostrom, palaeontologist, 1925–2005

CONTINENTS SHIFT AND **LIFE DIVIDES**

As continents move they carry with them communities of living things that have evolved over millions of years. Landmasses that split and collide pull species apart and bring others together. As land glides between poles and the equator, climate also affects species.

Land-based life rides on moving continental plates that are pushed and pulled as crust plunges into Earth's interior in some places and is reformed in others (see pp.92–93). Oceans between the crust expand and shrink, while coastal and marine life comes and goes. The shifting surface of Earth helps to explain why fossils found today end up in odd places – such as those of sea-floor animals appearing high in the Himalayas.

diversified, landmasses became centres for evolution. These events happened so long ago that there is scarcely any trace in the distribution of invertebrates and plants alive today. But over 300 MYA – as some amphibians were evolving into reptiles and some spore-bearing plants were evolving into seed plants (see pp.144–45) – the movement of the continents began to have more lasting impacts.

CRADLES OF LIFE ON LAND

Relatively early in Earth's history in the Cambrian period (541–485 MYA), giant land masses formed and split, creating the oceans in which life diversified. Once plants and invertebrates had invaded land and

LAND LIFE SPLITS APART

In the Carboniferous period (359–299 MYA), northern and southern land masses collided to form a huge supercontinent called Pangaea (see pp.152–53). It straddled the equator and contained most of Earth's land.

SOUTH AMERICA

> " **ALL EARTH SCIENCES** MUST CONTRIBUTE **EVIDENCE**... UNVEILING THE STATE OF OUR PLANET IN EARLIER TIMES. "

Alfred Wegener, geologist and meteorologist, 1880–1930

▶ Modern clue
The African ostrich is a species of flightless ratite bird. Other species of ratites include the South American rhea and Australian emu, providing evidence for a Gondwanan distribution for ratite birds.

Its effect on climate was dramatic – with the dry interior vastly different from the cold, polar extremes. This, coupled with the loss of many coastal habitats, sent many species into extinction, but helped seed plants, reptiles (see pp.154–55), and others diversify.

In the Mesozoic Era 100 million years later, Pangaea began to split. This created a sea barrier for land-based life, and plants and animals were isolated on two supercontinents; Laurasia in the north split from Gondwana in the south. Land-based life could wander across five continents that today are widely separated. Further splitting would produce recognizable landmasses: Laurasia into North America and Eurasia, and Gondwana into South America, Africa, India, Antarctica, and Australia.

We now know that Gondwana was covered in rich rainforests that encouraged diversity. Many groups alive today evolved there first – such as modern marsupial mammals – and spread throughout Gondwana, but could not reach Laurasia. Today, marsupials are restricted to South America and Australia, and have fossils in Antarctica. Flightless ratite birds, such as the Australian emu, also have a remnant Gondwanan distribution. Those evolving in Laurasia, such as salamanders and newts, were restricted to northern continents.

The distribution of fossilized species is evidence for continental drift (see pp.90–91). Certainly, the pattern and movement of continents has had a profound impact on the distribution of all life that followed.

| 0 MYA | FIRST LAND ANIMALS | 380 MYA | FIRST TREES AND FORESTS | 220 MYA | FIRST MAMMALS AND DINOSAURS | 65 MYA | ASTEROID KILLS THE RULING REPTILES |

◄ Clues about Gondwana

We can draw conclusions from the fossil sites of these four species as to which continents were connected as Gondwana 150 MYA. Some of these species are also found in Laurasia, indicating that they evolved before Pangaea split.

KEY

● *Glossopteris*
This tree lived before Pangaea split and was found in both Gondwana and Laurasia. Fossils are common in Gondwanan continents, indicating that much of the continent was forested.

● *Cynognathus*
This primitive mammal-like reptile lived before the Pangaea supercontinent split. Despite this, *Cynognathus* fossils are found only in the Gondwanan continents.

● *Lystrosaurus*
A common mammal-like reptile, *Lystrosaurus* thrived on Pangaea before it split. Its fossils are most abundant in southern Africa – but have been found in India, Antarctica, and also Eurasia.

● *Mesosaurus*
Fossils of *Mesosaurus*, an aquatic reptile, are only found between South America and South Africa, suggesting that its distribution was confined to the southern extreme of the continent.

AFRICA

INDIA

GONDWANA

ANTARCTICA

AUSTRALIA

CONTINENTS SHIFT AND LIFE DIVIDES | **159**

THE PLANET BLOSSOMS

One group of seed plants made the planet burst with colour. Flowers gave plants more effective ways of spreading their pollen and setting their seeds. Even before the demise of the dinosaurs, forests and other habitats were blooming – and buzzing with pollinators.

Around 90 per cent of all known plant species are flowering plants. As trees, shrubs, and climbers, they dominate rainforests; as grasses, they carpet open ground. Flowering plants thrive in the driest of deserts and cling to rocks on high mountains and Arctic tundra. Some, such as mangroves, even tolerate tidal inundations of salt water along shorelines. While some produce the deadliest of poisons, others supply most of humanity's food. All, in one way or another, provide habitats for animals. Such impressive diversity stems from a uniquely successful reproductive shoot: the flower.

female flowers are receptive. Female parts, the carpels, have special projections, their stigmas, that catch the pollen grains. Many plants rely on wind to disperse pollen, but early in their evolution, some species recruited animal partners to carry it for them. As insects diversified so did the variety of blossoms (see pp.164–65).

SCATTERING THE SEED

Insects were not the only animals to evolve alongside flowers. Fruit, another innovation of flowering plants, encased the seed and turned fragrant and colourful as it ripened.

Limonium sinuatum

Guzmania lingulata

> ❝ IT IS DIFFICULT TO CONCEIVE A **GRANDER MASS OF VEGETATION**... ONE MASS OF **BLOSSOMS**... ESPECIALLY THE WHITE ORCHIDS...WHITENING THEIR TRUNKS LIKE SNOW. ❞

Joseph Dalton Hooker, botanist, 1817–1911, *Himalayan journals*

THE FIRST FLOWERS

The first members of the flowering plant group, or angiosperms, evolved around 120 MYA. *Montsechia vidalii*, an aquatic plant with tiny flowers, is thought to have dispersed its pollen in water, similar to its ancestors (see pp.144–45). Angiosperms began to diversify 30 million years later and evolve the flowering structure so integral to their success. Water lilies and magnolias are some of the most primitive species – remaining unchanged for millions of years.

MOVING THE POLLEN

Flowers improve the transfer of pollen from male to female parts. Male flower parts, called stamens, split open to release their matured pollen grains at just the right time – when pollinators are active and when

This was perfect for attracting mammals with a nose for scent and birds with an eye for colour. Seeds, in turn, became resistant to their digestive processes so they could be dispersed in droppings, readily supplied with a dose of fertilizer.

When plants first used flowers in their reproduction, they were embarking upon an evolutionary pathway with far-reaching repercussions. Tens of millions of years later, animals with a taste for sugar, including humans, would have sweeter foods to plunder, such as fruits, as more seeds scattered and new seedlings grew.

▶ **Bloom of colour**
Today, over 250,000 species of flowering plants decorate our planet. Some kinds have specific animal pollinator partners, without whom they would not be able to spread.

Nymphaea

Anemone pulsat

Myrica gale

Globularia alypu

Kunzea baxteri

Agapanthus africanus

Austrobaileya scandens

Ostrya japonica

Narcissus pseudonarcissus

Anthericum liliago

Delphinium cardinale

Eriostemon spicata

Potentilla anserine

Rosa rugosa

Aesculus hippocastanum

Magnolia campbellii

Choisya ternata

Paulownia tomentosa

Xanthoceras sorbifolium

Primula veris

Protea cynaroides

Quercus robur

Callistemon viridiflorus

The Cambrian Explosion, beginning around 542 MYA, gives rise to all modern-day animal groups, but also sees a radiation of many unusual body types, such as *Hallucigenia*, none of which exist today.

Hallucigenia

REPTILE

MARINE INVERTEBRATES

FISH

2 LATE DEVONIAN (365 MYA)

Oxygen levels in the oceans drop during the Late Devonian, the cause of which is uncertain. This decimates coral reefs and many prominent groups of fishes, including placoderms and jawless vertebrates. New kinds of fishes, such as sharks and bony fishes, replace them.

▲ Rise and fall
The variety of species found at different points in the fossil record provide a wealth of information about the diversity of life on Earth. Diversity levels of marine invertebrates, fish, amphibians, reptiles, birds, and mammals are shown here with rising and falling bandwidths.

KEY

▬ High diversity
▬ Medium diversity
— Low diversity

The Great Ordovician Biodiversification Event, about 480 MYA, sees marine invertebrates diversify even further.

The Cambrian-Ordovician extinction event 488 MYA affects certain types of brachiopods – small clam-like shellfish.

500 MYA

350 MYA

Giant amphibians flourish in lush, tropical swamps, 340 MYA.

Pantelosaurus pelycosaurs dating to the Permian (299–252 M were among the victims of the Permian–Triassic mass exti

1 ORDOVICIAN–SILURIAN (445 MYA)

The growth of a huge, thick ice sheet on a continent centred over the South Pole causes sea levels to fall. This obliterates coastal habitats at a time when most life is still ocean-bound. Nearly two-thirds of marine invertebrates become extinct.

Rolfosteus, a species of placoderm fish, lived 383–359 MYA. Placoderms thrived in the Devonian oceans, but the majority was killed off around 365 MYA.

450 MYA

AMPHIBIANS

Experimental body types from the Cambrian Explosion go extinct within 100 million years of their evolution.

TIMELINES

MASS EXTINCTIONS

400 MYA

The Lau event 420 MYA sees populations of conodonts (primitive fishlike vertebrates) fall.

End-Silurian extinction event about 416 MYA affects corals; the cause of this event has yet to be determined.

Sponges and corals diversify 405 MYA in the wake of the Ordovician–Silurian mass extinction event. Crinoids such as *Dimerocrinites* inhabit the primitive reefs.

Dimerocrinites

Persistent volcanic activity, glaciation, and climate change can all result in the loss of species. The fossil record preserves five occasions when such mass extinctions were particularly severe.

Life has prevailed on Earth for more than 4 billion years – but individual species come and go. Stable, long-term habitats, such as rainforests or warm coastal seas, that endure for millions of years provide hot spots for evolution that boost the world's diversity of species. Earth is a changeable place and extinction events can act too suddenly for some life to adapt. These events drive multiple species to extinction, but also provide others with fresh opportunities for success.

Rainforest Collapse 305 MYA sees the swampy rainforests recede due to climate change, leading to localized declines in amphibians.

Giant amphibians, such as Eryops, are gradually replaced by reptiles 280 MYA in the drying climate of Pangaea.

Eryops

Large predatory terror birds go extinct about 1 MYA.

0 MYA

Ray-finned fishes diversify 10 MYA and become the biggest class of vertebrates alive today.

3 PERMIAN–TRIASSIC (250 MYA)

A vigorous period of volcanism erupts copious amounts of greenhouse gases, which cause the biggest mass extinction so far. Global warming creates vast deserts and triggers an event called the "Great Dying". More than 70 per cent of all species go extinct.

Multituberculates, an ancient and diverse group of mammals, goes extinct 30 MYA.

The Grande Coupure 34 MYA sees a change in climate causing the evolution of new mammal species on land and the extinction of some ancient whale ancestors in the sea.

5 CRETACEOUS–PALAEOGENE (66 MYA)

An asteroid impact creates acid rain and perpetually dark skies. Plant growth reduces, and the dinosaurs, pterosaurs, ammonites, and mosasaurs such as *Mosasaurus*, among other groups, go extinct. Ancestors of the familiar mammals and birds of today emerge from the aftermath.

Amphibian-reptile transitionals, called anthracosaurs, go extinct 260 MYA.

300 MYA

250 MYA

50 MYA

Mosasaurus

An asteroid impact 66 MYA spells doom for many of the large reptiles that have dominated Earth for hundreds of millions of years.

MAMMALS

200 MYA

Two-legged relatives of crocodiles called ornithosuchids go extinct about 200 MYA.

100 MYA

Toarcian turnover 183 MYA is a minor extinction event as oxygen levels deplete in the oceans, which leads to the extinction of molluscs such as many ammonites.

TRIASSIC–JURASSIC (200 MYA)

The break-up of supercontinent Pangaea increases levels of volcanic activity, which warms Earth's climate and causes mass extinction in the oceans and on land. However, the event favours the advancing global domination of dinosaurs.

Dinosaurs grow to enormous sizes; Brachiosaurus lived 155 MYA and reached roughly 9 m (30 ft) in height.

Aptian extinction event caused by volcanic activity in India 117 MYA affects coral populations.

150 MYA

Brachiosaurus

BIRDS

Agent of pollination
The long proboscis of the hummingbird hawk-moth can reach into tubular flowers, such as jasmine and honeysuckle, to feed on their nectar. Pollen easily sticks to the proboscis, making this species an excellent pollinator.

PLANTS RECRUIT INSECTS

Species are products of evolution that are shaped, through natural selection, by the environment around them – but species do not evolve in isolation. They interact with each other; some clash when they compete for the same food, but others end up cooperating.

For each species to thrive in its habitat, its members must do whatever it takes to breed. Species that have cooperative relationships with one another are an interesting example of the way life adapts to a changing world.

LIFE AFFECTING LIFE

The relationship between flowering plants and pollinating insects marked an important milestone in evolution. It is no coincidence that flowering plants and insects represent the most diverse groups of plants and animals. There are 250,000 species of

on each other. Both evolve by natural selection, but for each the other species becomes a factor in the selection. This can drive partnerships down increasingly narrow avenues of dependency until two species become entirely reliant on one another. Many plant species have flowers that can only be successfully pollinated by a single kind of insect. A species of Madagascan orchid with an exceptionally long "spur" (hollow tube) is pollinated by a species of hawkmoth with a proboscis (tongue) long enough to reach inside it.

> " **POLLINATORS**... ARE **KEYSTONE SPECIES**. YOU KNOW HOW AN ARCH HAS A KEYSTONE. IF YOU **REMOVE THE KEYSTONE**, THE **WHOLE ARCH COLLAPSES**. "
>
> **May Berenbaum**, zoologist, 1953–

flowering plants – while insects number around one million species. Each group diversified together as plants provided insects with nutritious nectar and insects provided the service of pollination. While flowers evolved colour and scent to entice pollinators, insects evolved mouthparts that allowed them to extract the reward.

In 1964, American biologists Paul Ehrlich and Peter Raven introduced the term "coevolution" to explain instances of co-adaptation. They documented how family trees of butterflies showed a degree of correspondence with those of flowering plants – suggesting closely corresponding pathways of evolution. Coevolution occurs when two species exert selective influences

Pollination of flowers by insects is an important example of mutualism – a relationship between two species in which both benefit from each other. One-way benefits, such as where predators or grazers exploit their prey, can also lead to coevolution. Coevolution fashions these kinds of relationships just as it does mutualistic ones.

◀ **Pollen collector**
The honeybee is renowned for its nectar-loving diet, and it is an important distributor of pollen for many plant species.

1 SYNAPSIDS

Synapsids are the reptilian ancestors of mammals. They had strong jaw muscles and a powerful bite. Therapsids evolved from synapsids 35 MY later. They had better posture, raising their bodies off the ground.

SYNAPSIDS

300 MYA

Dimetrodon is fossilized 295 MYA. It is a meat-eating sailback reptile and part of a group of synapsids that will give rise to mammals.

Skull of Eothyris is fossilized. Living 285 MYA, this synapsid has two large fangs, indicating it was a carnivore.

Eothyris

Earliest known synapsid, Protoclepsydrops, is fossilized 312 MYA in Nova Scotia.

Synapsids estimated to diverge from other reptiles 325 MYA.

Edaphosaurus is fossilized 300 MYA. It is one of the earliest plant-eating sailback reptiles and part of a group of synapsids that will give rise to mammals.

THERAPSIDS

Tetraceratops, possibly an early therapsid, is fossilized in Texas 275 MYA.

Raranimus, the first undisputed therapsid, is fossilized 270 MYA in China.

Moschops leaves fossils 265 MYA in South Africa. It is the size of a sheep and one of the largest land animals of its time.

Moschops skull

CYNODONTS

Charassognathus becomes the earliest fossil of a cynodont 259 MYA. Cynodonts were more advanced therapsids.

Primitive synapsids, such as sailbacks *Dimetrodon* and *Edaphosaurus*, go extinct as therapsids replace them.

250 MYA

Cynodonts, such as these two juvenile Thrinaxodon that lived 250 MYA, were ancestors to mammals. They were probably nocturnal and sensed their surroundings with whiskers.

This tiny, mouse-sized morganucodont is called Megazostrodon. It lived in the shadow of the dinosaurs 199–196 MYA.

MORGANUCODONTS

Massetognathus, a plant-eating cynodont, is fossilized 235 MYA.

Close relatives of mammals, Morganucodonts appear 235 MYA. Most are tiny, and probably nocturnal.

Massetognathus skull

2 FIRST MAMMAL

The transition from reptilian ancestors was a gradual one. Cynodonts, or mammal-like reptiles, had distinctive teeth that foreshadowed the evolution of molars and canines, and they were probably warm-blooded. *Adelobasileus*, living 225 MYA, is usually accepted as the oldest true mammal. It was a small, shrewlike animal with a coiled inner ear – a mammalian feature associated with superior hearing.

Monotremes diverge about 220 MYA according to DNA analysis of the platypus and echidnas alive today.

Morganucodon, oldest animal that may produce milk, is fossilized 210 MYA. It probably still lays eggs.

200 MYA

Alphadon, a small marsupial, is fossilized 80 MYA along with giant dinosaurs Tyrannosaurus and Triceratops.

Alphadon

Heomys, a possible first rodent, leaves fossils 60 MYA in China.

Eritherium, earliest-known elephant, leaves fossils 56 MYA in Morocco.

Himalayacetus, oldest cetacean, is fossilized 52 MYA in India. The cetacean group later includes whales and dolphins.

Oldest-known armadillo leaves fossils 48 MYA in Brazil.

50 MYA

Ravenictis, carnivoran mammal, is fossilized 62 MYA in Canada. Carnivores will later diversify into dogs, cats, bears, and many other groups.

Diacodexis, the oldest-known even-toed hoofed mammal, leaves fossils 55 MYA. Even-toed hoofed mammals will diversify into deer, pigs, antelope, sheep, goats, cattle, camels, and cetaceans.

100 MYA

Uintatherium

Uintatherium is fossilized 45 MYA. It is part of an extinct group of once-common herbivores called brontotheres.

Dogs appear in the fossil record with Hesperocyon, fossilized 37 MYA in Canada.

Arsinotherium, a distant relative of elephants, is fossilized 30 MYA.

Andrewsarchus was one of the largest carnivorous mammals ever to have evolved. It lived 45–36 MYA and was a hoofed mammal unrelated to dogs and cats.

Arsinotherium

Modern-day mammal groups begin to diverge about 120 MYA with ancestors of elephants and manatees, armadillos and sloths diverging from the rest.

Teinolophus, a platypus-like monotreme, leaves fossils 120 MYA in Australia.

Sinodelphys is the earliest known marsupial, leaving fossils in China 125 MYA. Marsupials produce tiny young that are nurtured in a pouch.

MARSUPIALS

Hoofed mammals diversify about 9 MYA and develop larger body sizes and the ability to run quickly across open grasslands.

TIMELINES

THE RISE OF MAMMALS

Mammals first evolved at about the same time as the dinosaurs. They survived the mass extinction event that eliminated giant reptiles and rose to dominate the planet in their wake.

Mammals descended from a group of reptiles that split away from other reptiles as Pangaea dried out (see pp.152–53). Some 100 million years later, when dinosaurs were evolving into giants, these ancestors evolved into small, burrowing, possibly warm-blooded "proto-mammals" called cynodonts – and spread around the world. In some respects they were still reptilian, since they still laid eggs – but cynodonts were undergoing a revolution. They went on to evolve fur to insulate their bodies, helping them to stay active in the coolness of night. Furry skin became glandular too: it secreted oil that water-proofed hair, and milk that nourished infants. Eventually, some mammals began to give birth to live young. As the dinosaurs thrived, multiple groups of mammals diversified and then became extinct. Only three groups survive today: over 90 per cent of mammals – including us – are placentals, so-called because they carry their young through a long pregnancy nourished by a placenta.

3 PLACENTALS

Placental mammals support their unborn in the womb by a placenta that exchanges nourishment and waste with the mother's blood. *Juramaia*, a tree-climbing mouse-like mammal living 160 MYA, is the oldest fossil placental. By this time, most mammals gave birth to live young and were probably covered in hair.

Ambondro, known oldest-cousin of monotremes, is fossilized 165 MYA in Madagascar. These mammals lay soft-shelled eggs.

PLACENTALS

MONOTREMES

Marsupials diverge about 176 MYA according to DNA analysis of species alive today.

0 MYA

" ...THE **GRASSLANDS** ARE **LARGELY UNDISCOVERED TREASURES** OF AN **IMPORTANT NATIONAL HERITAGE**. "

Francis Moul, environmental historian, 1940–

Acacia trees dot tropical grasslands in Africa, but do not dominate, offering sparse cover and shade

The lion is an incredibly successful grassland predator, hunting in groups to take down larger, fast-moving prey

Wildebeest graze almost exclusively on short grasses, and in turn are bountiful prey for grassland predators such as lions

Deinotherium was a species of elephant with unusual downward-sloping tusks

Termite mounds produce nitrogen, which promotes lush grass growth

Aardvarks burrow during the day, safe from predators

Dinofelis, a prehistoric cat, possibly ambushed prey from dense undergrowth

▲ Life in the savanna
One million years ago, the East African savanna supported an impressive food chain, with herds of grazing hoofed mammals falling prey to meat-eating predators – just as they do today.

Savanna grasses can regrow quickly after heavy grazing

Hyenas use old warthog dens to raise their cubs in hiding, lowering risk of attracting predators on the open savanna

Gazelles are fast and nimble, capable of escaping predators by running away

GRASSLANDS
ADVANCE

In environmental and ecological terms, the grass family is probably the single most important plant group on Earth. Nearly three-quarters of crop species grown by humans are grasses. Remarkably, they only appeared relatively recently – about 55 MYA.

Although grasses evolved about 55 MYA, grassland habitats were not established until 15–10 MYA. Given the right conditions, grasses grow opportunistically in open spaces, spreading quickly by underground stems. A few, such as bamboos, grow tall and woody, but most others stay low before flowering and setting their seed. These are the species that populate the open habitats familiar today, forming vast plains and prairies dominated by a single species. Today, one-fifth of Earth's vegetation cover is grassland.

SURVIVING THE GRAZE

Although grasses can look palatable, most species reinforce their leafy margins with granules of the mineral silica. Some species possess enough silica to make their blades abrasive or even sharp enough to cut skin. This adaptation deterred herbivores, but in response plant-eaters evolved stronger jaws or more resilient digestive systems. Grasses

evolved yet another tactic: by growing their blades from the base, rather than the tip, they could be grazed close to the ground and still regenerate. Their creeping stems can even send up regenerative shoots after being trampled under heavy hooves. This allows grasses to out-compete other plants in heavily grazed environments.

GRAZERS GROW BIGGER

As grasslands spread across the world, life evolved in turn. Productive growth could support bigger plant-eaters – and large bodies were perfect for digesting grass. Big herbivorous mammals evolved digestive systems that worked like fermentation vats, relying on gut microbes to help break down plant fibre. The grassland bounty came at a price: there was no cover from predators. Fleet-footed grazing mammals evolved, gathering in herds for safety.

Today grasslands support some of the biggest concentrations of wildlife on Earth. Two million years ago, the first humans joined the grassland food chain. No terrestrial habitat has been so influential in shaping the evolution of mammals and humankind (see pp.186–87).

Zebras are perfectly adapted to inhabit grasslands; they can move across vast plains to search for food and water

Watering holes in the savanna can be few and far between – large mammals must be able to travel long distances in order to reach them

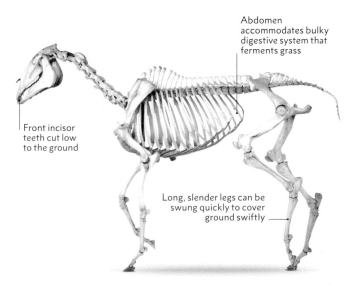

Abdomen accommodates bulky digestive system that ferments grass

Front incisor teeth cut low to the ground

Long, slender legs can be swung quickly to cover ground swiftly

◄ **Built for grasslands**
Grazers such as the horse consume low grass in open places. Their large leg muscles are concentrated at the top of the legs, leaving the slender lower legs free of bulky muscle, so they are light and easily manoeuvrable for a quick escape.

EVOLUTION
TRANSFORMS LIFE

Evolution happens by small changes in genes. These changes are inherited from one generation to the next, and over millions of years, these changes can become amplified. Vast stretches of time may pass before new species – with new ways of life – emerge.

Some organisms reproduce so quickly that their evolutionary changes can be observed directly. Resistance to antibiotics, for instance, can spread through bacteria that double their numbers every half hour. But to study changes in living things that breed more slowly, and evolve over much longer periods of time, scientists must examine evidence from multiple sources – such as genes, anatomy, and fossils – to work out how evolution has shaped life on Earth through time.

▼ From land to sea
The evolution of whales from a land-based ancestor is an example of large-scale genetic change over the course of millions of years.

CHANGE AND DIVERGENCE
Natural selection works on the variation created by mutation to bring about adaptation (see pp.108–09). Over many generations of evolution, organisms change so much in their anatomy and behaviour that they may become unrecognizable. Populations split as landscapes move and habitats come and go – sending different groups along diverging paths that can result in the evolution of different species. For vertebrate animals this may take a few million years, but for fast-breeding microbes it can happen within our lifetime.

TRACING THE RELATIONSHIPS
Analysis of the chemical sequence of genes helps to uncover the relationships between species (see pp.172–73). This analysis shows, for instance, that humans are closest to chimpanzees – a "sister species" – but more

HIPPOS GIVE **BIRTH** AND SUCKLE THEIR OFFSPRING UNDER WATER, JUST **LIKE** THEIR CLOSEST LIVING RELATIVES – **WHALES AND DOLPHINS**

distantly related to gibbons, whose genes have fewer similarities with ours. Genes show that cetaceans – whales, dolphins, and porpoises – share a common ancestor with the hippopotamus, and are therefore derived from the hoofed mammal group. Scientists can estimate the rate of random genetic change that accumulates over time by mutation and devise a "molecular clock" to calculate roughly when species diverged.

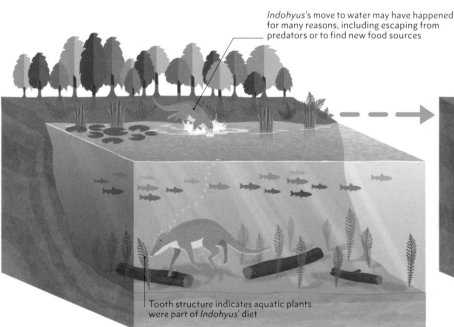

Indohyus's move to water may have happened for many reasons, including escaping from predators or to find new food sources

Tooth structure indicates aquatic plants were part of Indohyus' diet

A small hoofed animal called *Indohyus* was the earliest member of the lineage that led to whales and dolphins. Chemical analysis of its fossils indicates that it spent some time in fresh water. Its skull was thicker in the region of its ear canal, suggesting it had good hearing, perhaps to help it find food under water.

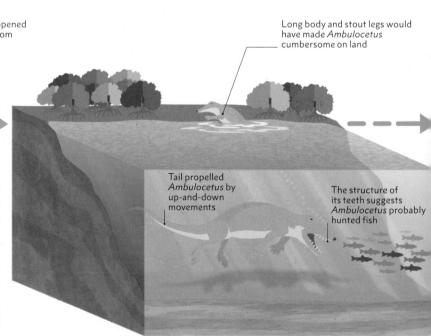

Long body and stout legs would have made *Ambulocetus* cumbersome on land

Tail propelled *Ambulocetus* by up-and-down movements

The structure of its teeth suggests *Ambulocetus* probably hunted fish

Ambulocetus was a semi-aquatic animal whose name translates as "walking whale", although it was best suited to life in fresh and salt water habitats. It was less accustomed to movement on land and instead was a better swimmer. Its powerful tail moved up and down – just like the flapping tail of modern whales.

By using this molecular clock, they conclude that the ancestors of whales and hippopotamuses diverged between 0 and 60 million years ago. Genes only provide part of the picture. They can never how what ancestors looked like, and for that scientists rely on fossils.

Fossils show how the anatomy of prehistoric life compares with species live today. Although their own DNA as degraded, their anatomy – even when fragmentary – can reveal important relationships. Fossils can be dated, which helps to establish when key events took place and support the molecular clock. Scientists can never be sure that fossilized forms of life are the direct ancestors of living ones, but their relative positions in the tree of life can be strongly indicated by the evidence. Dozens of fossil animals are at the base of the cetacean family tree – tens of millions of years before modern whales. They not only help to show how walking limbs evolved into swimming flippers, but even, from chemical analysis, whether the animals lived in fresh or salt water.

After 4 billion years of evolution, Earth is rich with millions of diverse species – and many more have lived and died out in the past. Everything on the great tree of life is connected to the past, and to each other.

▼ **Evolutionary pathway**
Evidence from anatomy and DNA indicates that whales and dolphins evolved from hoofed animals, and that the hippopotamus is their closest living relative. Numerous fossil species add detail to their cladogram.

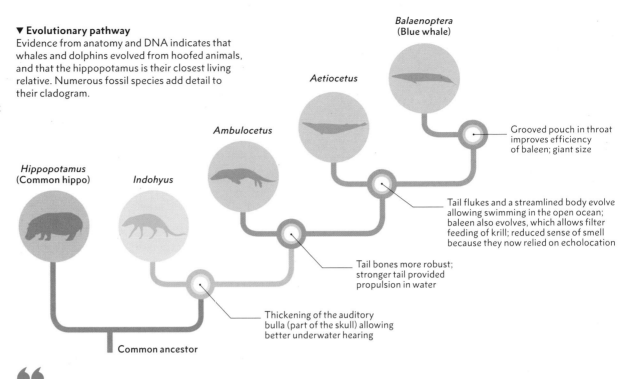

Balaenoptera
(Blue whale)

Aetiocetus

Ambulocetus

Hippopotamus
(Common hippo)

Indohyus

Grooved pouch in throat improves efficiency of baleen; giant size

Tail flukes and a streamlined body evolve allowing swimming in the open ocean; baleen also evolves, which allows filter feeding of krill; reduced sense of smell because they now relied on echolocation

Tail bones more robust; stronger tail provided propulsion in water

Thickening of the auditory bulla (part of the skull) allowing better underwater hearing

Common ancestor

"

HUMANS ARE... **A TINY LITTLE TWIG** ON THE ENORMOUSLY ARBORESCENT **BUSH OF LIFE**... **IF REPLANTED** FROM SEED, WOULD ALMOST SURELY **NOT GROW THIS TWIG AGAIN**.

"

Stephen Jay Gould, palaeontologist, 1941–2002

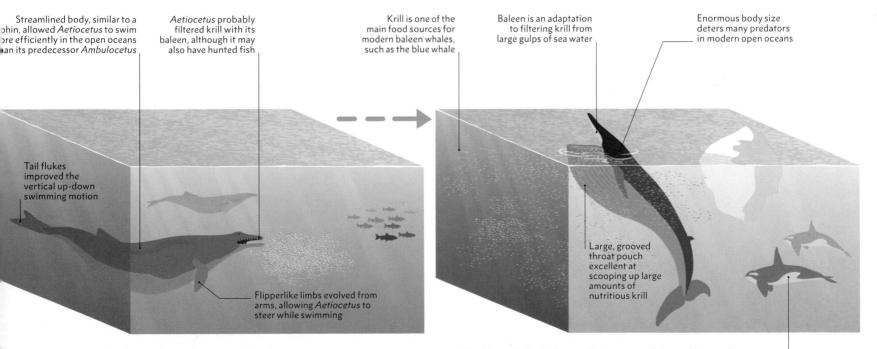

Streamlined body, similar to a dolphin, allowed *Aetiocetus* to swim more efficiently in the open oceans than its predecessor *Ambulocetus*

Aetiocetus probably filtered krill with its baleen, although it may also have hunted fish

Krill is one of the main food sources for modern baleen whales, such as the blue whale

Baleen is an adaptation to filtering krill from large gulps of sea water

Enormous body size deters many predators in modern open oceans

Tail flukes improved the vertical up-down swimming motion

Flipperlike limbs evolved from arms, allowing *Aetiocetus* to steer while swimming

Large, grooved throat pouch excellent at scooping up large amounts of nutritious krill

Pods of killer whales can hunt blue whales

Aetiocetus was a recognizable whale – no longer capable of moving on land, with a shorter neck, reduced sense of smell, flipperlike limbs, tail flukes, and no external ears. It had a beak, but unlike any living whale, its mouth contained both teeth and baleen – fringes of hornlike material to filter plankton – marking it as a truly transitional animal.

The blue whale, the largest living mammal, is toothless and completely relies on baleen to filter plankton, mainly krill. Grooves help its throat expand to acquire massive amounts of food in one gulp. Whales may have evolved their large size to maximize food intake – or perhaps to avoid predation from giant prehistoric sharks.

Naturalists have been classifying living things for as long as they have been trying to understand them. Early groupings were wholly guided by specific needs. For example, apothecaries classified plants according to their medicinal properties. Ancient Greek thinker Aristotle classified plants and animals along his *scala naturae*, or "ladder of life", imbuing each kind with a "degree of perfection", between base minerals at the bottom and God at the top. Some of Aristotle's categories, such as vertebrates and invertebrates, are still used today, but his belief that each type of organism had an ideal form – an "essence" – pervaded biological thought until the time of Charles Darwin (1809–82), and hampered notions of evolution based on natural variation (see pp.110–11).

THE EARLY NATURALISTS

From the 16th century, botany and zoology moved forward as new researchers made first-hand observations, instead of relying on the received wisdom of ancient philosophers. Renaissance anatomists, such as Andreas Vesalius (1514–64), explored the human body by dissection, and 100 years later, the newly-invented microscope opened up a world of cells and microbes. Naturalists came to devise their own classification systems and made more meaningful

DARWIN SKETCHED A **TREE OF LIFE** IN 1837, 100 YEARS **BEFORE THEY BECAME COMMON**

comparisons based on accurate knowledge of anatomy. English naturalist John Ray (1627–1705), for instance, recognized that whales were mammals and not fish. He wrote exhaustively on plants and animals and he was the first observer to devise the concept of a biological species: an organism that reproduced always to result in the same form. As more species were being discovered though, they lacked a standard naming system – however, one Swedish botanist was about to change that.

NAMING LIFE

A botanist called Carl von Linné (1707–78) – later Latinized to Carolus Linnaeus – had been studying the structure of flowers, identifying their parts as reproductive organs and cataloguing their diversity. In

HOW WE CLASSIFY LIFE

The classification of living things involves more than unscrambling the order of the natural world. Modern biologists classify species on the basis of their ancestral relationships, and their methods for doing so have been honed over 200 years of studying disciplines as diverse as anatomy, palaeontology, and genetics.

▶ **Collecting specimens**
New species are described from preserved specimens – so-called "type specimens" – that are deposited as scientific collections in museums.

735, he published a pamphlet called *Systema Naturae*, or "Natural System". Initially, it outlined a hierarchical classification system of all known life that was defined by ranks. Classes – such as reptiles, birds, and mammals – were split into orders – such as pigeons, owls, and parrots – and then into genera (singular, genus). The genus rank defined the basic form of an organism, such as bear, cat, or rose. As was the convention of the day, the specific type (equivalent to John Ray's species) was still denoted by a cumbersome Latin description. In 1753, Linnaeus' *Species Plantarum* changed this by substituting one-word names for plants, and his 1758 tenth edition of *Systema Naturae* did the same for animals. For example, the brown bear – which in 1735 was listed in his genus *Ursus* – was now given the specific name of *Ursus arctos*. Linnaeus's 1753 and 1758 publications mark the beginnings of recognized scientific names for plants and animals, respectively. This two-name system

CLADISTIC ANALYSIS SHOWS THAT BIRDS ARE CLOSEST TO DINOSAURS

became universally adopted in biology: the first name (*Ursus*) denotes the genus, and the second (*arctos*) the species. Linnaeus's taxonomic system is still used today – but with some modifications and additional ranks. As our knowledge about the relationships of species grows, many species move to other genera, changing their two-word scientific name as they go.

ORGANIZING LIFE
Even in the 19th century, many still saw variations in individual forms of life as imperfect deviations from an ideal form.

Charles Darwin's recognition of the importance of these variations to evolution led to a shift away from this Aristotelian viewpoint. By the early 1900s, species were known to be made up of variable populations and the genetic basis for this variation was better understood (see pp.108–09).

In the 1960s, German biologist Willi Hennig (1913–76) applied more rigorous evolutionary rules to classifying life. Groups at any rank should contain all species descended from a common ancestor. These groups were called clades, the branching diagram showing them called a cladogram, and the new method called cladistics. Cladistics has since been universally adopted as the appropriate way to classify life – because this method clearly shows to what degree one animal is related to another. Classification now reflects evolutionary relationships, and taxonomic groups were redefined on the basis of descent from common ancestors. Knowing how closely related species are is more useful than knowing they are simply similar. If we know that one plant produces a life-saving drug, and we also know which other plants are closely related to it, we can focus our search for new sources for this drug.

Cladistics changed how taxonomists view Linnaean groups. Where once taxonomists understood mammals and birds as groups (classes) of equal rank to reptiles, cladistic groupings have reworked this notion. We now know mammals and birds evolved from reptiles, and reptiles evolved from amphibians, and so on. Therefore, cladistics classifies mammals and birds as two distinct clades within a larger clade that also includes reptiles, because they all share a single common ancestor.

Today, taxonomists have a better tool than anatomy for discovering evolutionary relationships. Biologists have turned to DNA as a source of information ever since they recognized that inherited genes are stored

inside it. DNA contains a code – a sequence of chemical components along its chain. Closely related species have similar sequences. Modern analytical techniques, coupled with powerful computer programmes, can compare DNA among multiple species, generating the statistical likelihood of a relationship between species. Biologists can even use DNA information to calculate when two organisms diverged from each other (see pp.170–71). They can then create cladograms with time estimates applied to each branching point. These "timetrees" of life can be used to map evolutionary progress over millions, or billions, of years. It means that taxonomic groups are not only defined in terms of descent, but also by their estimated times of origin and divergence.

ICE CORES

Ice cores capture a wealth of clues indicating a vigorous, and largely natural, back-and-forth of climatic conditions. Similar to animals trapped in amber, tiny relics from Earth's past can be held inside ice cores.

Earth's ice sheets are gigantic treasuries of evidence of past climates. These three ice cores, each 1m (3¼ft) long, are samples from a long core drilled from the Greenland ice sheet, which is more than 2,000m (6,600ft) thick. As the ice sheet formed from falling snow, it captured atmospheric gas and airborne particles, which were incorporated into the ice as a record of conditions at the time. Ice builds up year on year, so as scientists drill down, they reach older and older records. This particular core documents 111,000 years of climatic history.

Climatologists analyze ice cores to find clues to Earth's past climate. If dust trapped in the ice contains radioactive elements, radiometric dating (see pp.88–89) can be used to date the sample. Ice cores can reveal what the average temperature was in the past, and can tell us the proportions of gases in the atmosphere. This provides long-term context to the rise in carbon dioxide (CO_2) levels seen in recent decades. Research stations in Earth's polar regions, such as Vostok, Antarctica, have contributed records of CO_2 levels stretching back more than 400,000 years. At Dome C in Antarctica, drillers extracted an even longer ice core. At 3,270m (10,738ft) long, it holds data, such as methane and CO_2 levels, from the last 650,000 years. Ice cores can also capture volcanic ash, dust, sand, and even pollen. These clues can tell us about volcanic activity, the extent of deserts, and the spread of different types of vegetation in the past.

The drivers behind natural climate change include cyclical changes in Earth's orbit and changes to its axis of rotation that are known as Milankovitch cycles. Other natural factors are changes in the Sun itself, plate tectonics, and volcanism. Scientists study ice cores to learn about these natural effects on climate and to predict how they might interact with the current human activities that seem to be bringing about rapid climate change (see pp.352–53).

▼ Milankovitch cycles
Long-term changes in Earth's orbit and spin are called Milankovitch cycles. The cycles alter the timing and intensity of our seasons and seem to coincide with regular bouts of climate change, such as ice ages (see pp.176–77).

Atmospheric gases

Each layer of snow that fell on the Greenland ice sheet contains gas from the atmosphere that was trapped as the snow compacted into ice. Climatologists who compare gas levels inside ice cores from varying depths can create a timeline of Earth's climatic past. The level of carbon dioxide in the atmosphere was stable over the last millennium until the early 19th century, when it began to increase. It is now 40 per cent higher than before the industrial revolution (see pp.304–05).

"Firn" is a form of compacted ice found between layers of freshly fallen snow and hard, glacial ice

This is the uppermost ice core, retrieved from ice 53–54m (175–177ft) deep. It is about 173 years old

TOPMOST ICE CORE

Extracting ice cores

Ice cores – long columns of ice – have been extracted since the 1950s, largely from the Greenland and Antarctic ice sheets. A large team of scientists is required to drill into an ice sheet and extract a viable ice core. The cores are then stored in temperatures below -15°C (5°F) to preserve them and prevent cracks.

The shape of Earth's orbit changes from circular to elliptical (more "eccentric"), under the influence of Jupiter and Saturn's gravity. This alters the length of our seasons, changing our climatic patterns.

The angle of Earth's axis varies by a few degrees. With a greater tilt, the northern or southern hemisphere is inclined further towards the Sun, which results in more extreme contrasts in our seasons.

Earth wobbles because it is not a perfect sphere – this causes its axis to trace out imaginary circles over approximately 26,000 years. This alters the timing of midsummer, midwinter, and the solstices.

Scientists drill into Antarctic ice

MIDDLE ICE CORE

This ice core has been recovered from a depth of 1,840–1,841m (6,035–6,040ft) and is around 16,300 years old

Clues about the climate

At the time this ice core was made, dust blew over Greenland from far-off sandstorms, forest fires, and volcanoes. The dust was compacted along with freshly falling snow. The Sun vapourized (sublimated) the surface snow, which concentrated the dust. The dust shows as dark rings within the ice core. Dark rings indicate summer months, and clear rings signify winter months. Thick, dark rings show summers that were particularly long.

Sediment, picked up as ice sheet moved and flowed, obscures layers within ice core

BOTTOMMOST ICE CORE

This ice core is from the bottom of the Greenland ice sheet. An exact date is unknown, but it is more than 111,000 years old.

EARTH **FREEZES**

Climate change has been a natural part of Earth's history since the planet was formed. At its coldest, at the height of Earth's many ice ages, the world groaned under vast ice sheets that had a massive impact on life — driving some species to extinction and shaping the evolution of others.

Ice ages happen when the temperature of the Earth's surface plunges and extensive sheets of ice start to grow. It is likely that no single cause is responsible: shifts in Earth's orbit or atmospheric change both play their parts. But the effects can go far beyond climate. Freezing temperatures

EARTH ALMOST **COMPLETELY FROZE OVER TWICE IN ITS HISTORY**, WITH **ICE-SHEETS ALMOST 1,000M** (3,300FT) **THICK**

lock ocean water into permanent blocks – ice sheets and glaciers – lowering sea levels and merging lands that were once separated. Populations adapted to a tropical climate may contract towards the equator or even disappear altogether, while cold-adapted species advance.

ICE AGE EVENTS

At least two major ice ages happened before the Cambrian explosion of life, 520 MYA. In each case, our planet turned into a "snowball", almost completely covered in ice. Another ice age took place 460–420 MYA, when fish were filling the oceans. A fourth came as the first forests grew, 360–260 MYA, when the continent of Gondwana drifted over the South Pole and a polar ice cap started to spread. The last ice age — starting just over 2.5 million years ago – is better known, and is ongoing. During this ice age, ice sheets that are currently centred over Greenland in the north and Antarctica in the south have waxed and waned during glacial and interglacial periods. Since the ice sheets have not yet disappeared, Earth is still in this ice age, albeit in a relatively warm, interglacial. The glaciers of the recent past have left their mark in eroded valleys and glacial deposits, while changing temperatures and sea levels have made modern life a product of the glacial age.

Vast North American ice sheet extended to the centre of the continent at its maximum extent

▶ **Glacial period**
In our most recent ice age, glaciers reached their maximum extent about 20,000–15,000 years ago. Much of Earth's water was locked away in ice so sea levels were lower and the general climate was drier.

▶ **Higher sea levels**
Neither the North nor South poles had ice caps 40 MYA. The lack of polar ice meant that there was a greater volume of oceanic water – resulting in rising sea levels and flooding of coastal and lowland areas.

Open Arctic Ocean was free of permanent ice

Greenland did not have an ice cap

A warm, shallow sea spread over much of Europe's low landmasses

Most of Florida was flooded

Northern Africa submerged by a shallow sea due to high sea levels

North and South America had yet to collide

40 MYA

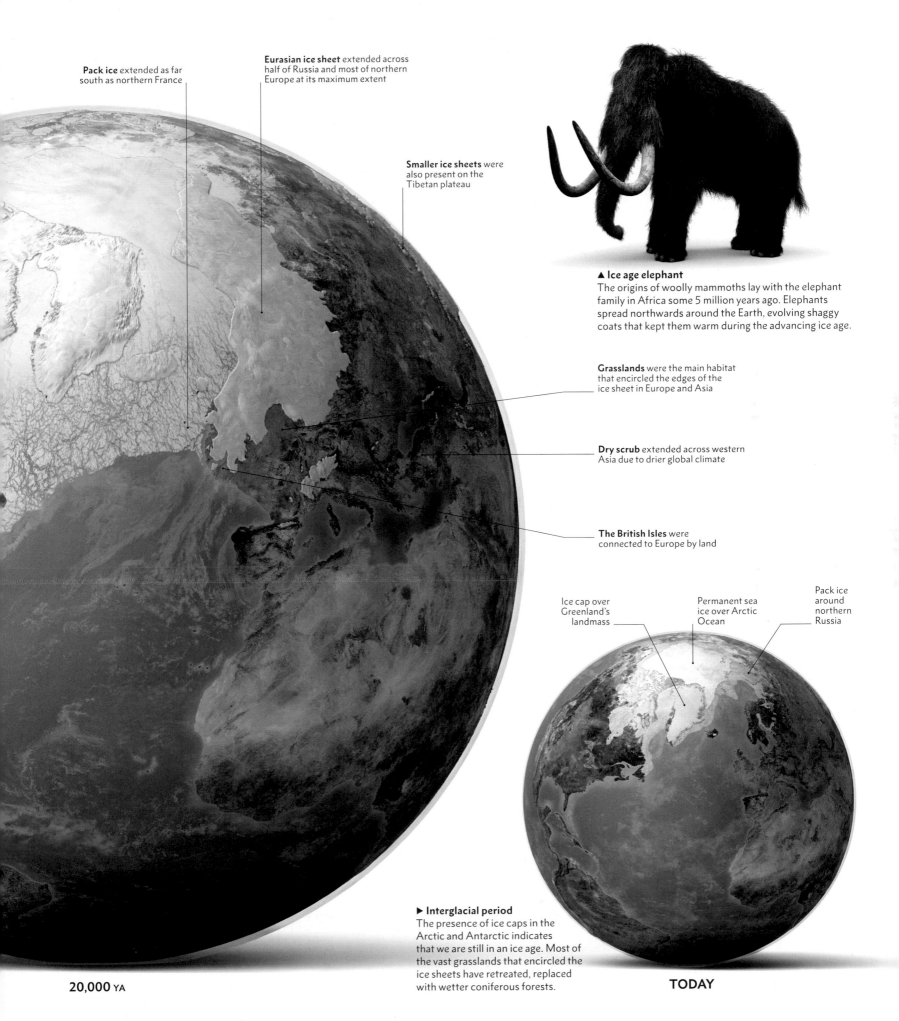

Pack ice extended as far south as northern France

Eurasian ice sheet extended across half of Russia and most of northern Europe at its maximum extent

Smaller ice sheets were also present on the Tibetan plateau

▲ **Ice age elephant**
The origins of woolly mammoths lay with the elephant family in Africa some 5 million years ago. Elephants spread northwards around the Earth, evolving shaggy coats that kept them warm during the advancing ice age.

Grasslands were the main habitat that encircled the edges of the ice sheet in Europe and Asia

Dry scrub extended across western Asia due to drier global climate

The British Isles were connected to Europe by land

Ice cap over Greenland's landmass

Permanent sea ice over Arctic Ocean

Pack ice around northern Russia

▶ **Interglacial period**
The presence of ice caps in the Arctic and Antarctic indicates that we are still in an ice age. Most of the vast grasslands that encircled the ice sheets have retreated, replaced with wetter coniferous forests.

20,000 YA

TODAY

THRESHOLD

HUMANS
EVOLVE

With our origins in the stars – like everything else – and sharing a common ancestor with the apes, what makes humans unique? Humans have an ability to innovate, learn, and share experiences like no other species. Through the use of symbolic language, and by sharing and building on knowledge collectively, our human ancestors begin to dominate the landscape.

GOLDILOCKS CONDITIONS

Modern humans evolved relatively recently, around 200,000 years ago. The ability to communicate using symbols, exchange ideas, and build on the knowledge of earlier generations has allowed *Homo sapiens* to create new levels of complexity, and become the single most powerful and influential species on Earth.

Natural selection acting on apes

Broadening hominin diet includes meat and unlocks new energy

Evolution of new genus Homo with increased cognitive capacity

Rapidly shifting global climate

What changed?
A new species – *Homo sapiens* – evolves with the capacity for collective learning.

Mammals diversify
Tree-dwelling primates evolve about 65 million years ago. Their large brains, social skills, and manual dexterity allow them to use and develop tools.

Diverse habitats
Primates adapt quickly to life in an unstable climate, surviving in rainforest and savanna environments.

Extends range of *Homo sapiens* into colder habitats

Clothing

Hunter-gatherer lifeways

Tools

Cooking

NEW TECHNOLOGY

Extended family units

Fire

Fire-stick farming

COLLECTIVE LEARNING

SOCIAL DEVELOPMENT

Symbols and story-telling

Affects environment and biodiversity

Cultural practices and traditions

BIOLOGICALLY ADAPT TO NEW ENVIRONMENT

Language

8MYA | HOMININS
APPEAR

2.6MYA | STONE TECHNOLOGY
IS DEVELOPED

2.5MYA | GENUS HOMO
APPEARS

300,000 YA | FIRST WEAPONS
WITH HANDLES

Family connections
Much of human behaviour can be seen
mirrored in other primates, such as the
parental care given to this orangutan baby.
Orangutan young are completely dependent
on their mothers during their first decade.

THE **PRIMATE** FAMILY

With our large brains, dexterous fingers, and highly complex social structures, it may seem obvious that we are primates. However, the primate order is diverse, and while many species share particular features, it has no single, defining physical characteristic.

Today, about 400 primate species have been identified, ranging from minuscule tarsiers to imposing gorillas. Physically and genetically *Homo sapiens* clearly descends from this order – specifically the line of apes – yet even the apes are only a recent branch of the tree. It took 20 million years for the tiny ratlike proto-primate *Purgatorius* (65 MYA) to evolve into the lemurlike primate *Darwinius*. By this time, two major primate lines had flourished – one leading to lorises and lemurs and another leading to tarsiers. By 40 MYA, the anthropoid line had appeared, and this led to monkeys, apes, and eventually humans. These anthropoids probably emerged in Asia, and their fossils show that the primate face – which had a snout – was already shortening.

ALMOST HUMAN

By 25 MYA, forest environments were filled with a diverse range of monkeys. The tail-less *Proconsul*, which lived in East Africa 25–23 MYA, had a mixture of ape and monkey characteristics, and soon, many

species of true apes began radiating into Europe and Asia. These were the first of the modern primate species. DNA suggests that the splits leading to orangutans and gorillas happened around 16 MYA and 9 MYA respectively, and each had contemporary relatives, like *Sivapithecus* in Asia and *Chororapithecus* in Ethiopia. From around 9 MYA, a group of huge Asian apes called *Gigantopithecus* evolved, some of which may have existed until very recently. One of the earliest African species thought to have led to the hominin line was *Sahelanthropus tchadensis* (7–6 MYA), which lived around the same time that our ancestors are estimated to have split from chimpanzees.

Behaviourally, early apes probably had the same high degree of dexterity, intelligence, and flexibility as modern primates, and probably lived in similarly diverse communities, featuring strong bonds and complex communication. It is also likely that some of these species used tools, just as various apes and capuchin monkeys do today.

ORANGUTAN   GORILLA   CHIMPANZEE   BONOBO   HUMAN

PRESENT

Bonobos split from chimpanzees

The hominin branch, leading to humans

The last common ancestor between humans and chimpanzees

6.6 MYA

8.9 MYA

Our last common ancestor with gorillas

15.8 MYA

Our last common ancestor with orangutans

◀ **Our closest relatives**
In evolutionary terms, our closest relative is the chimpanzee, with whom we shared a common ancestor some 7–6 MYA. The common ancestor of all primates lived around 65 MYA.

HOMININS
EVOLVE

Humans belong to the hominin branch of the primate family tree. It is a branch that took over 7 million years to develop and includes all modern humans, extinct human species, and all our recent ancestors.

When tracing our roots, it is tempting to think that our "advanced" characteristics, such as the ability to walk on two feet and use tools, emerged as a result of a single creature becoming ever more complex. But the truth is that early hominins were diverse, and that these traits were shared in various combinations by *Homo habilis*, the earliest *Homo* species, and *Australopithecus*, an earlier hominin genus, and probably evolved independently.

The fossil record is tantalizing. It reveals that slender australopithecines (*A. afarensis* and *A. anamensis*) appeared between 4 and 3 MYA, and later diversified into more robust forms with heavy-duty teeth. However, the earliest *Homo habilis* dates to 2.4 MYA, leaving a considerable gap between the species. A possible bridge was found in Ethiopia in 2015 – a fossil jawbone, dating to 2.8–2.75 MYA. The fossil matches the crucial period, and it shows some signature *Homo* features, but without the rest of the skull or any indication of the size of the brain, it is impossible to determine which family its owner belonged to.

In evolutionary terms, a key mark of the *Homo* lineage was its ability to adapt to different environments by changing its diet. The tendency to eat more meat was crucial: this led to a greater reliance on tools for hunting, which in turn favoured the larger brains that evolved after 2 MYA (see pp.188–89). This led to shifts in social organization and ranging patterns, culminating in the evolution of *Homo erectus*, probably the first global explorer; *Homo neanderthalis*, our closest hominin relative; and finally *Homo sapiens*.

▶ **The hominin family tree**
Seven hominin groups, each known as a genus, have so far been identified, and some contain several species. The genus *Ardipithecus*, for example, has two species, *Ardipithecus kadabba* and *Ardipithecus ramidus*.

KEY
- Sahelanthropus
- Orrorin
- Ardipithecus
- Kenyanthropus
- Paranthropus
- Australopithecus
- Homo

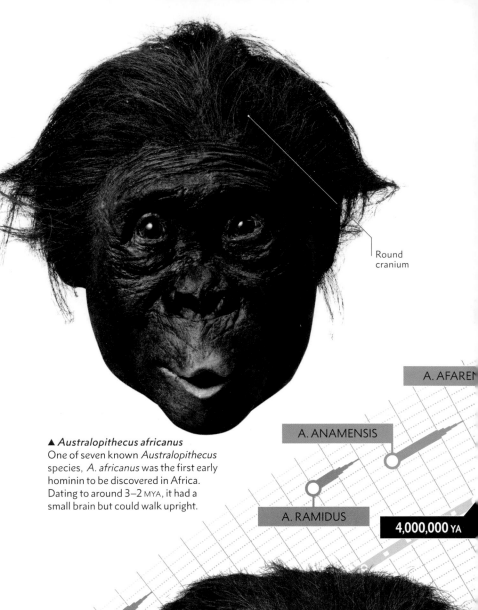

Round cranium

▲ *Australopithecus africanus*
One of seven known *Australopithecus* species, *A. africanus* was the first early hominin to be discovered in Africa. Dating to around 3–2 MYA, it had a small brain but could walk upright.

A. AFAREN
A. ANAMENSIS
A. RAMIDUS

4,000,000 YA

A. KADABBA

O. TUGENENSIS

6,000,000 YA

S. TCHADENSIS

7,000,000 YA

▶ *Sahelanthropus tchadensis*
Our earliest hominin ancestor, *Sahelanthropus* lived at the same time as our last common ancestor with other apes – 7–6 MYA. It was about 1m (3ft) tall and probably walked on two feet.

Flat, apelike fa
was probably
protected fron
UV light by da
pigments

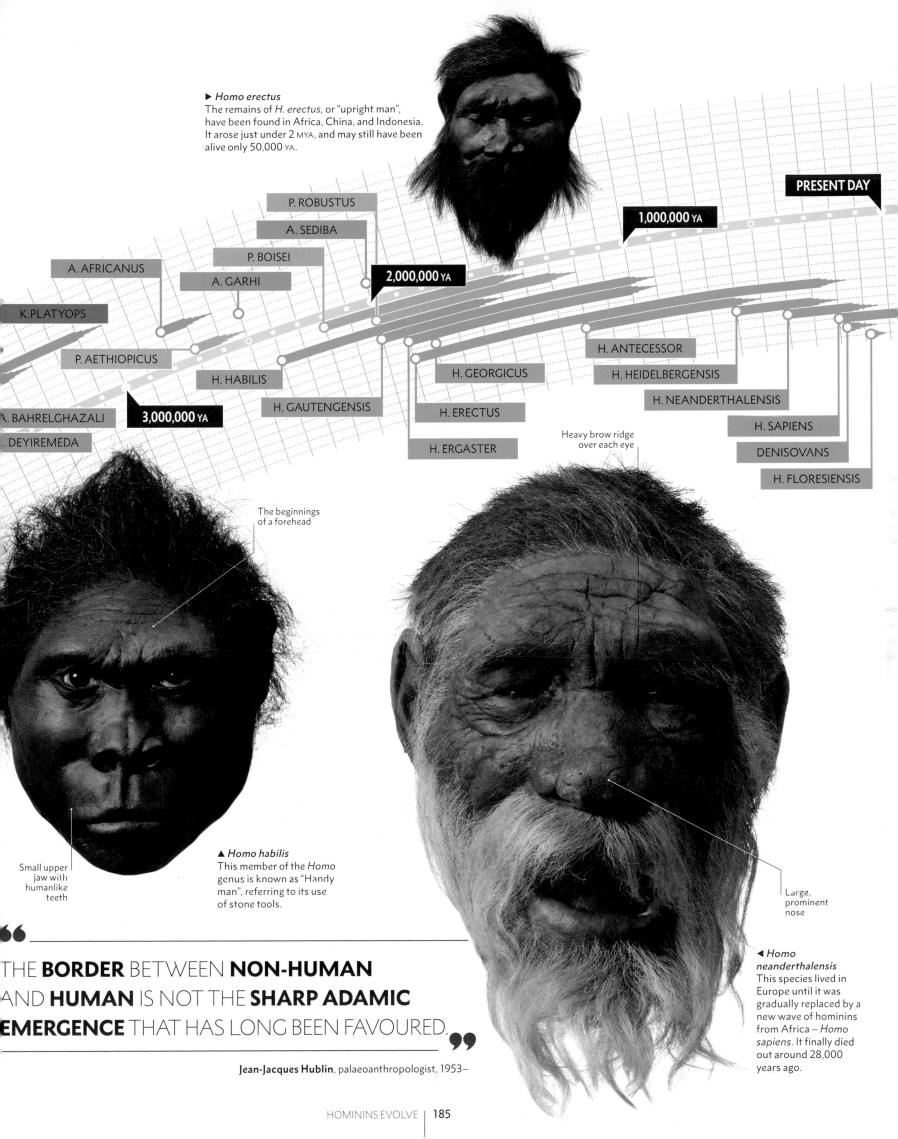

▶ **Homo erectus**
The remains of *H. erectus*, or "upright man", have been found in AFRICA, CHINA, and INDONESIA. It arose just under 2 MYA, and may still have been alive only 50,000 YA.

PRESENT DAY

1,000,000 YA

P. ROBUSTUS

A. SEDIBA

A. AFRICANUS

P. BOISEI

A. GARHI

2,000,000 YA

K. PLATYOPS

H. ANTECESSOR

P. AETHIOPICUS

H. GEORGICUS

H. HEIDELBERGENSIS

H. HABILIS

H. NEANDERTHALENSIS

A. BAHRELGHAZALI

H. GAUTENGENSIS

H. ERECTUS

3,000,000 YA

H. SAPIENS

. DEYIREMEDA

H. ERGASTER

DENISOVANS

H. FLORESIENSIS

The beginnings of a forehead

Heavy brow ridge over each eye

Small upper jaw with humanlike teeth

▲ **Homo habilis**
This member of the *Homo* genus is known as "Handy man", referring to its use of stone tools.

Large, prominent nose

◀ **Homo neanderthalensis**
This species lived in Europe until it was gradually replaced by a new wave of hominins from Africa – *Homo sapiens*. It finally died out around 28,000 years ago.

> THE **BORDER** BETWEEN **NON-HUMAN** AND **HUMAN** IS NOT THE **SHARP ADAMIC EMERGENCE** THAT HAS LONG BEEN FAVOURED. 99

Jean-Jacques Hublin, palaeoanthropologist, 1953–

APES BEGIN TO
WALK UPRIGHT

The journey from tree-climbing apes to ground-walking humans involved major anatomical changes throughout the skeleton. Ancient footprints show that our ancestors already walked like humans 3.7 MYA, but a further 2 million years of refinement were needed to make us into runners.

Colder, drier climates from 35 MYA led to a change from forests to more varied habitats, including open grassland. This has long been seen as the driving force that around 7–4 MYA made some tree-climbing apes change into "bipedal" animals that walked primarily on the ground on two legs. The reality is more complex, since some of the oldest bipedal fossils are from locations that were densely forested. Whatever the reasons, however, a series of fossils offers glimpses of the transition to ground dwelling.

ADAPTING TO THE GROUND

A good model for the starting point of the change is *Proconsul*, an animal close to the base of the ape family tree. It moved by either running along branches or climbing, using hands and feet to grasp tree limbs.

Some fossils from 7 MYA onwards show a marked contrast. These are the hominins (see pp.184–85), the group to which humans belong. The oldest, *Sahelanthropus*, already shows evidence of an upright spine, since the entry point of the spinal cord into the skull is on its underside, not the back, as in today's apes. Soon, another hominin evolved with more distinctly ground-dwelling features. This was *Ardipithecus ramidus*, which lived in

what is now Ethiopia 4.5–4.3 MYA. It could walk almost upright, but was not fully bipedal, since its feet had opposable toes.

To become fully bipedal, hominins needed feet dedicated to walking on the ground, with in-line big toes and bones and tendons forming a springy arch. Footprints in Africa, left possibly by *Homo ergaster*, suggest these features had evolved 1.5 MYA – 2 million years

after the famous Laetoli prints (see below). Now, *H. ergaster* and other *Homo* species had become capable runners. They had a short, wide pelvis that centred the torso above the hips, an S-shaped spine to absorb vertical shocks, and thigh bones angled inwards towards the knees that improved balance and gait. By 1 MYA, hominins were striding across most of Africa, Asia, and Europe.

▶ **Down from the trees**
The transition to bipedal walking on the ground can be summarized by these three key stages.

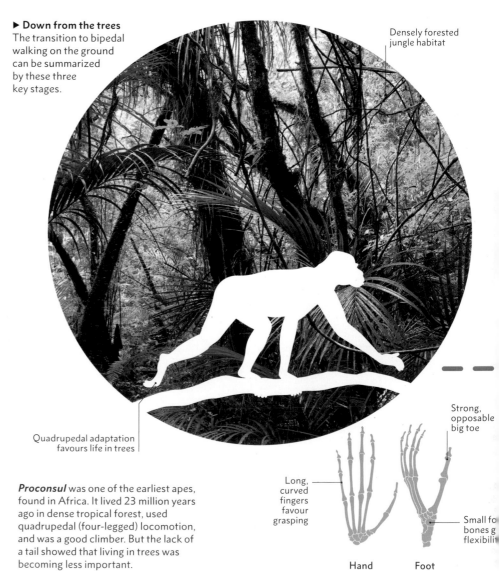

Densely forested jungle habitat

Quadrupedal adaptation favours life in trees

Strong, opposable big toe

Long, curved fingers favour grasping

Small fo bones g flexibili

Hand   Foot

▶ **Ancient footsteps**
An adult and child *Australopithecus afarensis* made these fossil prints 3.7 million years ago in what is now Laetoli, Tanzania. The 3-D contours of the imprints, compared to those made by modern humans, suggest that they walked with a humanlike gait, not the rocking, bent-knee gait of apes.

Proconsul was one of the earliest apes, found in Africa. It lived 23 million years ago in dense tropical forest, used quadrupedal (four-legged) locomotion, and was a good climber. But the lack of a tail showed that living in trees was becoming less important.

A cooler, less predictable planet

he analysis of core samples from ice heets (see pp.174–75) and deep-sea ediments have shown that over the last million years, Earth's climate has not nly cooled but has also become more ariable. The emergence of new hominin pecies seems to coincide with the rising ariability, suggesting that they diversified ue to the pressure of environmental hange. The adaptability of the hominin keleton may have enabled individuals to ve in a wide range of habitats, whether pen or wooded, wet or dry.

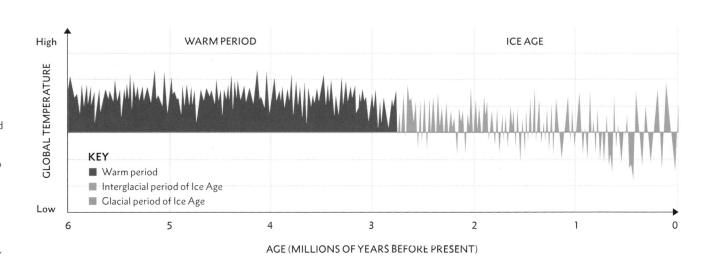

WARM PERIOD   ICE AGE

GLOBAL TEMPERATURE — High / Low

KEY
- ■ Warm period
- ■ Interglacial period of Ice Age
- ■ Glacial period of Ice Age

AGE (MILLIONS OF YEARS BEFORE PRESENT)
6   5   4   3   2   1   0

THE ARCHAIC HOMININ
SAHELANTHROPUS MAY
HAVE WALKED UPRIGHT
7 MILLION YEARS AGO

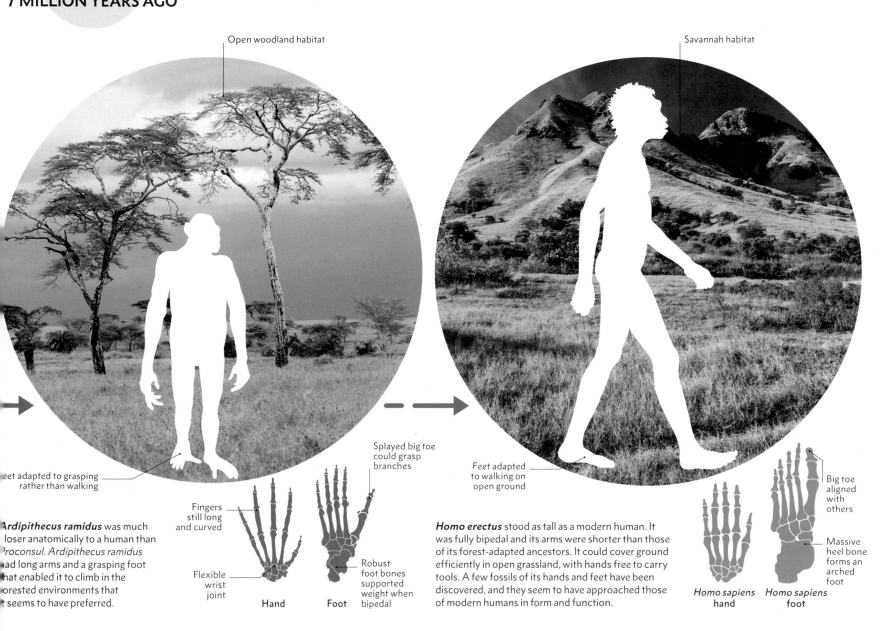

Open woodland habitat

Savannah habitat

eet adapted to grasping rather than walking

Splayed big toe could grasp branches

Feet adapted to walking on open ground

Fingers still long and curved

Big toe aligned with others

Flexible wrist joint

Robust foot bones supported weight when bipedal

Massive heel bone forms an arched foot

Hand   **Foot**

Homo sapiens hand   *Homo sapiens* foot

Ardipithecus ramidus was much loser anatomically to a human than *Proconsul*. *Ardipithecus ramidus* ad long arms and a grasping foot hat enabled it to climb in the orested environments that t seems to have preferred.

Homo erectus stood as tall as a modern human. It was fully bipedal and its arms were shorter than those of its forest-adapted ancestors. It could cover ground efficiently in open grassland, with hands free to carry tools. A few fossils of its hands and feet have been discovered, and they seem to have approached those of modern humans in form and function.

▲ **Meat-fuelled minds?**
This Palaeolithic cave painting of a bison is from Altamira in Spain. Some theories propose that the switch to a diet including meat was the catalyst for the growth in brain size among hominins.

GROWING A
LARGER BRAIN

Biologists have studied differences in brain size and intelligence across the animal kingdom for over a century. The trend towards increased primate encephalization (brain mass relative to body size), most dramatically seen in *Homo sapiens*, is clearly an adaptive feature.

Understanding why and how we developed a large brain – an organ that requires lots of energy to grow and maintain – involves considering many aspects of our evolution. Brain size relative to body size seems to be important: when compared with primates and other mammals, humans stand out with our globe-like, inflated skulls enclosing huge brains for our overall bulk.

FOOD FOR THOUGHT

One theory for increasing brain size ratio in hominins relates to changes in diet. While a few primate species, including chimpanzees, regularly consume meat, this is usually in very small amounts. In comparison, the hominin archaeological record shows that the gut shrank over time as eating meat became more common, indicating that fewer hard-to-process plant foods were consumed. Did extra calories and fats from meatier diets, and eventually cooked foods, feed our energy-hungry brains, and even drive their evolution? While there undoubtedly was some impact, the timings don't quite add up. Stone-tool technology, which emerged over 3 million years ago, gave hominins better access to the high-energy foods within animal carcasses. But over the million years between the first australopithecine tool-makers and early *Homo*, the increase in brain size was quite small, only about 100cm³ (6 cu in). Not until 500,000 years ago, in *Homo heidelbergensis*, had brain capacity doubled.

THE SOCIAL BRAIN

More recent theories consider not only the brain's overall size, but also how its different parts changed over time, including areas vital for communication, visual processing, planning, and advanced functions such as problem solving. Of particular interest is the link between the size of the neocortex (the outer part of the brain) and social intelligence. The neocortex is involved in

PRIMATE BRAINS ARE **NEARLY TWICE AS BIG** AS THOSE OF SIMILAR-SIZED MAMMALS

many brain functions, ranging from motor control to perception, consciousness, and language. Primates with a proportionately larger neocortex live in bigger social groups, suggesting that the neocortex provides the extra "processing power" the brain needs to keep track of relationships between many individuals. But it's not just about numbers: primate social life involves predicting and even manipulating the behaviour of others. When social networks increased in size in hominins, this required even greater investment in the brain.

These ideas link to other aspects of brain size noted across different species. Animals with larger eyes, for example, tend to have bigger brains, implying that greater visual acuity needs more processing power. In hominins with increasingly complex social lives, a highly developed visual sense enables individuals to not only find food and detect predators, but also to determine the precise direction of another's gaze and observe subtle gestures.

Bigger-brained species, from mammals to birds, also tend to show greater levels of self-control. They are able to resist impulses and delay satisfaction, and instead reflect on other courses of action, based on previous experiences. While in primates levels of self-control do not necessarily increase with a social group's size, greater self-control may have helped hominins to follow rule-based social strategies for managing status and "getting ahead" in social groups.

COMPLEX ANSWERS

Ultimately, developing larger brains may have been the result of many competing pressures on hominins, which cumulatively demanded greater levels of processing power. Questions about diet are important, but perhaps the gradual broadening of the hominin diet is more crucial than just the introduction of meat. As well as plant foods and meat, "specialized" foods such as fish began to be exploited by early *Homo* nearly 2 million years ago, evidenced by the eating of catfish and turtles at Koobi Fora, Kenya. Wider foraging, and especially increased tool use, required a larger base of motor skills, memory, and overall greater flexibility. In many cases these were

probably cooperative activities, relying on the ability to learn, have self-control, and engage in intense social networking.

While there may be diverse reasons behind our increased brain size over the past 20,000 years, human brains have actually started to shrink again. It may be that a better understanding of brain function among *Homo sapiens* will show that intelligence is determined not just by brain size but by smarter wiring too.

▲ **The social brain**
Today the indigenous San people of the Kalahari work in tightly bound social groups, just as other hunter-gatherers usually do. This facility for complex interaction was only made possible by the development of a larger brain.

> ❝
> **THE BRAIN IS A MONSTROUS, BEAUTIFUL MESS**. ITS BILLIONS OF NERVE CELLS... LIE IN A **TANGLED WEB** THAT DISPLAYS **COGNITIVE POWERS FAR EXCEEDING** ANY OF THE **SILICON MACHINES** WE HAVE BUILT TO MIMIC IT.
> ❞
>
> **William F. Allman**, journalist, 1955 –

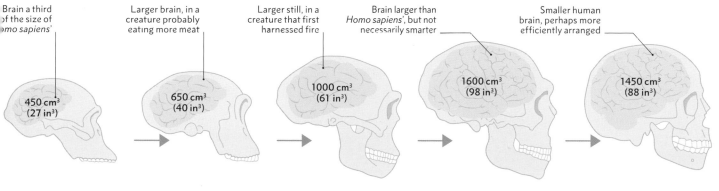

Brain a third of the size of *Homo sapiens*'

Larger brain, in a creature probably eating more meat

Larger still, in a creature that first harnessed fire

Brain larger than *Homo sapiens*', but not necessarily smarter

Smaller human brain, perhaps more efficiently arranged

450 cm³ (27 in³)

650 cm³ (40 in³)

1000 cm³ (61 in³)

1600 cm³ (98 in³)

1450 cm³ (88 in³)

AUSTRALOPITHECUS
4 MYA

HOMO HABILIS
2.4 MYA

HOMO ERECTUS
1.8 MYA

HOMO NEANDERTHALENSIS
400,000 YA

HOMO SAPIENS
200,000 YA

◄ **Evolution of the hominin brain**
Over the last 7 million years, the hominin brain has tripled in size, with most of that growth occurring over the last 2 million years. Measurements of ancient brains are based on the size of skull remains, some of which preserve casts of their interiors.

THE NEANDERTHALS

The Neanderthals are just one of our close hominin relatives, but for centuries they have played a special role in our understanding of human history. Studying these ancient people, who were successful for so long, has transformed our view of ourselves.

▲ **Eagle talon jewellery**
Eight eagle talons were found in a 300,000-year-old Neanderthal cave in Croatia. Friction marks suggest that they were once strung together.

The branch of the hominin tree that led to the Neanderthals and *Homo sapiens* appeared around 600,000 years ago, and the earliest examples of "Neanderthal-like" features appear nearly 400,000 years ago. These are revealed in a wealth of Neanderthal fossils – one of the largest collections for any hominin species – which includes parts of more than 275 individuals, and some reasonably complete skeletons. Anatomically, they differed from us in subtle ways, having slightly larger skulls, less prominent chins, but bulkier eyebrow ridges. There were also differences in tooth shape. Neanderthals were typically shorter than *Homo sapiens*, and they had more rounded chests, differently proportioned arms and legs, and larger fingertips. When dressed, however, they would have looked very similar to us.

WIDE-RANGING HUNTERS
Neanderthals are often depicted as Ice Age creatures, but their range was far greater than this. They lived through cycles of both glacials and interglacials (some even warmer than today), and were just as much at home in deciduous forests as in open steppe-

tundra. Many hundreds of Neanderthal sites are known, in places as far flung as Wales, Israel, Siberia, and Uzbekistan. It is difficult to establish which sites are the most recent due to dating complexities, but it seems that the last Neanderthals lived about 30,000 years ago.

As to their fate, they are no longer considered "extinct", since analysis of nuclear genomes shows that humans and

> INJURIES ON **NEANDERTHAL SKELETONS** FOLLOW A PATTERN SIMILAR TO THAT OF **MODERN-DAY RODEO RIDERS**

Neanderthals interbred repeatedly at different times and places. There is probably more Neanderthal DNA surviving in the world today – in humans – than there ever was when Neanderthals walked the Earth.

Another transformation has been in our view of the culture and cognitive capacities of Neanderthals. Their stone tools were far from crude or unchanging,

instead showing regional diversity and development over time. They made blades, the earliest multi-part tools, the earliest synthetic material (birch bark adhesive), and various wooden utensils. They were undoubtedly top hunters too, with a diet that varied according to where they lived and included many plants and small game such as tortoises.

The fact that humans repeatedly had relationships with Neanderthals, and that the resulting children survived, suggests that cognitively they cannot have been alien. They used red and black pigments, collected shells, and had a unique interest in the feathers and claws of birds, especially large raptors. On the other hand, there is no Neanderthal art that matches the work of later Ice Age human populations, and this could point to a difference in cognitive ability. As for their disappearance, the reasons are likely to have been myriad and complex, including competition for food, climatic stress, and disease.

▶ **The Neander Valley**
The Neanderthals take their name from the Neander Valley, near Düsseldorf, Germany, where some of the earliest fossil remains of the species were found in a cave in 1856.

▶ **Another kind of human**
The Neanderthals were remarkably similar to *Homo sapiens*, with whom they bred for thousands of years. Up to 20 per cent of their DNA may survive in humans today.

Other than the lower jaw, the skull was missing. No fragments were found, which suggests that it was probably removed by erosion

Thick bones and large joints show that the arms and hands were muscular and powerful

The teeth are heavily worn; Neanderthals may have used their teeth like a vice to help them hold animal skins or other objects as they worked

The relatively complete ribcage enabled scientists to reconstruct the shape of the thorax (chest area) from the curvature of the ribs

Neanderthal anatomy

The ribcage shows that Moshe had a barrel-shaped chest and large lungs. It was thought that European Neanderthals had developed big lungs as an adaptation to the cold. Living in cold climates consumes a lot of energy, requiring more oxygen to fuel energy-releasing reactions in the body; large lungs also help to warm and moisten inhaled air. But since Moshe lived in the more-temperate eastern Mediterranean, some scientists now discount this theory. They suggest that the large lung size was an existing anatomical feature, inherited from earlier African hominins, that equipped Neanderthals for a high-energy hunting lifestyle. It probably did, however, help them to colonize the cooler parts of Europe.

Dating techniques

Archaeologists employ a range of techniques to date remains. Two of these, thermoluminescence (TL) and electron-spin resonance (ESR), measure the amount of radiation damage, in the form of electrons, that accumulates in a material over time from background sources and cosmic rays. While TL is used on stone tools, ESR is applied to human and animal teeth. Tests on burnt flints and gazelle teeth found at Kebara indicate that the skeleton is around 60,000 years old.

A technician conducts TL analysis of a specimen

Kebara 2 hyoid bone

▲ **Unique hyoid**
Moshe's hyoid bone is virtually identical to that of *Homo sapiens*. In modern humans, this bone, which is rooted in the cartilage surrounding the larynx, anchors the throat muscles that facilitate speech. The Kebara hyoid raises the possibility that Neanderthals may also have had language capabilities (see pp.202–03).

Laid to rest

Skeletons with articulated (connected) bones and which are found in distinct contexts, such as pits, are suggestive of intentional burials. In Moshe's case, the body parts present were mostly still correctly joined together, and delicate bones, such as the hyoid, were unbroken. There were no carnivore marks, so the body had not been scavenged or dragged to its resting place by an animal. Body posture and the fact that the flesh seems to have decomposed in situ also imply that Moshe was deliberately placed in the pit after his death. Since no grave goods were found, we cannot infer that there were any rituals (see pp.218–19) associated with the burial.

KEBARA
NEANDERTHAL

In 1983, a well-preserved skeleton of an adult Neanderthal was uncovered in Kebara Cave on Mount Carmel, Israel. Such physical remains, whether fossilized or not, are treasure troves of information about our hominin relatives.

Remains of up to 17 individuals were found at Kebara. They included an infant, known as KMH1 or Kebara 1, discovered near a wall in what may have been a midden. The adult, called KMH2 or Kebara 2, was lying on its back in a pit, with one arm across its chest and the other across its abdomen. Bone growth, dental wear, and the shape of the pelvis showed that it was a male aged 25–35. Nicknamed "Moshe", he was about 1.7m (5ft 7in) tall – slightly taller than the average Neanderthal. Although the skull and most of the legs were missing, the skeleton provided the first full sets of Neanderthal ribs and vertebrae, the first complete pelvis, and the only Neanderthal hyoid bone, which enables speech in modern humans.

A clue to diet comes from chemical analysis of the ratio of carbon to nitrogen in bones. Neanderthal bones have a higher proportion of carbon, indicating that they ate a lot of meat (high nitrogen levels signify a more herbivorous diet). This is supported by the many gazelle and deer bones at Kebara that bear the cut marks of butchery and signs of burning.

Recent studies of Neanderthal teeth reveal different information to analysis of bones, showing that plants may have been consumed more often than scientists once thought. Plant remains in Kebara cave, including charred peas in hearths, suggest these Neanderthals consumed a range of wild legumes, grasses, seeds, fruits, and nuts, though in what quantities we cannot be sure.

While Moshe's bones show no evidence of injury, many Neanderthals had healed fractures, possibly sustained when hunting large animals at close quarters. As well as being an indication of health, signs of disease and injury can sometimes suggest some level of care between group members. Shanidar 1, a male Neanderthal from Shanidar Cave, Iraq, had received a blow to the skull that probably blinded him and perhaps caused brain damage; he also had one withered arm and had lost his other forearm entirely. He could only have survived to his estimated age of 40–45 years with the help of others in his community.

Burial site

Moshe's body lay in the cave's main living area, which had the greatest concentration of hearths and animal bones. It was found in a shallow grave cut into the thick black hearth deposits. The grave contained a yellow sediment that differed from the surrounding hearth layer. This is evidence that the pit had been filled in after the body was placed inside it.

Kebara Cave, where Moshe was found

▼ Spreading around the world

Archaeologists use the distribution of hominin skeletons and artefacts such as tools to reconstruct routes of dispersal. The routes and timings are constantly being refined as more evidence comes to light.

KEY

Dispersal route of *Homo sapiens*

- *Homo sapiens*
- *Homo habilis*
- *Homo erectus*
- Denisovans
- *Homo antecessor*
- *Homo floresiensis*
- Unknown species
- Neanderthals

Red Deer Cave people Fossils found at Maludong Cave in southwest China are remarkable because they seem to be from a species of human that is found nowhere else and yet they are relatively recent – dating from just 14,500–11,500 years ago, long after modern humans had already reached China.

Manot Cave

Skhul Cave

Qafzeh Cave

Kebara

Tabun

Pontnewydd

Happisburgh

Feldhofer

Saint Cesaire

Gran Dolina

Peștera cu Oase

Saccopastore

Gibraltar caves

Dar es-Soltan

Mezmaiskaya

Dmanisi

Shanidar Cave

Ust'Ishim

Okladnikov

Denisova Cave

Mal'ta

Teshik-Tash

Xujiayao

Zhoukoudian

Lantian

Nanjing

Fuyan Cave

Maludong Cave

Callao Cave

Herto

Sulawesi

Liang Bua

Wolo Sege

Malak

Blombos Cave

25,000 YA

44,000–41,000 YA

125,000–70,000 YA

35,000 YA

120,000–80,000 YA

200,000 YA

55,000 YA

120,000 YA

The Levant was one of the routes out of Africa taken by early hominins – some species appear to have moved in and out of here as the climate fluctuated

Neanderthal and Denisovan fragments of bones and teeth, dated at 110,000–30,000 YA, have been found here

Fossils of a subspecies of *Homo erectus* provide evidence of the first phase of dispersal from Africa

Homo sapiens were the first species of humans to reach Australia

Gorham's Cave This limestone cave contains evidence of some of the most recent Neanderthal occupation, dating from about 28,000 years ago. It is now on the Gibraltar shoreline, but when first inhabited, 55,000 years ago, it was about 5km (3 miles) inland.

This cave contains a remarkable record of life about 75,000 years ago – its inhabitants made art using ochre and ate a diet that included land animals, fish, and shellfish

Olduvai Gorge This vast ravine in northern Tanzania was formed as a stream cut downwards through lake deposits, volcanic ash, and lava flows. Not only do the layers contain the remains of several hominin species, they can also be accurately dated, providing a valuable record of human evolution spanning a period from about 1.75 MYA to 15,000 years ago.

AT ABOUT **1M (3FT 3IN) TALL**, THE HOMININS DISCOVERED AT LIANG BUA CAVE IN **FLORES**, **INDONESIA**, ARE THE SMALLEST EVER FOUND

Bering Strait For much of the last 2 million years, Europe and Asia were linked by a landmass called Beringia. But for much of that time, the route across it was blocked by vast ice-sheets.

18,000 YA

EARLY HUMANS DISPERSE

The first hominins were found only in Africa. Helped by the ability to adapt to new environments, the various species of the genus *Homo* dispersed around the world and inhabited almost all parts of Earth's land surface.

Early humans probably dispersed from their African savanna habitat in at least two phases. The first of these may have begun about 2 million years ago, resulting in fossil finds of a species similar to *Homo habilis* at Dmanisi, Georgia, dated at 1.8 million years old. The same dispersal may also account for fossil finds in China and Indonesia dated at 1.6–1.1 million years old, although these are more similar to *Homo erectus*. A later phase of dispersal followed. This led to the occurrence in Europe of *Homo antecessor* in Spain and Britain at least 900,000 years ago.

These two phases of dispersal placed hominin species in Africa, Asia, and Europe. The populations diversified and new hominin species developed. For example, between 500,000 and 400,000 years ago, Neanderthals originated in Europe and, simultaneously, other species, such as the Denisovans, were emerging in Asia.

At some time between 150,000 and 120,000 years ago, groups of modern humans (*Homo sapiens*) left Africa, moving first into Asia and later into Europe. The demanding sea crossings to New Guinea and Australia were made by 55,000 years ago, although colonization of North, South, and Central America had to wait for the traversal of the Bering Strait after the peak of the last ice age, about 18,000 years ago.

Compared with earlier hominins, modern humans dispersed relatively quickly. Adapting to new environments required them to exploit new sources of food, adjust to colder, more seasonal climates, and withstand climate change. Crucial to their survival were the abilities to invent new technologies, learn new skills, and exchange resources and information.

Manis

Calgary

Anzick Child

Meadowcroft

Paisley 5-Mile Point

15,500 YA

Buttermilk Creek Complex

Yucatan Caves

Huaca Prieta

Pedra Furada

Cuncaicha

Cueva Bautista

Well-preserved remains at this site include wooden frames, hide coverings of huts, medicinal plants, and the first evidence of humans using potatoes

Monte Verde

14,800 YA

ANCIENT DNA

Over the past decade, advances in analyzing ancient DNA – the genetic material found in cells – have revolutionized our understanding of human evolution and led to some surprising discoveries.

DNA (deoxyribonucleic acid) is a very long molecule made up of small individual units. DNA is found in the cells of all living things. The order of the small units is like a set of coded instructions, genes, that determine the characteristics of an individual.

The oldest DNA so far obtained is from 400,000-year-old Neanderthals at Sima de Los Huesos, Spain, and suggests *Homo sapiens* split from other ancient hominins between 760,000 and 550,000 years ago. This and other samples show that Eurasia was always a melting pot, and that globally there was more interaction and breeding between ancient groups and with *Homo sapiens* than we previously suspected based on evidence from fossils and archaeology.

One 40,000-year-old human from Oase, Romania, may be as few as four generations removed from a Neanderthal ancestor. Other branches of our family were genetic

"dead-ends": an individual from Ust'-Ishim, Siberia, dated to 45,000 years ago, had Neanderthal ancestry but did not contribute genetically to later *Homo sapiens* populations. Similarly, there were at least four large population replacements in Europe between the earliest *Homo sapiens* colonizers and modern times.

We have only just begun to decipher the details of this ancient DNA and understand how genetic differences between species impacted on their – and our – success. As techniques advance and early DNA is decoded, especially from African and Asian remains, we can expect to unlock more secrets about our origins, migrations, and unique genetic adaptations, and also uncover further links between different branches of the hominin tree.

Mitochondrial DNA

We inherit mitochondrial DNA (mtDNA) from our mothers. This type of DNA is found not in the cell nucleus but in other cell structures called mitochondria. Since mtDNA only traces the maternal lineage, studying samples from many thousands of people has enabled scientists to construct a genetic "family tree" that indicates a common female ancestor for everyone alive today. This "Mitochondrial Eve" had many contemporaries, but they did not contribute to our mtDNA. She lived between 200,000 and 100,000 years ago, and was probably African or one of the earliest *Homo sapiens* to colonize Eurasia.

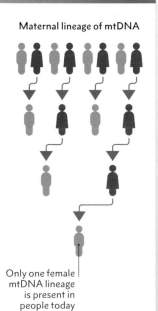

mtDNA is circular in shape

MTDNA

Maternal lineage of mtDNA

Only one female mtDNA lineage is present in people today

Mitochondria are small capsules inside cells where sugar is oxidized to release energy for use in the cell. Each one has its own DNA containing 37 genes that allow it to function

Nuclear DNA

Nuclear DNA lineage

Most DNA is located within the cell nucleus. Both parents pass on nuclear DNA to their offspring, so this type of DNA reveals much more about the relatedness of species, genetic differences, and adaptive traits. Recent studies have shown that during early dispersals from Africa, *Homo sapiens* populations interbred with hominins already living in Eurasia, but at different times and places, leaving living humans with varying amounts of their DNA. Genes from Neanderthals and other hominins probably aided our survival and eventual global success, such as by improving our immunity and metabolism.

Both sets of parental DNA present today

Double-helix structure

NUCLEAR DNA

Extracting DNA

Archaeologists extract DNA from teeth, bones, and mummified tissues. Mitochondrial DNA is easiest to recover intact: there are up to 1,000 mitochondria in every cell, each with 5–10 copies of the short mtDNA strands. The much longer strands of DNA in a cell's single nucleus are more likely to degrade over time and with changing soil temperature. Often the best chance of recovering nuclear DNA is from dental cementum – the mineralized outer layer of the tooth root. This is because the hard mineral matrix helps to preserve any cellular material trapped within it.

Discovering the Denisovans

In 2010, DNA analysis of a 50,000-year-old fragment of a girl's finger bone from Denisova Cave, Siberia, revealed a mystery hominin population. The "Denisovans" had brown eyes, hair, and skin, and showed an ancient relationship to Neanderthals, whom they lived alongside in Eurasia. By 2015, two further individuals had been identified at the site, one of whom lived 60,000 years earlier. Studies show that non-Africans alive today have varying proportions of Denisovan DNA, up to 4 per cent in the island populations of Melanesia. This indicates that only some early *Homo sapiens* migrants interbred with the Denisovans, but where this occurred remains uncertain.

Bone fragment

Size of Denisovan bone fragment

Nucleus, the cell's control centre, contains 20,000 to 25,000 genes

▶ Herto skull
This skull from Herto, Ethiopia, shows slight differences to others from early *Homo sapiens*. Some anthropologists suggest it represents a subspecies, *Homo sapiens idaltu*.

Typical steep forehead

The brow ridges are more pronounced than on most *Homo sapiens* skulls

Globe-shaped skull is a little longer than usually seen in *Homo sapiens*

SIDE VIEW

Homo sapiens have relatively small jaws and teeth for hominins

Large, high, rounded skull to accommodate increased brain capacity

Short, flat face with narrow cheekbones

FRONT VIEW

WE CAN SEE THE FOCUS, THE **CENTRE OF EVOLUTION,** FOR MODERN **HUMANS IN AFRICA** APPARENTLY **MOVING AROUND** FROM ONE PLACE TO ANOTHER, **DRIVEN BY CLIMATE CHANGES**.

Chris Stringer, anthropologist, 1947

THE FIRST HOMO SAPIENS

Of all the hominin species, and all the variants of genus *Homo*, only *Homo sapiens* remains today, having survived the challenges of the last ice age. It did so thanks to its unique anatomy, which came together in Africa nearly 200,000 years ago.

The distinctive "package" of anatomical features that identify living people today as *Homo sapiens* developed gradually, beginning around 500,000 years ago. Some key characteristics include: globular skulls, very large brains, shorter tucked-under faces, and smaller teeth, together with a more slender, lighter skeleton, smaller arm-to-lower-limb proportions, and narrower ribs. The appearance of these modifications was complex, occurring at different times and places, and in different combinations, but brain size continued to increase everywhere.

The oldest *Homo sapiens* fossils come from Omo Kibish, Ethiopia. Dated to around 195,000 years ago, the fragmented skulls and skeletons of two individuals show a modern morphology (form and structure), but one has less modern features than the other. Other early modern fossils have been discovered at Herto in Ethiopia, Singa in Sudan, Laetoli in Tanzania, Jebel Irhoud in Morocco, and Border Cave and Klasies River Mouth in South Africa. All of these are between 200,000 and 100,000 years old and display modern characteristics, albeit with variation in morphology.

BEGINNING THE LONG WALK

By 120,000 to 80,000 years ago, early *Homo sapiens* had moved into the Middle East and western Asia. The remains of over 20 individuals recovered from the caves at Skhul and Qafzeh in Israel still show some morphological differences. However, 47 distinctly modern teeth, with flat crowns and thin roots, have been found thousands of kilometres further east at Fuyan Cave, Daoxian, China. It is clear from this that we are missing fossils from large swathes of *Homo sapiens*' long journey into Asia, and that at least some of the stone tools found along their route in this period, such as in India, were made by anatomically modern people. It also makes it very likely that the oldest stone tools in Australia, dating back 55,000 years, were made by *Homo sapiens*, since they had already been in Asia a long time.

We cannot be sure what stimulated *Homo sapiens*' dispersal from Africa, leading eventually to a single global human species. It is unlikely to have been technological progress, since their stone tools were little more advanced than those made 100,000 years previously. Populations may have been increasing and climate change may have played a part, but important cognitive and social changes were also taking place at the time. Increased symbolic expression after 150,000 years ago point to innovations that probably coincided with *Homo sapiens* acquiring a brain size similar to that of people living today.

Jebel Irhoud

Skhul-Qafzeh

Singa   Herto
         Omo Kibish

Laetoli

Border Cave/
Klasies river mouth

▶ **African origins**
Early *Homo sapiens* fossils have been found at a variety of African sites. Genetic and skeletal evidence shows that African populations were already regionally distinct by 120,000 years ago.

▶ **Sole survivor**
Homo sapiens is the last hominin species, but for long periods it coexisted with other humans, including *Homo erectus*, *Homo floresiensis*, and the Neanderthals.

A family affair
Unlike the young of other primates, human children spend years being cared for by parents, grandparents, and friends of the family. These prolonged childhoods provide ample time for learning the ways of the world.

BRINGING UP
BABIES

Changes in the human reproductive cycle played an important part in the success of *Homo sapiens*. Increasing brain size probably made childbirth harder, but it also enabled us to evolve the very culture we need to rear our relatively undeveloped young.

Homo sapiens labours are long, painful, and risky. Our infants are large, have big heads, are mostly helpless, and are born with only 30 per cent of their adult brain size. Pregnancies would need to be 16 months long to attain the same development as newborn chimpanzees. Our childhood development is also extended, demanding high levels of care, not just by parents, but by other family members and friends.

To explain these complications, it is often said that greater brain size (see pp.188–89) coupled with bipedalism – which gave us narrower pelvises – created a biological trade-off. Potentially fatal births were avoided by limiting the length of pregnancies, forcing babies to be born early. It is certainly possible that by about 500,000 years ago, hominins were already experiencing tricky births, and that women may have had some level of assistance, or at least company, during labour. Other social primates, such as bonobos, exhibit similar behaviour. However, it is also true that non-bipedal primates have a tight fit in the birth canal, that capuchins and chimpanzee babies have relatively undeveloped brains, and that human gestation is actually longer

than expected given our body size. It may be that the upper limit on pregnancy length is actually metabolic – the point at which mothers can no longer biologically support a growing baby.

CO-OPERATIVE BREEDING
Anatomical changes also affected how we bring up our young. As australopithecine feet lost the "big toe" associated with tree climbing, infants were less able to cling to their mothers, and required greater care. It is possible that the exploitation of animal skins may have been driven more by the need to make baby slings and wraps than a need for warm clothing.

Although the length of time spent breastfeeding was probably comparable to that of other apes – lasting several years, as it does today – the greater demands of a hominin infant may have promoted the evolution of co-operative breeding, by which several adults bring up a child. The role of non-related adults and older generations in caring for children probably became important too, creating a rich environment in which experienced individuals could be observed finding food and making tools – vital skills that were then passed on to the next generation.

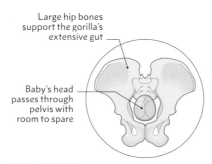

▲ **Gorilla birth**
Due to its small brain, a baby gorilla's head passes through its mother's birth canal with room to spare, making labour shorter and less risky.

Large hip bones support the gorilla's extensive gut

Baby's head passes through pelvis with room to spare

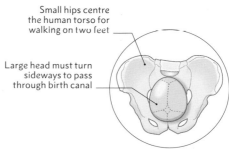

▲ **Human birth**
The head of a human baby must rotate to descend through its mother's birth canal, making childbirth longer and more painful.

Small hips centre the human torso for walking on two feet

Large head must turn sideways to pass through birth canal

HOW **LANGUAGE** EVOLVED

Many animals call to each other with sounds that stand for "Danger!", "Food!", or "Here!", but only humans can think conceptually – can talk, for example, about the nature of food or danger. For this, language had to evolve, and with it came story-telling, information-sharing, and our first attempts at understanding the world.

In evolutionary terms, the ability to speak emerged as a result of the hominin larynx lowering in the throat, enabling our ancestors to produce more diverse sounds than those of any other primate. The biological price of this was high, as an elevated larynx had enabled us to breathe and swallow simultaneously; now, we ran the risk of choking when we ate. At the same time, the hyoid bone, which connects the larynx to the root of the tongue, also changed position in a way that helped facilitate vocalization. Judging from the fossil record, this happened between 700,000 and 600,000 years ago, as Neanderthals and probably our common ancestor both had a "modern" hyoid bone. Our exceptional breath control, essential when speaking, also seems to date from this time.

Casts of fossil skulls show that Neanderthals had structures in the brain that were equivalent to our own "Broca's

TODAY THERE ARE NEARLY **7,000 LANGUAGES**, BUT EACH USES **ONLY A SMALL NUMBER** OF THE SOUNDS THAT A **HUMAN BEING** CAN MAKE

area". This area is vital to speaking and understanding language, and to perceiving meaningful gestures. Indeed, gestures may have been key: studies show that chimpanzees repeatedly use hand signs when vocalizing, indicating that early language may not have been purely vocal. However, the functions performed by different parts of the brain can change over time, so even if other hominins had brain structures similar to ours, they may not have been used for language.

2. Broca's area plans the response

3. The motor cortex controls the muscles used in the response

1. Wernicke's area deciphers speech

Tongue

Hyoid bone

Larynx

4. Mouth, tongue, and throat articulate the response

▲ **How humans process speech**
The emergence of speech required the evolution of several key stuctures in the throat and brain. This included the hyoid bone, which is vital in producing varied vocal sounds.

SYMBOLS AS EVIDENCE

The artefacts left by our ancestors are better forms of evidence. Among the most striking are those created by early *Homo sapiens* in South Africa between 100,000 and 50,000 years ago. At Blombos Cave, for example, red ochre blocks were shaped and carefully covered with delicate cross-hatch designs (see p.207). Even more impressive are the ostrich eggshells found at Diepkloof Cave, also in South Africa (see p.208). These were engraved with complex geometric patterns that show changes over time, hinting at shifts in meaning. Very much older than these, however, is a seashell from Trinil, Indonesia, which bears the incised zig-zag markings of a *Homo erectus* who lived some 540,000–430,000 years ago (see p.206). It reveals that the common ancestor of several hominins used graphic symbols, and so had probably developed language – a fact that is supported by anatomical evidence.

Another type of symbolic evidence comes from personal ornaments, which often communicate social meanings – for instance, about personal status or group affiliation – which can only be established through language. For example, the first use of shell beads occurs at the same time as engravings become more common; beads from Skhul Cave in Israel date from 135,000–100,000 years ago, while those from Grotte des Pigeons in Morocco date from 80,000 years ago. At Blombos Cave, too, groups of beads were excavated from layers dating from around 80,000 years ago, many showing areas of polish that suggest they were strung together, possibly as necklaces. The markings also show that the arrangement of the beads changed over time, suggesting not only that they were symbolic, but that their meanings evolved, like those of the Diepkloof eggshells.

FROM SYMBOLS TO STORIES

Taken together, the evidence shows that *Homo sapiens* had evolved symbolic culture and language by 70,000 years ago – and that Neanderthals did this independently. However, the evidence for language being used in narrative, story-telling senses comes much later, after 45,000 years ago. For example, the famous Lion-man ivory statue

from Hohlenstein-Stadel, Germany (see p.208) was carved around 40,000 years ago. It merges a lion's head with a human body, indicating both an imaginative leap by the artist, and a narrative to give it meaning.

The most striking examples of Palaeolithic narrative come from later European cave art. One scene painted at Lascaux, France, around 17,000 years ago, features a wounded bison charging a male figure who lies above some fallen spears and a line topped by a bird. There are many interpretations of the scene, but all of them agree that the man, the bison, and the bird only make sense in a story-telling context. This and other examples indicate that rich oral traditions, full of

◄ **Almost talking**
Campbell's monkeys from Ivory Coast seem to be on the verge of speaking. They have a "proto-syntax" composed of alert calls, which they use to communicate detailed information – such as what type of predator is coming and how it was detected.

meaning and symbolism, were part of Palaeolithic life, and likely had been for many thousands of years. They were our first attempts at fathoming the world around us – of giving it a narrative shape.

> A COMPLEX **TRAIN OF THOUGHT** CAN BE NO MORE **CARRIED OUT** WITHOUT **WORDS**... THAN A **CALCULATION** WITHOUT THE USE OF **FIGURES**.
>
> **Charles Darwin**, *The Descent of Man*, 1871

◄ **The birdman of Lascaux**
Dating from around 17,000 years ago, this strange image of a man – apparently dressed as a bird – being charged by a bison is probably evidence of story-telling. It may also show a shamanic experience.

COLLECTIVE LEARNING

The emergence of language set *Homo sapiens* apart from other species: with language came the ability to share and store information across generations. This ensured that new generations could know more than the last, and so be more effective in the world.

The practice of sharing and storing information is called "collective learning". At its simplest, this means that we only need invent the wheel once, for that knowledge can then be stored and shared publicly. The alternative is to imagine us as a group of networked computers. Without the network – without connectivity – how could human history unfold?

SURVIVING COOPERATIVELY

Humans appear to be predisposed to work together to a far greater degree than other animals. The roots of this tendency can be seen in primates, the majority of which live in social groups, with strong kin relationships and friendships. However, humans live in unusually diverse societies, and our high level of cooperation is a unifying characteristic. Hunter-gatherer groups, for example, typically number between 25 and 50 individuals, but they are usually part of extended social networks, consisting of blood relations and other types of kinship. Within and between these groups, food, labour, and childcare are shared – as is vital information about water, predators, and the availability of food.

The evolution of this ability to cooperate can be seen in the archaeological record. Stone tools began to be transported increasingly long distances around 200,000 years ago, pointing to expanding social networks. By then, multi-part tools, such as spears, were being made, probably collaboratively. More spectacular examples of these, such as atlatls and bows, came later, and after 40,000 years ago many of these were lavishly ornamented. The Mas d'Azil atlatl, for example, is one of five almost identical objects found at different sites in the Pyrenees. Each is carved into the shape of an ibex, demonstrating a common artistic tradition, and probably some level of apprenticeship. Moreover, an atlatl, like a bow, is a "tool for using a tool" – in this case a tool for propelling spears – which is of a whole new order of complexity. It shows that by 17,000 years ago we were adapting ourselves ever more cleverly to our environment – alone of all creatures through cultural rather than genetic change. Thanks to collective learning, human history could begin.

The Ibex seems to be giving birth, or possibly excreting. The projection was needed to make a durable hook for the spear

Hook holds the spear in place until it is launched by the hunter

▲ **Mas d'Azil atlatl**
Found in the Mas d'Azil Cave in the Pyrenees, France, this exquisite atlatl, made of reindeer antler, is an early example of mass-produced art. Its mysterious symbolism was briefly common in the region, proof of shared story-telling devices.

▶ **Sharing information**
Today, the San people of the Kalahari make fire using knowledge passed down for tens of thousands of years by their forebears.

▶ **Throwing power**
An atlatl, or spear-thrower, is a device that uses leverage to amplify throwing power. The spear is kept in place by a hook at the rear of the atlatl, and this gains energy as the hunter throws the spear.

ENERGY GAIN

ENERGY INCREASE

ENERGY RELEASE

MULTI-PART TOOLS ARE EASIER TO **REPAIR**, AND SO ARE **MORE COMMONLY FOUND** IN **HARSHER, HIGHER LATITUDES**

> " A GROUP CAN POOL THE **HARD-WON DISCOVERIES** OF **MEMBERS**, PRESENT AND PAST, AND END UP **FAR SMARTER** THAN A **RACE OF HERMITS** "

Steven Pinker, cognitive scientist, 1954 –

Ibex motif is carved in naturalistic detail from a single piece of antler

Lines represent changes of colour in the ibex's fur

▶ **Strange symbolism**
There are subtle differences between the five versions of the Mas d'Azil atlatl, but all share the motif of the ibex looking back at her rear. Its meaning remains a mystery.

The spear is held against this side of the atlatl

Great skill went into hollowing out the space between the animal's legs, leaving only the denser outer cortex of the antler

FULL VIEW

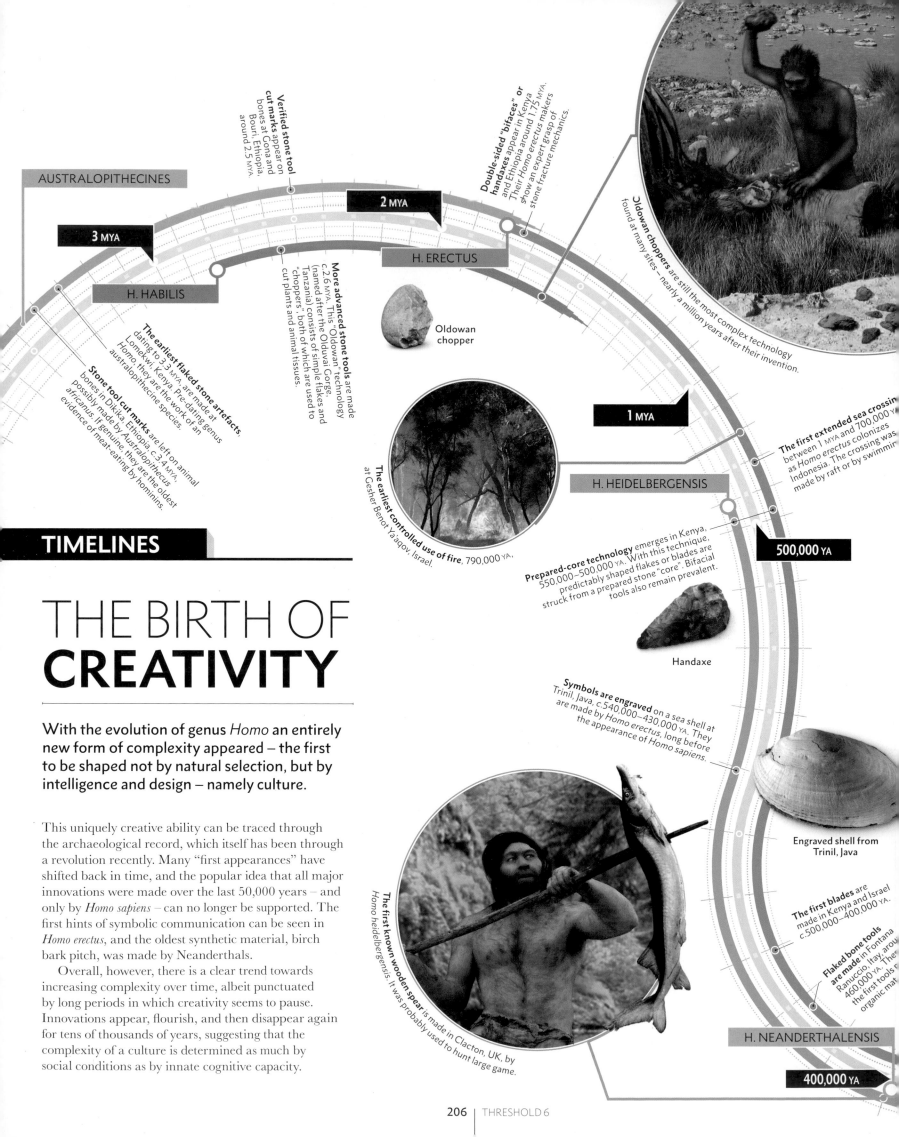

THE BIRTH OF CREATIVITY

With the evolution of genus *Homo* an entirely new form of complexity appeared – the first to be shaped not by natural selection, but by intelligence and design – namely culture.

This uniquely creative ability can be traced through the archaeological record, which itself has been through a revolution recently. Many "first appearances" have shifted back in time, and the popular idea that all major innovations were made over the last 50,000 years – and only by *Homo sapiens* – can no longer be supported. The first hints of symbolic communication can be seen in *Homo erectus*, and the oldest synthetic material, birch bark pitch, was made by Neanderthals.

Overall, however, there is a clear trend towards increasing complexity over time, albeit punctuated by long periods in which creativity seems to pause. Innovations appear, flourish, and then disappear again for tens of thousands of years, suggesting that the complexity of a culture is determined as much by social conditions as by innate cognitive capacity.

AUSTRALOPITHECINES

3 MYA

H. HABILIS

2 MYA

H. ERECTUS

1 MYA

H. HEIDELBERGENSIS

500,000 YA

H. NEANDERTHALENSIS

400,000 YA

Verified stone tool cut marks appear on bones at Gona and Bouri, Ethiopia, around 2.5 MYA.

The earliest flaked stone artefacts, dating to 3.3 MYA, are made at Lomekwi, Kenya. Pre-dating genus *Homo*, they are the work of an australopithecine species.

Stone tool cut marks are left on animal bones in Dikika, Ethiopia c.3.4 MYA, possibly made by *Australopithecus africanus*. If genuine, they are the oldest evidence of meat-eating by hominins.

More advanced stone tools are made c.2.6 MYA. This "Oldowan" technology (named after the Olduvai Gorge, Tanzania) consists of simple flakes and "choppers", both of which are used to cut plants and animal tissues.

Double-sided "bifaces" or handaxes appear in Kenya and Ethiopia around 1.75 MYA. Their *Homo erectus* makers show an expert grasp of stone fracture mechanics.

Oldowan chopper

Oldowan choppers are still the most complex technology found at many sites – nearly a million years after their invention.

The first extended sea crossing between 1 MYA and 700,000 YA, as *Homo erectus* colonizes Indonesia. The crossing was made by raft or by swimming.

The earliest controlled use of fire, 790,000 YA, at Gesher Benot Ya'aqov, Israel.

Prepared-core technology emerges in Kenya, 550,000–500,000 YA. With this technique, predictably shaped flakes or blades are struck from a prepared stone "core". Bifacial tools also remain prevalent.

Handaxe

Symbols are engraved on a sea shell at Trinil, Java, c.540,000–430,000 YA. They are made by *Homo erectus*, long before the appearance of *Homo sapiens*.

Engraved shell from Trinil, Java

The first blades are made in Kenya and Israel c.500,000–400,000 YA.

Flaked bone tools are made in Fontana Ranuccio, Italy, around 460,000 YA. These are the first tools made of organic material.

The first known wooden spear is made in Clacton, UK, by *Homo heidelbergensis*. It was probably used to hunt large game.

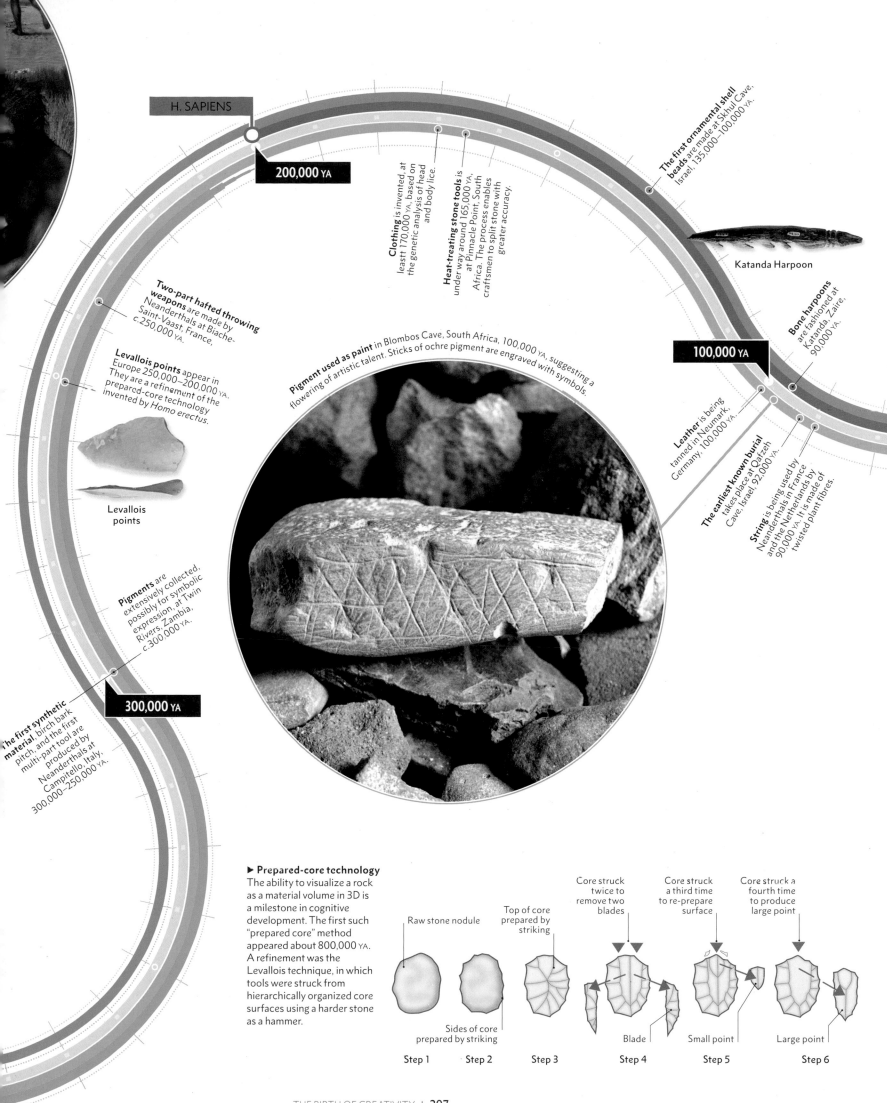

H. SAPIENS

200,000 YA

Clothing is invented, at the least 170,000 YA, based on the genetic analysis of head and body lice.

Heat-treating stone tools is under way around 165,000 YA, at Pinnacle Point, South Africa. The process enables craftsmen to split stone with greater accuracy.

The first ornamental shell beads are made at Skhul Cave, Israel, 135,000–100,000 YA.

Katanda Harpoon

Bone harpoons are fashioned at Katanda, Zaire, 90,000 YA.

Two-part hafted throwing weapons are made by Neanderthals at Biache-Saint-Vaast, France, c.250,000 YA.

Levallois points appear in Europe 250,000–200,000 YA. They are a refinement of the prepared-core technology invented by Homo erectus.

Levallois points

Pigment used as paint in Blombos Cave, South Africa, 100,000 YA, suggesting a flowering of artistic talent. Sticks of ochre pigment are engraved with symbols.

100,000 YA

Leather is being tanned in Neumark, Germany, 100,000 YA.

The earliest known burial takes place at Qafzeh Cave, Israel, 92,000 YA.

String is being used by Neanderthals in France and the Netherlands by 90,000 YA. It is made of twisted plant fibres.

Pigments are extensively collected, possibly for symbolic expression, at Twin Rivers, Zambia, c.300,000 YA.

The first synthetic material, birch bark pitch, and the first multi-part tool are produced by Neanderthals at Campitello, Italy, 300,000–250,000 YA.

300,000 YA

▶ **Prepared-core technology**
The ability to visualize a rock as a material volume in 3D is a milestone in cognitive development. The first such "prepared core" method appeared about 800,000 YA. A refinement was the Levallois technique, in which tools were struck from hierarchically organized core surfaces using a harder stone as a hammer.

Raw stone nodule

Sides of core prepared by striking

Top of core prepared by striking

Core struck twice to remove two blades

Blade

Core struck a third time to re-prepare surface

Small point

Core struck a fourth time to produce large point

Large point

Step 1 Step 2 Step 3 Step 4 Step 5 Step 6

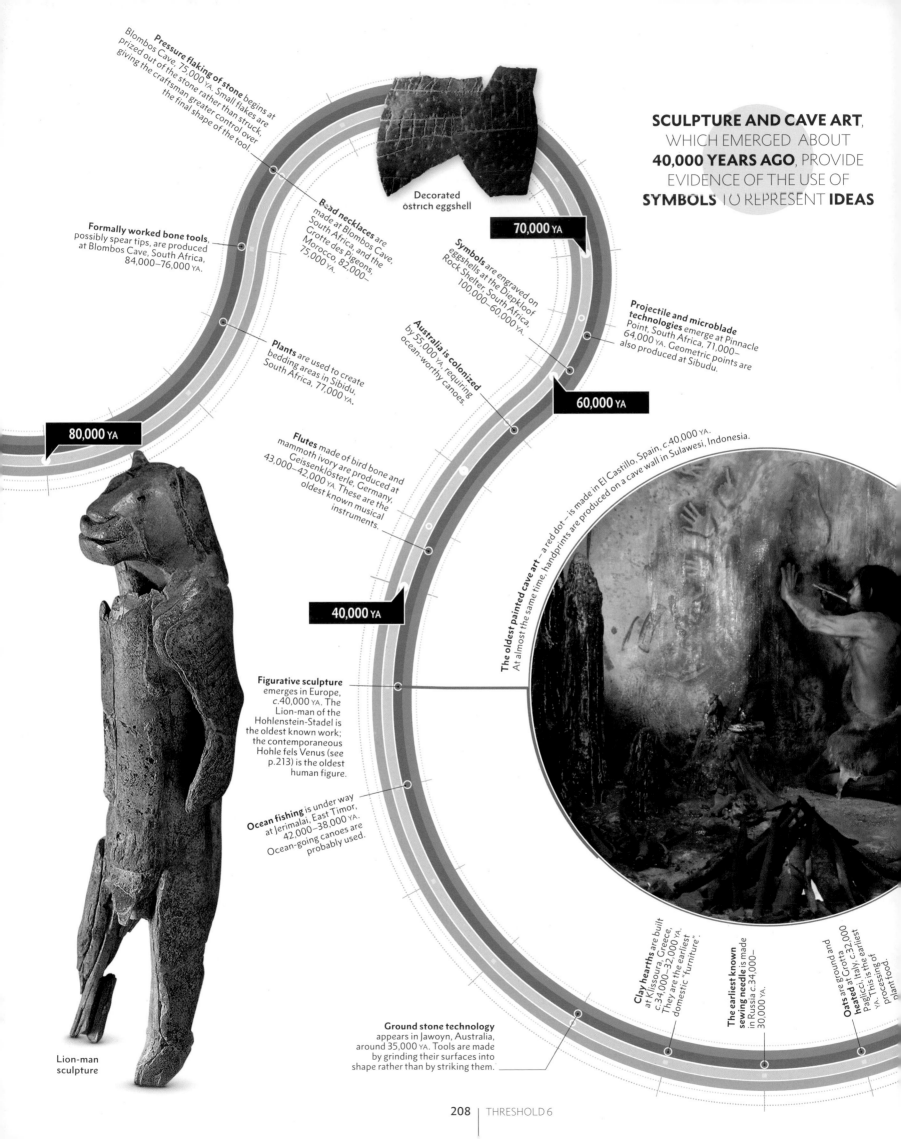

Pressure flaking of stone begins at Blombos Cave, 75,000 YA. Small flakes are prized out of the stone rather than struck, giving the craftsman greater control over the final shape of the tool.

Decorated ostrich eggshell

SCULPTURE AND CAVE ART, WHICH EMERGED ABOUT **40,000 YEARS AGO,** PROVIDE EVIDENCE OF THE USE OF **SYMBOLS** TO REPRESENT **IDEAS**

Formally worked bone tools, possibly spear tips, are produced at Blombos Cave, South Africa, 84,000–76,000 YA.

Bead necklaces are made at Blombos Cave, South Africa, and the Grotte des Pigeons, Morocco, 82,000–75,000 YA.

70,000 YA

Symbols are engraved on eggshells at the Diepkloof Rock Shelter, South Africa, 100,000–60,000 YA.

Projectile and microblade technologies emerge at Pinnacle Point, South Africa, 71,000–64,000 YA. Geometric points are also produced at Sibudu.

Plants are used to create bedding areas in Sibidu, South Africa, 77,000 YA.

Australia is colonized by 55,000 YA, requiring ocean-worthy canoes.

80,000 YA

60,000 YA

Flutes made of bird bone and mammoth ivory are produced at Geissenklösterle, Germany, 43,000–42,000 YA. These are the oldest known musical instruments.

The oldest painted cave art – a red dot – is made in El Castillo, Spain, c.40,000 YA. At almost the same time, handprints are produced on a cave wall in Sulawesi, Indonesia.

40,000 YA

Figurative sculpture emerges in Europe, c.40,000 YA. The Lion-man of the Hohlenstein-Stadel is the oldest known work; the contemporaneous Hohle fels Venus (see p.213) is the oldest human figure.

Ocean fishing is under way at Jerimalai, East Timor, 42,000–38,000 YA. Ocean-going canoes are probably used.

Lion-man sculpture

Ground stone technology appears in Jawoyn, Australia, around 35,000 YA. Tools are made by grinding their surfaces into shape rather than by striking them.

Clay hearths are built at Klissoura, Greece, c.34,000–32,000 YA. They are the earliest domestic "furniture".

The earliest known sewing needle is made in Russia c.34,000–30,000 YA.

Oats are ground and heated at Grotta Paglicci, Italy, c.32,000 YA. This is the earliest processing of plant food.

Shamanism is possibly practised in Europe by 26,000 YA. This is suggested by ... ...ls buried with typically shamanic effects, such as ochre, beads, and a staff.

20,000 YA

Fish hooks for large-scale ocean fishing are made at Jerimalai, East Timor, 23,000–16,000 YA.

The first clay pots are produced at Xianrendong, China c.20,000 YA.

Woven textiles, basketry, nets, and string are produced in Pavlov and Dolni Vestonice, the Czech Republic, 28,000–25,000 YA. The linen-like textiles were probably made on a loom.

Replica of house made from mammoth bones and hide

Atlatl

The first houses are built in Dolni Vestonice, the Czech Republic, c.26,000 YA. They are made of mammoth bones and possibly coated with daub.

Ornately carved atlatls (spear-throwers) are widely used in Western Europe 17,000–12,000 YA. Their decoration is proof of story-telling, and their use proof of apprenticeship.

Wild cereals and starchy plant foods are used intensively, such as at Grotte des Pigeons, Morocco, 15,000–14,000 YA. Plants are becoming a major part of Homo sapiens' diet.

Microblades are produced in Mongolia c.28,000 YA, using a prepared-core technique.

Clovis point arrowheads appear in New Mexico c.13,500 YA. These are struck from a stone core, then pressure-flaked around the edges.

The dog is ...nesticated ...30,000 YA.

The Chauvet Cave, France, is painted, beginning 32,000 YA. The images are largely of local animals, many of which are shown in perspective, and some with a sense of movement.

The bow and arrow is widely used in Europe, particularly among the Ahrensburgian people of Germany, 15,000–10,000 YA.

The earliest known fish trap is made in Dublin, Ireland, 10,000–9,000 YA. Fish resources are increasingly exploited.

30,000 YA

Clovis point

10,000 YA

8 MYA | HOMININS APPEAR   2.6 MYA | STONE TECHNOLOGY IS DEVELOPED   2.5 MYA | GENUS HOMO APPEARS   300,000 YA | FIRST WEAPONS WITH HANDLES

Ancient practices
The San people have been hunting the landscapes of the Kalahari for thousands of years. Large game accounts for about 20 percent of their diet – the remainder is made up of plants and smaller animals caught in traps.

HUNTER-GATHERERS
EMERGE

From the earliest times, most hominins survived by gleaning what they could from the world around them, rather than producing their own food. The range of items eaten and the ways of sourcing them varied according to the environment, and demanded high levels of social organization.

Early members of the hominin family had diverse diets – primarily of fruit, leaves, and insects – and some probably used cobbles to crack nuts, as primates do today. The first stone tools made food processing easier, and while these were being made by pre-*Homo* species at least 3.3 MYA, the earliest evidence of their function comes from around a million years later. Analysis of the surfaces of tools found at Kanjera South, Kenya, shows that plants and meat were being processed, probably by *Homo habilis*. Dating to about 2 MYA, the tools were made using an early technology known as Oldowan. At the same site, there is also evidence of hunting – or at least of scavenging kills made by other animals. Whole carcasses of small gazelles were brought in and cut up; because tooth marks from carnivores overlie them, it is clear that hominins had first access.

Around 1.8 MYA, with the emergence of *Homo erectus* and an improved way of making handaxes, called Achelean technology, hunting seems to have increased. Hundreds of footprints found at Ileret, Kenya, dating to 1.5 MYA, reveal that small groups of adults circled the lake shore – just as carnivores do. At the very least, it shows cooperative foraging was under way.

By around 700,000 years ago, diets had diversified. At Gesher Benot Ya'aqov, in Israel, there is evidence of nut-cracking as well as the exploitation of large animals, including elephants, although it is unclear whether the elephants were hunted or scavenged. Various plant resources are also thought to have been important during the European ice ages, both for Neanderthals and, later, *Homo sapiens*, but large amounts of fat and meat were still vital for survival.

LEARNED ADAPTABILITY

Making the most of varied food resources across different environments required an investment in complicated technologies and a dedication to preserving knowledge. The ability to hunt large animals suggests that hominins from *Homo erectus* onwards were learning how to track, probably from early childhood. From 200,000 YA, Neanderthals were hunting birds, and at least 120,000 YA *Homo sapiens* were exploiting shellfish. Our species colonized the harshest environments, including the Arctic, suggesting that we had especially flexible skills.

Foragers typically lived in mobile communities, which were broadly egalitarian. However, abundant and predictable resources, such as fish, could encourage people to stay in the same locations, and even to become semi-sedentary – eventually, an alternative to the hunter-gatherer way of life would emerge.

▼ **Evolving technologies**
Homo sapiens spread across the globe by inventing new technologies, such as this three-pronged spear used by the Inuit for fishing in the Arctic.

> THERE WAS **NOTHING** THAT THEY COULD NOT **ASSEMBLE** IN **ONE MINUTE**, WRAP UP IN THEIR **BLANKETS** AND CARRY ON THEIR **SHOULDERS** FOR A JOURNEY OF **A THOUSAND MILES**.

Laurens van der Post, writer and conservationist, 1906–1996, on the San bushmen of the Kalahari

PALAEOLITHIC **ART**

For many, the word "art" means representational imagery, and "Palaeolithic art" is shorthand for a purely European tradition. However, Palaeolithic art is much more diverse than this, and can be traced back to symbolic graphic creations produced over 100,000 years ago.

Early stirrings of artistic expression can be seen in the engraved eggshells found at the Diepkloof Rock Shelter in South Africa (see p.208), dating to over 100,000 years ago. However, we have no clear depictions of recognizable figures before 50,000 years ago. Currently, the two oldest paintings in the world (both *c.*40,000 YA) are a single red dot found in El Castillo cave, Spain, and a hand stencil found in Leang Timpuseng cave in Sulawesi, Indonesia. This proves that art was being practised far beyond Europe at the time, even though most of the surviving dated examples are European. The Chauvet Cave in France, for instance, preserves some of the most stunning images of the era, including representations of nearly 450 animals. They were painted in two phases, the first starting nearly 37,000 years ago, the second over 2,000 years later. The walls of the cave were carefully prepared by the artists, and the images show a profound understanding of movement and perspective.

Around the same time, a pig-like animal was painted in Leang Timpuseng. The very first Australian Aboriginal cave painting to have been firmly dated appeared soon after (*c.*28,000 YA), and from 20,000 years ago multiple traditions began flowering across the world. Throughout this time, "portable" art was also produced, including a female carved pendant discovered at Hohle Fels, Germany (*c.*40,000 YA). Known as the Hohle Fels "Venus", it is the oldest known depiction of a human being. Other traditions included the carving of ivory, bone, and antlers, and, in Eastern Europe, firing clay to make animal and human figurines. The meaning of these works can only be guessed at, but their growing significance to the people of the time is beyond doubt.

▼ **Painted cave**
The Chauvet Cave, in France, features huge panels of animals, including bison, horses, and lions – but not one single complete human being.

◀ **The Zaraysk bison**
This reconstructed figurine from Russia is a masterpiece of naturalistic carving. Made from ivory and rubbed with red pigment, it was smashed before being buried in a pit.

Hohle Fels Venus
This ivory pendant is the oldest known female figurine.

> " [ANCIENT ART] MAY BE AN **ATTEMPT TO NEGOTIATE**... WITH THE **HUMAN INTELLECT** AND ITS CAPACITY TO **OCCUPY OFTEN ILLUSORY REALMS DISTINCT** FROM **THE REALITY** OF THE **REST OF NATURE** "

Jill Cook, archaeologist, 1960 –

THE INVENTION OF **CLOTHING**

Clothing protects us from the cold, from sunburn, from insect bites, and even from certain weapons. In short, it makes us more adaptable. In Palaeolithic times, it allowed us to live in a range of hostile environments, and to begin our spread across the globe.

We know from physical evidence that early *Homo sapiens* and Neanderthals used pigments and may have worn jewellery, but the earliest evidence for clothing is mostly indirect as clothing does not survive well in the ground. Biological studies suggest that during very cold glacial phases hominin species in the northern hemisphere needed tailored body coverings. Even the Neanderthals, who are thought to have been physically cold-adapted, needed to cover at least 80 per cent of their body, especially their hands and feet. Another clue comes from the study of parasites. Body lice are adapted to living in clothes, and the estimated age for their split from head lice, based on DNA studies, is at least 170,000 years ago. That long ago there were numerous types of human – including Neanderthals, Denisovans, *Homo floresiensis*, and ourselves – and it is possible that exchanges between the different types of human led to both the habit of wearing clothes and the spread of these parasites.

THE FIRST FABRICS

The earliest clothes were probably animal-based. Tiny scraps of tannin-soaked organic material were found stuck to a stone tool in Neumark-Nord, Germany, suggesting that over 100,000 years ago Neanderthals were tanning skins. They didn't have needles, but could have sewn pieces of leather and fur using existing tools designed for piercing and threading. Bone tools with rounded ends have been found in 40,000-year-old Neanderthal sites, and these were probably "lissoirs" – leather-softening tools very like the ones still used today. The oldest bone needles date to 20,000 years ago, but these were probably used for bead embroidery as much as sewing other materials.

The use of plants for producing fabrics seems to begin with *Homo sapiens*. Dyed plant fibres have been found at Dzudzuana Cave in Georgia, dating to 30,000 years ago. Other sites show that from at least 28,000 years ago fabric was being woven.

Tiny impressions in baked clay fragments from the sites of Pavlov and Dolni Vestonice, in the Czech Republic, show fine textiles comparable to linen, possibly made from flax or nettle, alongside netting and basketry. We cannot be sure that these fabrics were used for clothing, but some of the carved human figurines from the same region and period seem to show that plaited or woven caps and belts were worn. Other carvings from the Siberian site of Mal'ta, a few thousand years later, may represent full-body outfits with hoods, possibly made from fur.

The production of plant-fibre textiles continued through Mesolithic times, when bast (from tree bark) was spun into clothes. However, there is no evidence for their replacement with softer animal fibres, such as wool, until the advent of farming.

> [THE DISTINCTION BETWEEN **HEAD** AND **BODY LICE**] PROBABLY AROSE WHEN **HUMANS** BEGAN TO MAKE **FREQUENT USE OF CLOTHING**.

Mark Stoneking, American geneticist, 1956–

▶ **Buried prince**
Only the shells remain of the clothes worn by the "Young Prince" found in the Arene Candide cave, Italy. He was buried over 23,000 years ago.

Prehistoric dress

This reconstruction of a prehistoric person is based on remains found in the Abri Pataud site, Aquitaine, France. The site contained human remains, figurines, tools, and cave paintings from between 47,000 and 17,000 years ago, a period during which archaeologists believe clothing had become relatively sophisticated.

Hair may have been twined together to form dreadlocks, to keep it easy to clean and to avoid the potential illnesses associated with matted hair. Evidence for caps or simple hats has also been found, as have bandeaux – thin strips of fibre that hold the hair in place

EVIDENCE SUGGESTS THAT **HUMANS** MAY HAVE BEEN WEARING **JEWELLERY** AS FAR BACK AS **75,000 YEARS AGO**

Snoods made from fur would have provided warmth during winter and at night

Tunics may have been made from woven nettle and hemp stalks

Clothes may have been dyed, with the dyes obtained from berries, roots, and leaves of plants

Elaborate jewellery made from stone, shell, bone, ivory, and antler was worn around the wrists and neck, and sewn onto clothing

Long string skirts and simple belts may have been common, as were boots made from animal skins laced together

100,000 YA | HOMO SAPIENS APPEARS 135,000 YA | FIRST USE OF SYMBOLS 110,000 YA | LAST ICE AGE BEGINS 41,000 YA | EARLIEST PAINTED CAVE ART 12,000 YA | LAST ICE AGE ENDS

HUMANS
HARNESS FIRE

The ability to use fire is uniquely human, and may have been a significant source of impetus for the evolution of genus *Homo*. However, we may not have fully controlled it until relatively late in hominin evolution.

The earliest evidence of fire comes from Wonderwerk Cave, South Africa, where careful analysis of sediments nearly a million years old reveals that bones and plants were deliberately burnt deep inside the cave. However, it is possible that early hominins took advantage of fires started by natural events, such as lightning strikes. The first repeated, controlled use of fire dates from just after 800,000 years ago, at Gesher Benot Ya'aqov, Israel, where burnt materials recur over a 100,000-year period, shows that *Homo erectus* was both making and maintaining fire.

TECHNOLOGY AND SOCIAL LIFE

After 400,000 years ago, the increased frequency of sites with deep layers of ashes, charcoal, and burnt bone reveals a habitual control of fire. In Europe, this coincides with the appearance of the Neanderthals, who seem to have been the first to use it for manufacturing purposes. At the Italian site of Campitello (*c.*300,000 YA), stone tools were found covered in birch bark pitch, which was used to make multi-part tools.

Familiarity with fire also changed our social life. Domestic spaces centred on fires appear by 200,000 years ago, and may have played a key role in the development of language. The campfire increased the amount of light to work by, but not sufficiently to perform difficult tasks, thereby creating opportunities for conversation and storytelling. It was also where the first experiments in cooking took place, nearly 800,000 years ago.

From around 35,000 years ago, in eastern Europe, people experimented with fire and clay for some 5,000 years, producing animal and human figurines; by 20,000 years ago, the first pottery was produced in China. From then on, fire drove many new technologies, especially as people abandoned hunter-gatherer lifestyles.

Birch tar and leather lashings hold the blade in place

▲ Copper weapons
Copper was the first metal to be smelted, probably in the Middle East around 5,800 years ago. The first furnaces were simple holes in the ground, in which copper was extracted from ores such as malachite. Blades such as the one belonging to Ötzi the Iceman were then cold-hammered into shape (see pp.282–83)

Hearths are a sure sign that fire is being controlled. Many have been found at the Neanderthal site of Abric Romani, Spain, and evidence suggests that at least some were used at the same time.

The first campfires were probably sourced from bush fires that had started naturally. Typically, a fire would be kept alive in a cave, where it was sheltered from the elements.

50,000
Neanderthals cook plant foods, as proved by starch grains found on teeth

200,000 YA
Activity areas in Palaeolithic sites become centred on hearth areas

165,000 YA
Heat treatment to improve stone tool-making by early *Homo sapiens* in South Africa

400,000–300,000 YA
Evidence of the controlled use of fire, such as burnt bones, becomes more common

300,000–250,000 YA
Neanderthals use fire to make birch bark pitch, the first synthetic material

780,000 YA
Habitual use of fire by late *Homo erectus*. Evidence of burnt seeds suggests cooking

500,000 YA

1 MYA

1 MYA
Early hominins use fire occasionally, perhaps sourced from bush blazes

Impression made by wooden haft, probably for a knife

▲ Birch bark tar
This 80,000-year-old piece of birch bark tar comes from Königsaue, Germany. On its reverse side, it bears the thumbprint of a Neanderthal – possibly its maker – who used it as an adhesive to attach a piece of flint to a wooden shaft.

◀ Clay vessels
Clay vessels, such as this pot made by the Jomon people from Japan, greatly enhanced our ability to cook and store food. Their production became widespread with the adoption of the agricultural lifestyle, when strong containers for grain and other foodstuffs were needed.

35,000–30,000 YA
Clay-lined hearths, clay lamps, and the first fired ceramic figurines

20,000 YA
The first known pottery made in containers made in China

13,500 YA

5,800 YA
The earliest crucibles, evidence of copper smelting

5,500 YA

5,000 YA
Pottery vessels found worldwide, with varied techniques of manufacture

3,800–3,200 YA
The earliest evidence of iron smelting

3,000 YA

2,000–1,800 YA
Glass manufacture begins in Egypt and possibly India

40,000 YA

◀ Clay figurines
The oldest fired figurine is the "Venus of Dohlni Vestonice", from Croatia. Made some 29,000–25,000 years ago, she is proof that her makers were experimenting with fire.

▲ Bronze armour
Bronze was produced by adding tin to copper during the smelting process. It was considerably harder than copper, giving bronze-clad soldiers a distinct advantage in battle. This helmet was worn by a Greek soldier around 2,650 years ago.

Skull-shaped helmet made from a single piece of bronze

> ## HEARTHS ARE PLACES TO SIT AND **EXCHANGE NEWS**... **MAKE AND REPAIR STONE TOOLS**, DISCUSS THE DAY'S **HUNT**, AND **MAKE PLANS** FOR THE **FUTURE**.

John McNabb, archaeologist, 1960 –

▼ Making birch bark pitch
Birch bark pitch, the first synthetic substance, was used as an adhesive from Palaeolithic times onwards. First made by the Neanderthals, it was produced by "cooking" birch bark in a fire for several hours under controlled temperatures. The liquefied tar was then collected and allowed to cool. As it was hardening it was applied like putty to the joints of multi-part tools.

Strips of bark wrapped tightly together

Packed earth to retain high temperatures

Fire maintained above 348°C (658°F)

Bark is packed into pit under fire

After 4–8 hours, all the tar is released

Tar applied to spear joint

Spear point

Spear shaft

Preparing the bark

Extracting the tar

Finishing a spear

BURIAL PRACTICES

The Palaeolithic period saw the emergence of that most human of characteristics – having respect, even concern, for the dead. The rituals of the day were simple, but they foreshadowed a time when tombs would be built for entire generations of ancestors.

Practices relating to death are important because they point to key intellectual capacities, such as an understanding of time. The ability to comprehend that an individual has moved from a living state to one of death seems uniquely human, but other species show hints of understanding. Elephants, for example, can be reluctant to leave the bodies of dead group members, and chimpanzees show an extraordinary range of reactions, from extreme agitation to quietly staying by a body for hours, and sometimes carrying infants' corpses for weeks. However, it is impossible to know if these reactions are simply the effects of confusion and distress or true expressions of loss and sadness.

THE FIRST **OPEN-AIR BURIALS** TOOK PLACE AROUND **40,000 YEARS AGO**. BEFORE THEN, **ALL FUNERARY PRACTICES** TOOK PLACE IN **CAVES**

THE FIRST BURIALS

The earliest evidence of hominins acknowledging the dead is the practice of "caching", or collecting, bodies. Around 430,000 years ago, at Sima de Los Huesos, Spain, at least 28 hominins were deliberately placed in a deep pit, accompanied by a single strikingly coloured stone tool. The complete interment of bodies began much later. Some 92,000 years ago, a number of *Homo sapiens* were buried at Qafzeh and Skhul, in Israel. These included a young adult and a child who were buried together, and a teenager who was interred with antlers covering his chest.

After 40,000 years ago, the frequency of burials increases, as does the number of bodies buried with objects. At Sungir, Russia, around 25,000 years ago, two children were buried head-to-head in a single grave, accompanied by spears, thousands of beads, and a single adult femur filled with red pigment. Such rich burials were rare, however. Simpler burials were common, and isolated body parts were sometimes interred separately

EATING THE DEAD

Cut marks from stone tools found on both Neanderthal and *Homo sapiens* remains suggest another facet of Palaeolithic funerary practices. The marks, which occur on various bones, were caused by the deliberate removal of flesh from the body or by cutting the body to pieces. This may have been a means to interact with or honour the dead, but may also indicate that the population had to resort to cannibalism for nutritional purposes. A number of such bones was found at Gough's Cave, in the UK, in 1898. Dating to 14,000 years ago, and almost certainly evidence of cannibalism, the bones included several carved "skull cups" – the earliest examples of human skulls being used as drinking vessels.

The area of the skull used as a cup

Cut marks show that the interior of the skull was cleared of tissue

▶ **Skull cup**
The skull remains found at Gough's Cave show all the signs of manufacture. The meticulous cutting and cleaning of the bone suggests that the skull was used for ritualistic purposes.

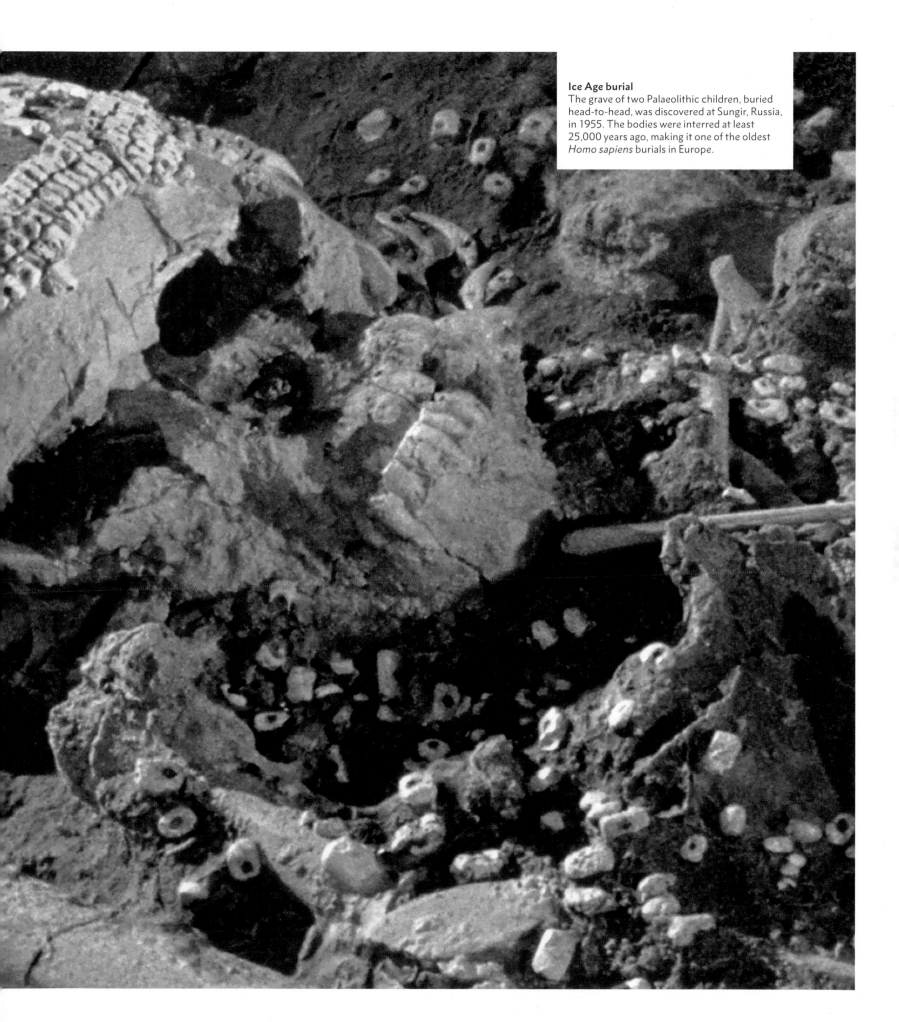

Ice Age burial
The grave of two Palaeolithic children, buried head-to-head, was discovered at Sungir, Russia, in 1955. The bodies were interred at least 25,000 years ago, making it one of the oldest *Homo sapiens* burials in Europe.

HUMANS BECOME
DOMINANT

The end of the last Ice Age nearly 12,000 years ago marked the beginning of the Holocene – our current geological epoch. Climatic change was nothing new for the hominin family. However, two things were different: there was now only one surviving human species, and we had already begun to alter the habitats and landscapes around us.

▼ **Fire-stick farming**
The practice of burning vegetation to create grassland habitats that suit the animals humans wish to hunt may have been in use in Australia for 50,000 years. It can radically change the landscape and even a region's climate.

The end of the Pleistocene brought warmer, wetter conditions to most of the planet. In many areas grasslands gave way to mixed deciduous forests, and desert areas grew increasingly moist. Over tens of thousands of years, *Homo sapiens'* dispersal had resulted in settlement all the way from the South African coast, through Eurasia, into Australia and up to the tip of South America. The unfamiliar, often harsh, surroundings they found, along with climatic changes, required innovative survival strategies. Humans exploited their ability to problem-solve and learn skills – including forging new relationships with flora and fauna. These new relationships, in turn, started to shape the local environments in which *Homo sapiens* lived.

EFFECT ON ANIMAL LIFE

The earliest known examples of hominins exploiting marine resources are the gathering of shellfish by *Homo sapiens* at Pinnacle Point, South Africa, around 160,000 years ago, and by Neanderthals at Bajondillo Cave, Spain, some 150,000 years ago. Such small-scale activity made little impact on shellfish populations, but as harvesting escalated over time it began to have a negative effect. In South Africa, the average size of some shellfish species decreased around 50,000 years ago, which indicates that collecting had become more intense. This may, perhaps, be due to changing settlement patterns, with more humans moving to coastal areas, or may have been caused by an increase in the existing local human population. There were similar reductions in shellfish size following the human colonization of Papua New Guinea 30,000 years ago and southern California 10,000 years ago.

Most animal populations no doubt recovered from temporary local pressure exerted by humans, but our species may have a deep history of more permanent, catastrophic impacts on biodiversity. The so-called megafaunal "overkill" hypothesis correlates reductions in the diversity of large animal species with evidence of increasing *Homo sapiens* occupation towards the end of the last Ice Age. This is most obvious in Australia and North America, where the arrival of humans, 55,000 years ago and 15,000 years ago respectively,

MELTING GLACIAL ICE AT THE BEGINNING OF THE **HOLOCENE** EPOCH CAUSED **WORLD SEA LEVELS** TO **RISE 35M (115FT)**

corresponded with the disappearance of a great number of animal species, including the spectacular giant ground sloths. However, climate changes around the same time may also have played a part, and certainly *Homo sapiens* had been present in Europe since before 40,000 years ago with no clear associated mass extinctions.

even ventured beyond. But not so far back in time – within the blink of an eye in geological terms – humans were few in number, scattered, and surviving on what they could find or catch. Yet even during these early stages of our history, we were making an impact on the world around us through our daily lives.

was conducted so systematically that it could justifiably be described as quarrying. Even if this occurred over a long period of time, the mounds of waste material dramatically changed the local landscape.

More subtle open-air artistic traditions begin to appear around 40,000 years ago, sometimes involving the transformation of

> ## " THE FACT THAT **HOMO SAPIENS** IS THE **ONLY HOMINID SPECIES** ON THE EARTH TODAY MAKES IT EASY TO ASSUME THAT OUR **LONELY EMINENCE** IS HISTORICALLY A NATURAL STATE OF AFFAIRS – **WHICH IT CLEARLY IS NOT**.
>
> **Ian Tattersall**, British palaeoanthropologist, 1945 – "

It may be that in especially challenging environments the arrival of a new, skilled predator, *Homo sapiens*, was just enough to push particular species into extinction. One of the strongest cases to support the overkill hypothesis is the Caribbean ground sloth, which went extinct less than 5,000 years after the arrival of humans; even then, however, the process seems to have taken about 1,000 years.

While there is no evidence of *Homo sapiens* having an extinction-scale impact on plant communities at this time, we may have been significantly altering some environments. Charcoal from sediment cores may indicate that people were burning forest in Southeast Asia around 50,000 years ago and also in Australia between 60,000 and 50,000 years ago. Although natural causes of forest fires cannot be entirely dismissed, "fire-stick farming", where forest is burned to increase ecological productivity and attract animals, is known to have a long history in North America and Australia, and there is evidence that Mesolithic communities may also have developed similar practices in some areas.

CULTURAL LANDSCAPES

Homo sapiens' world-spanning civilization is today easily visible from space; our robotic craft have explored the Solar System and

By persistent activity at a particular place, organisms begin to change their surroundings. For hominins, this can be seen in the accumulations of detritus within caves. Thousands of caves around the world show deep sediments formed from the waste of countless generations. These unintentional creations were not limited to caves, but also occurred where people continually inhabited the same open-air sites, and they provide evidence of how people lived. For example, some shell middens (refuse heaps) may have had symbolic significance. At some sites they contain human remains, as well as discarded mollusc shells. One such place is Klasies River Mouth, South Africa, in a region where very few burials have been found.

Hominins interacted with cultural deposits in other ways, too, including the digging of burial pits through older occupational layers left by Neanderthals and *Homo sapiens*. They often found cultural deposits to be a useful resource, and it became common practice to recycle old stone tools made centuries earlier.

The overall effect on the landscape of using vast amounts of rock for stone tools over millions of years is hard to calculate, but some sites show intense activity. The exploitation of flint in Israel over 500,000 years ago, for example,

entire valleys into outdoor symbolic arenas, such as the 5,000 engravings at Côa, Portugal. The alteration of stone on such a large scale foreshadows the oldest megalithic structures, built at Gobekli Tepe, Turkey. They were made by hunter-gatherers some 11,000 years ago, within a few centuries of the beginnings of early agriculture.

> ## " WE ARE **PROBABLY** THE MOST **ADAPTABLE MAMMAL** THAT HAS **EVER EVOLVED** ON **EARTH**. "
>
>
>
> **Rick Potts**, American palaeoanthropologist, 1953–

THRESHOLD

CIVILIZATIONS
DEVELOP

As our highly adaptable and ingenious species starts to modify nature in order to sustain itself, we turn from hunter-gatherers into farmers. This is a pivotal point in the story of our species. Farming sets us on a path of expansion. The population grows, and small nomadic communities turn into permanent cities, states, and – eventually – empires with complex new power structures.

GOLDILOCKS CONDITIONS

Agriculture developed after years of collective learning enabled humans to extract more resources from their environment. The ability to innovate and manipulate nature altered both the biosphere and society itself: larger populations required organization to function effectively, and new, more complex power structures began to emerge.

Warmer climate

Population and resource pressures of denser human communities

Build up of collective learning

Hunter-gatherers
Armed with information accrued through generations of collective learning, foragers band together to collect a variety of seasonal foods from large areas of land. Populations remain small and highly mobile, but teamwork is important, particularly when hunting or trapping large animals for their meat.

What changed?
The warmer climate transforms the landscape, and the food and energy sources available to humans, reducing the need to move on. With the elderly, infirm, and very young no longer left behind, communities settle, grow, and learn to cultivate their own food, and extract more from the environment.

Fire-stick farmers
Hunters with knowledge of local flora and fauna use fire to clear land to create favourable grassland habitats for hunting and gathering.

Affluent foragers
Foraging communities in areas with abundant natural resources devise methods of storing food to consume out of season, and enjoy a more settled way of life.

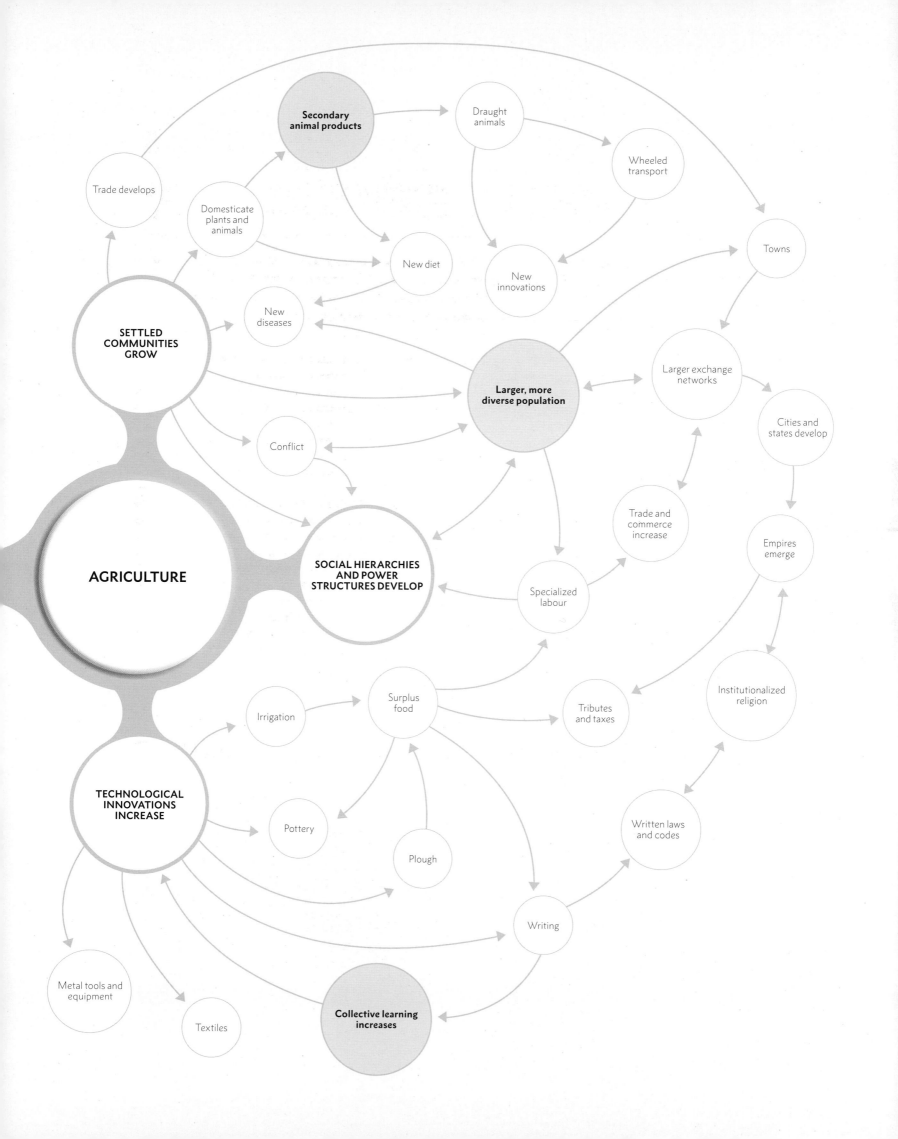

AGRICULTURE

SETTLED COMMUNITIES GROW

TECHNOLOGICAL INNOVATIONS INCREASE

SOCIAL HIERARCHIES AND POWER STRUCTURES DEVELOP

Trade develops

Domesticate plants and animals

Secondary animal products

Draught animals

Wheeled transport

Towns

New diet

New innovations

New diseases

Larger exchange networks

Cities and states develop

Larger, more diverse population

Conflict

Trade and commerce increase

Empires emerge

Specialized labour

Tributes and taxes

Institutionalized religion

Irrigation

Surplus food

Pottery

Plough

Written laws and codes

Writing

Metal tools and equipment

Textiles

Collective learning increases

CLIMATE CHANGES THE **LANDSCAPE**

From around 9600 BCE, global temperatures rose rapidly, beginning the current geological period known as the Holocene ("wholly recent"). Humans were forced to find new ways to hunt and gather. Eventually, they discovered a very different way of life – one based on farming.

As the climate warmed up, the ice sheets melted. This raised sea levels and released more water into the atmosphere, which increased rainfall. Asia was cut off from America, and Britain and Japan became islands. The wetter climate produced forests, grasslands, and new lakes and rivers. There was a mass extinction of Ice Age big game, such as the mammoth, the woolly rhino, and the giant elk.

MESOLITHIC ABUNDANCE

During a transitional period called the Mesolithic, or Middle Stone Age (280,000–25,000 BCE), people adapted to the new conditions by hunting smaller animals, such as deer, using the bow and arrow – a new invention, ideal for stalking animals in woodland. They also caught more fish and learned to eat a wider range of plant foods, including grasses and acorns, which required processing or cooking. By trial and error, people discovered which plants were poisonous and which could be made edible. In fact, some coastal regions were so rich in food resources that hunters and gatherers were able to settle down, for the first time, in permanent villages.

Throughout this period, people were building up and sharing their knowledge about plants and animals, which would contribute towards the new way of life.

At the same time, there was a dramatic rise in the human population, which had by now spread to every inhabitable part of the world. Rising sea levels also meant that huge areas of land that were once rich hunting grounds were now lost under water. Our planet may have reached its carrying capacity for the hunter-gatherer way of life. Climate change, and the pressure of competition for resources, eventually led some people, in different parts of the world, to begin farming.

> IN MANY PARTS OF THE HABITABLE GLOBE **THE CHANGE IN CLIMATE** MUST HAVE BEEN **REMARKABLE** EVEN IN **ONE** LONG **LIFETIME**.

Geoffrey Blainey, Australian historian, 1930–, *A Short History of the World* (2000)

▶ **Climatic ups and downs**
Although the Holocene era has been generally warm, climatic fluctuations have occurred within it, as shown on this chart. The first farmers may have begun to grow crops in response to cool and dry periods, when there was a decline in the availability of wild food plants.

End of glaciations

Post-glacial optimum

8000 7000 6000 5000 4000 3000 2000 1000 1 CE 1000 2000

BCE   CE

KEY ■ Warmer ■ Cooler

A good day's hunting
This African rock painting shows hunters using bows and arrows to kill deer. During the Mesolithic period, Africa's Sahara – which is now desert – was a grassland habitat, and a plentiful source of game.

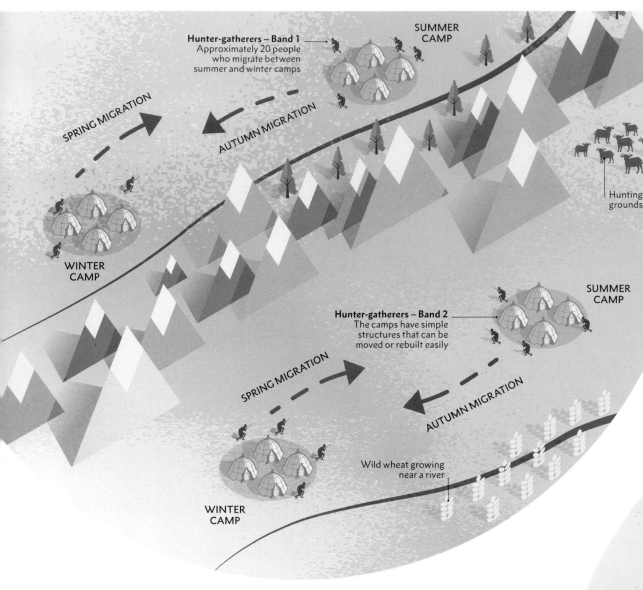

Hunter-gatherers – Band 1
Approximately 20 people who migrate between summer and winter camps

SUMMER CAMP

SPRING MIGRATION

AUTUMN MIGRATION

WINTER CAMP

Hunting grounds

Hunter-gatherers – Band 2
The camps have simple structures that can be moved or rebuilt easily

SUMMER CAMP

SPRING MIGRATION

AUTUMN MIGRATION

Wild wheat growing near a river

WINTER CAMP

NOMADS – FIRST PHASE

◄ Nomads
23,000–13,000 BCE
People are organized into small family groups (bands) that rely on hunting and gathering for food. They live a nomadic lifestyle, moving to new sites as the seasons and resources change. A nomadic lifestyle puts natural restrictions on population growth.

▼ Early settlers and affluent foragers
13,000 BCE
The climate becomes warmer and wetter. Rivers swell, grasslands and forests spread, creating a richer landscape. Some bands continue their nomadic lifestyle, but others settle in one prime spot.

Hunter-gatherers – Band 1
Foraging resources at the winter camp improve as the climate warms

SPRING MIGRATION

AUTUMN MIGRATI

WINTER CAMP

Settlers – Band 2
This group stops moving between winter and summ camps and settles in one place, where the river floo and creates fertile land

SETTLED CAMP

FORAGERS BECOME FARMERS

As the warming climate transformed the landscape, hunter-gatherers and foragers across the world discovered new ways to boost their food supplies, most dramatically by farming. Instead of continually moving to find food, they could now settle permanently in one place.

Settling down had many unforeseen consequences. Without the need to move on, technology became heavier and more complicated. This led to quern stones for grinding grain, looms for weaving, and pottery. More permanent settlements meant children did not have to be carried over long distances on the annual migrations, and the elderly and infirm were no longer left behind to fend for themselves until the band returned. As a result, the birth rate went up and people lived longer, but there were now more mouths to feed.

Gradually, these settled populations came to depend on the limited number of crops they could grow, rather than the wide but seasonal range of wild foods obtained by foraging. In ways, settling down was a trap. Although farming could support significantly larger populations than foraging, people had to work much harder for their food.

EARLY FARMING COULD SUPPORT **50 TO 100 TIMES** AS MANY PEOPLE **AS FORAGING** IN A SIMILAR AREA

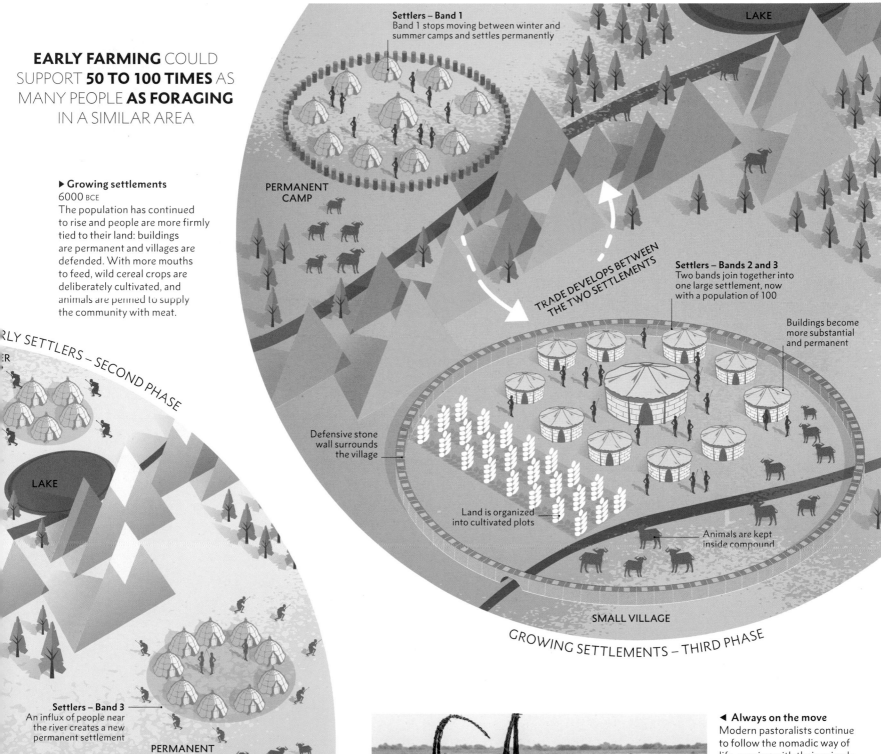

▶ **Growing settlements**
6000 BCE
The population has continued to rise and people are more firmly tied to their land: buildings are permanent and villages are defended. With more mouths to feed, wild cereal crops are deliberately cultivated, and animals are penned to supply the community with meat.

Settlers – Band 1
Band 1 stops moving between winter and summer camps and settles permanently

LAKE

PERMANENT CAMP

TRADE DEVELOPS BETWEEN THE TWO SETTLEMENTS

Settlers – Bands 2 and 3
Two bands join together into one large settlement, now with a population of 100

Buildings become more substantial and permanent

Defensive stone wall surrounds the village

Land is organized into cultivated plots

Animals are kept inside compound

SMALL VILLAGE

GROWING SETTLEMENTS – THIRD PHASE

EARLY SETTLERS – SECOND PHASE

LAKE

Settlers – Band 3
An influx of people near the river creates a new permanent settlement

PERMANENT CAMP

Wild wheat has spread due to harvesting

◀ **Always on the move**
Modern pastoralists continue to follow the nomadic way of life, moving with their animals to find better pasture and water if climatic conditions change. This gives them a substantial advantage over settled farmers, who can lose their crops and animals in periods of drought.

Jomon hunters caught game, including wild boar, deer, and bears, using pit traps and bows and arrows

Jomon houses were usually 3–4m (10–13ft) across

This cross-section shows how the huts may have been constructed. The main evidence comes from sunken floors and post-holes for timber

Meat was a vital food source in winter, when fresh plant foods were scarce

Outlet for smoke

Sunken floor, whose soil sides provided natural insulation from the weather

Pots with their bases buried in the earth floor of the hut

Subsurface chimney inside Jomon huts, on which Jomon women probably cooked meals.

Smoke escapes through channel below ground

Cooking pot enables the Jomon to boil shellfish and nuts

Pots being fired to use for cooking food

It is likely that the roofs and sides were thatched, helping to ventilate the interior

The forest was rich in plant foods, such as berries, walnuts, chestnuts, and acorns, which the women gathered in autumn

Life in the village
This is a typical Japanese Jomon village of c.13,000 BCE. At the time, villages were small, consisting of around five pit-houses. Settlements gradually grew larger until, by 9000 BCE, some contained as many as 50 or 60 houses.

Salmon drying on a wooden frame. This process involved many people, and is evidence of community cooperation

The Jomon fished using specialized tools: spears, nets, basket traps, and lines

Boat made from a hollowed-out log

Rivers and lakes yielded salmon and other freshwater fish, while tuna, mackerel, turtles, and shellfish were harvested from the sea

and other plant ds were kept in nd storage pits

Grinding grain collected from wild plants

AFFLUENT
FORAGERS

At the end of the last ice age, climates became warmer and wetter, which enabled human communities to stay in the same place for longer, while still living as hunter-gatherers. They are described as "affluent foragers".

Affluent foragers settled in areas of natural abundance and were able to live off the fruits of the land. Among the most successful affluent foragers were the Jomon of Japan, who first settled in villages around 14,000 BCE. They lived in small communities – without adopting farming – for more than 13,000 years. The Jomon lived beside forests, but also stayed close to the coasts, river estuaries, and lakes. Their mixed environment provided a rich, varied diet of seasonally available plant foods, fish, and wild animals. This, combined with their more sedentary lifestyle, allowed affluent foragers to invest more energy in larger specialized tools and technology rather than just portable objects. The Jomon were the first people to invent pottery, in around 13,000 BCE, which they used to cook fish, and store food to consume out of season.

▶ **Flame-rimmed vessel**
Jomon pottery was fired in the open air, in bonfires. From simple beginnings, Jomon pots grew more elaborate. This richly decorated vessel dates from the late Jomon period.

HUNTERS BEGIN TO **GROW FOOD**

The first farmers worked the land with wooden digging sticks and stone-bladed hoes and adzes. This method, called horticulture, was not productive enough to create a surplus. It was subsistence farming, in which people grew only enough crops to feed their own families.

The simplest agricultural tool is a digging stick – a strong, straight, pointed stick, often hardened in a fire. To remove weeds, farmers used a hoe, which had a blade made of stone or antler set at an angle to the handle. Without ploughs or draught animals, people could grow crops only in light, easily worked soils, such as loess, a fertile topsoil formed by wind-blown dust.

FARMING WITH FIRE

Long before farming, hunter-gatherers had burned forest to create open areas where they could hunt grazing animals, and encourage the growth of useful plants such as hazel and willow for basket making. The first farmers used fire in a similar way. After cutting down an area of forest with stone-bladed adzes, they left the vegetation to dry and then burned it. The ash made the soil fertile for planting seeds. But after two years, the fertility of a field dropped, and farmers had to move on to create a new one.

Using fire to create fields is called slash-and-burn or swidden farming, from an old Norse word for "burnt ground". It is still practised by between 200 million and 500 million people worldwide, mostly in the tropical rainforests of South America, South East Asia, and Melanesia. Slash-and-burn is sustainable in these regions because high rainfall and a warm climate permit a year-round growing season. But it is only practical where there are relatively few people and the area of forest is large enough to support the population's size.

Slash-and-burn proved unsustainable in the cooler, drier latitudes of Eurasia, where farming began. The short growing season meant that vegetation took much longer to recover after a fire. As the population grew, people were forced to invent new ways to increase the yield from their fields. Their challenge was to find better tools than the hoe and digging stick, and new ways to fertilize the soil.

Despite this, we know that slash-and-burn was once practised across large areas of Eurasia. Studies of ancient peat bogs in northern Europe show the disappearance of pollen from oak trees, accompanied by a rise in pollen from cereal crops along with layers of powdered charcoal – clear evidence of slash-and-burn farming.

FOREST GARDENING

Human interaction with the forest was not always quite so devastating. As people living beside rainforest rivers and on wet foothills in monsoon regions began to adapt to their immediate surroundings, they learned which species were helpful to the growth of food plants, and which were a hindrance. They protected useful plants and removed unwanted species. Later, they introduced beneficial plants from elsewhere to these "forest gardens".

▲ **Wooden adze**
Flint-bladed tools are remarkably strong. An adze can cut a large hardwood tree in a matter of hours.

THE **PROUD GETAE** LIVE HAPPILY, GROWING FREE FOOD FOR THEMSELVES ON LAND THEY **DO NOT WANT TO CULTIVATE FOR MORE THAN A YEAR**.

Horace, Roman poet, 1st century BCE

Destructive harvest
Areas of Laos still follow a tradition of slash-and-burn cultivation. However, it is highly destructive to the rainforest – crops are only grown for one year as they quickly deplete the soils, and harvests are poor. The area then has to be left for between four and six years to regenerate.

North East America 2000–1000 BCE
In the Americas, native foods included sunflowers, sumpweed, and goosefoot, which were gradually domesticated, even though these plants were not very nutritious. There were no potential animal domesticates in this region

Mesoamerica 3000–2000 BCE
Mesoamerican farmers had an ideal combination of crops, with maize and beans grown alongside each other. Turkeys and dogs were the only domesticable animals, and were raised for meat

AMERICAS

FARMING
BEGINS

Farming began once people started to store and plant seeds and tubers. Archaeology shows that within a few millennia agriculture had emerged separately in different parts of the world that had no contact with each other.

Reasons for becoming farmers may have varied. In some places, people responded to a shortage of wild foods, due to climate change or a rising population. In other areas, they may simply have preferred one food crop over others. They would not have made a conscious decision to become farmers – they had no idea what the new way of life would be like. However, food production could only begin where there was a source of animals and plants suitable for domestication. The range varied from region to region and as a result, farming had different impacts in each world zone. The crops of eastern North America and New Guinea were much less nutritious than those of other farming areas, so people continued to depend on wild foods, and farmers lived alongside hunter-gatherers. It was very different in the Fertile Crescent and China, where agriculture offered such a complete food production package that farmers were able to out-compete their hunter-gatherer neighbours.

Maize became the most important crop in Mesoamerica. It was easy to store for long periods and soon domesticated.

The llama was domesticated in the Andes. Llamas were a source of meat and wool, and also beasts of burden.

EACH OF THE **FOUR WORLD ZONES** WAS ITS OWN WORLD FOR A TIME.

Cynthia Stokes Brown, American historian, 1938–

The Andes 3000–2000 BCE
The main crops of the Andes region were quinoa, potatoes, and amaranth – all were highly nutritious. Only two large animals were suitable for domestication in the whole of the Americas, and both – the llama and the alpaca – were found in the Andes

The Fertile Crescent 9000 BCE
The range of plants and animals available in this region, including cereals (wheat and barley), cattle, goats, and sheep may explain why farming emerged here in very early times

EURASIA

AFRICA

China 7000 BCE
The first Chinese farmers grew rice along the Yangtze River, in the warm, wet south, and millet along the Yellow River, in the cool, drier north. They domesticated water buffalo, pigs, and chickens

Sheep were first domesticated in the Fertile Crescent and herding remains a way of life in Egypt today.

New Guinea 7000–4000 BCE
In this zone, true agriculture only emerged in New Guinea, where the main crop was taro. This is very low in protein, which was provided by frogs, mice, and insects

Sub-Saharan Africa 3000–2000 BCE
Early crops were sorghum, millet, yam, groundnut, cowpea, and oil palm.

The cowpea was first domesticated in Africa and remains an important and widely cultivated legume there today.

AUSTRALASIA

Polynesia 1400 BCE –1100 CE
Farming was only adopted after the settlement of Polynesia began around 1400 BCE, when people from Southeast Asia moved out into the ocean, bringing taro, pigs, and chickens with them

Agriculture in the four world zones
Each zone is an area in which humans interacted. This map shows how and when agriculture emerged in each of the four unconnected world zones, and reveals that, with the right conditions and resources, humans have the ability to innovate and often find similar solutions to similar problems.

KEY

The Americas
North, Central, and South America, and islands including the Caribbean Islands.

Afro-Eurasia
Africa and the Eurasian landmass, including islands such as Britain and Japan.

Australasia
Australia, the island of Papua New Guinea, and neighbouring islands in the Pacific Ocean.

The Pacific Islands
Societies such as New Zealand, Micronesia, Melanesia, and Hawaii.

WILD PLANTS
BECOME CROPS

Domestication is a process through which plants are brought under human control. As a result of human selection, plants changed until they were unable to reproduce successfully in the wild. Domestication was a two-way process, which benefited plants as well as people.

The most important domesticated plants are the grass-like grain crops, which offer little nutrition individually but can be gathered in bulk. The heads of wild grasses shatter when ripe, so that the grains can spread in the wind. However, it was easier for early foragers to harvest grains that stayed longer on the plants. Eventually, a new plant developed with heads that no longer needed to shatter: domesticated plants wait to be harvested.

The growing season was also changed by domestication. Wild seeds tend to germinate piecemeal over a long period, which ensures that in a changing climate some plants will survive. Humans created plants that all germinated at the same time. Domesticated plants also grew to around the same height, which made them easier to harvest. The grains themselves grew bigger and became easier to remove from their husks.

These changes were not consciously planned by farmers. They occurred as a natural result of selecting seeds from the most desirable plants to harvest and sow in the following year. Yet the more plants were brought under human control, the more human lives revolved around the needs of

▲ **Vital commodity**
Rice now provides one-fifth of all the calories consumed by humans worldwide. It can be grown even on steep hillsides, using terraces.

domesticated plants. As farming developed, people found themselves forced to spend long days caring for wheat, rice, and maize.

FIRST CROPS

Domestication of wheat began in the region known as the Fertile Crescent, in the Middle East. Here, between 11,000 and 9000 BCE, early farmers domesticated two types of wheat – wild emmer and einkorn. Then, in Iran around 7000 BCE, domesticated emmer wheat crossed with a wild goatgrass to become bread wheat; this has larger grains, easily removable husks, and higher gluten levels, which creates an elastic dough that rises to form soft bread.

Unlike other cereals, rice is a marsh plant, suitable for growing in water. It was domesticated between 4900 and 4600 BCE in southern China, south of the Yangtze River. Wild rice has a long awn, a hard husk, a tiny grain, and a strong stem, allowing the plant

to regenerate itself. Domesticated rice developed a bigger grain, and lost its awn, hard husk, and ability to regenerate itself.

In the 5th millennium BCE, farmers in southwest Mexico transformed the wild teosinte plant into maize. Teosinte yields less than 12 kernels, while maize produces up to 600. Teosinte kernels are protected by a hard outer covering, but maize kernels are naked. The plants look so different that the relationship between them was only discovered in the 20th century.

Beans were domesticated 6,000 years ago in Mesoamerica and also in the Andes. The plants selected produced bigger beans or better yields and were easier to harvest. In the Andes, the plant changed from a tall vine to a more productive bush.

▼ **Held for harvest**
The difference between wild and domesticated wheat grains is subtle, but significant. The change from an easily breakable rachis (shaft) on wild plants to one that needed to be threshed meant that more grain could be collected – but it took a lot more effort.

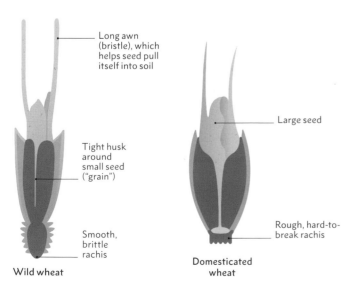

Long awn (bristle), which helps seed pull itself into soil

Tight husk around small seed ("grain")

Smooth, brittle rachis

Wild wheat

Large seed

Rough, hard-to-break rachis

Domesticated wheat

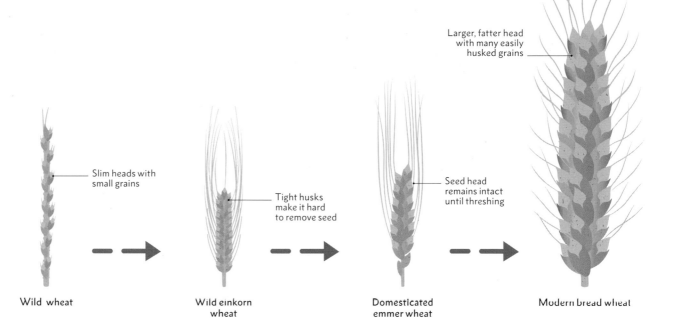

More gatherable grains

Over time, wheat evolved from wild shattering varieties, with small grains, to a plant with non-shattering heads and bigger grains. Farmers also selected for head size, plant height, growing season, and grains that were easy to remove from their husk. Scientists have recently begun making hybrids by crossing modern varieties with their wild relatives to reintroduce old characteristics such as resistance to drought, heat, and pests.

Larger, fatter head with many easily husked grains

Slim heads with small grains

Tight husks make it hard to remove seed

Seed head remains intact until threshing

Wild wheat → Wild einkorn wheat → Domesticated emmer wheat → Modern bread wheat

Bigger beans

Wild beans were a staple of the Mesoamerican diet because they contain amino acids that maize does not have. Wild plants have small pods that twist when ripe, splitting open to release their seeds (the beans). Domesticated species have more beans in bigger pods, but the beans stay in their pods until humans split them open. In Mesoamerica, beans were planted alongside maize, which acted as a support, and squashes, to suppress weeds, in what is known as the "three sisters" planting scheme.

Casing splits and flings out beans

Small pods contain 3–4 small beans

Longer pods contain more or bigger beans

Pods have to be shucked by hand to release beans

Wild bean · Ripe wild bean · Domesticated bean · Ripe domesticated bean

> ## PLANTS DOMESTICATED HOMO SAPIENS, RATHER THAN VICE VERSA.

Yuval Noah Harari, Israeli historian, 1976–, *Sapiens: A Brief History of Humankind*

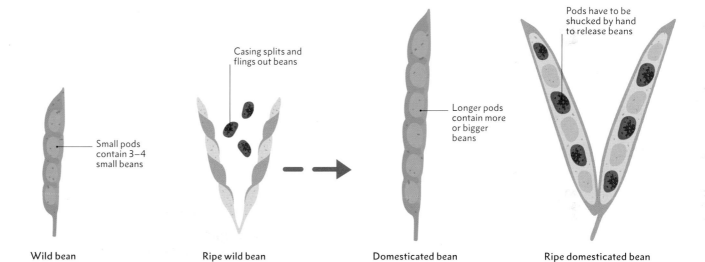

Modern maize has 400–600 kernels arranged in 16–20 rows

Gigantic improvement

Teosinte, a wild form of maize, has only a few kernels on a head less than 2.5cm (1in) long. A modern domesticated maize cob, packed with kernels, can measure more than 30cm (12in). The discovery of phytoliths (plant microfossils) and starch grains from a number of sites in Mexico suggests that domesticated forms of maize may have existed much earlier than previously thought.

6–12 kernels in two interleaved rows

Naked kernels fixed to the stem

Multiple rows of kernels

Teosinte · Early domesticated maize · Later domesticated maize · Modern maize

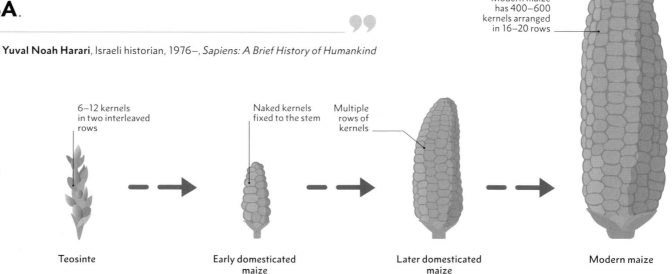

POLLEN GRAINS

Small amounts of plant residue can reveal a wealth of information about climatic conditions, the history of agriculture, and the lives of our ancestors thanks to forensic techniques such as pollen analysis.

The study of pollen, plant spores, and microscopic plant organisms is known as palynology. Pollen grains, which are the male reproductive bodies of flowering plants, are produced in vast quantities in nature. Thanks to its hard outer shell, a pollen grain can survive for millions of years in favourable conditions. Different plants have distinctively shaped pollen grains, which makes it possible to identify the plants that produced them.

Pollen survives best in peat bogs, lake beds, and cave sediments. Ancient pollen associated with humans is also found in mud bricks, storage pits, boats, pottery vessels, tombs, preserved bodies, and coprolites (fossil faeces). It can also be detected on the surfaces of grinding stones and stone tools.

Palynologists use an electron microscope to identify individual pollen grains, counting the grains of each type. Using this data, they recreate a picture of the climate and environment in one area at a particular time. By repeating the study with different depths of soil deposits, they build up a pollen chronology, which shows how the range of plants changed over time. Archaeological sites can be dated by matching the range of pollen collected with the known chronology.

Palynology has revealed the huge impact that early farming had on the environment. Wherever it was practised, agriculture was marked by a decline in tree pollen and a rise in pollen from cereals and opportunistic weeds, such as darnel, that are associated with their growth.

The spiny surface of pollen from the morning glory vine (*Ipomoea*) helps it to attach itself to pollinating insects

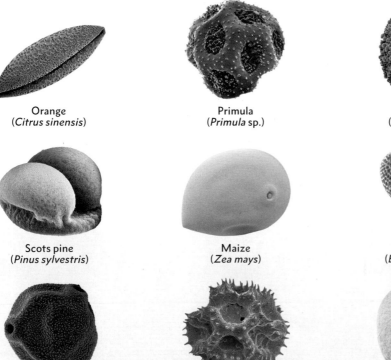

Orange
(*Citrus sinensis*)

Primula
(*Primula* sp.)

Geranium
(*Geranium* sp.)

Scots pine
(*Pinus sylvestris*)

Maize
(*Zea mays*)

Rapeseed
(*Brassica napus*)

Silver birch
(*Betula pendula*)

Narrow-leaved hawksbeard
(*Crepis tectorum*)

Wheat
(*Triticum spp.*)

▲ **Pollen gallery**
This selection of pollen shows how distinctly shaped the pollen from different plants is. Pollen also ranges widely in size, from 5 to 500 microns (1 micron is 0.001 mm).

Travel and trade

Pollen grains from pottery found on a shipwreck can identify the ship's cargo, and pollen trapped in the resin used to seal the hull may reveal where the ship was made. The hull of a small, 2,000-year-old boat wrecked off the French coast contained pollen that showed it was built east of Italy – which indicates that small boats traded further afield than previously thought.

Pollen evidence in context

The amount of pollen plants produce varies from species to species, and is spread in different ways, so the results of palynology are interpreted alongside findings from other disciplines such as archaeology or climate science. The *Ipomoea* genus includes plants with hallucinogenic properties; *Ipomoea* pollen in a cave in Belize suggests the plants may have been taken there by pre-Mayan people for ritual purposes.

Morning glory vine

The tough, rigid, waterproof shell prevents the pollen grain from rotting or drying out.

Climate change

Global warming at the end of the Ice Age caused a dramatic change in vegetation across northern latitudes. Pollen collected from lake sediments in Britain shows that before 9600 BCE the only trees there were cold-hardy dwarf birches. As the climate warmed, birches were replaced by Scots pines, which in turn gave way to a wider variety of trees, including hazels, elms, and oaks.

This pollen grain can be identified as *Ipomoea purpurea* from its size, shape, and surface features.

Agriculture and food

Pollen can help us understand what past peoples farmed and ate. Pollen from grass and other fodder plants stored in dwellings tells us how livestock were fed. Similarly, pollen clinging to grinding stones used by New Mexico's Anasazi people shows that alongside domesticated maize they also harvested a wide variety of wild plants. In the American Southwest, palynologists recreated a prehistoric individual's diet from pollen found in coprolites (fossilized faeces), while in Scotland pollen on 5,000-year-old pottery shards was used to recreate the recipe for heather ale, drunk by early Celtic farmers.

Stone quern with sandstone rubber

FARMERS
DOMESTICATE ANIMALS

The domestication of animals began at roughly the same time and in the same areas as the domestication of plants. The process probably began with men guarding a local herd of animals as it moved, assisted by dogs. Eventually the herd was enclosed, fed, and protected.

A domesticated animal is one that has been bred in captivity and has become modified from its wild ancestor. Some animals, such as elephants and bears, can be tamed, but this is not the same as domestication. Tamed elephants remain wild animals, and never adapt completely to their new conditions.

Animals needed certain characteristics to be suitable for domestication. They had to be a manageable size and relatively docile with social structures, early sexual maturity, and a high reproductive rate. Herbivores were better than carnivores because they would survive on local plants. Just 14 large mammals met all these requirements, almost all of them in Eurasia.

Attempts to domesticate other animals failed: bison are related to cattle, but they are more aggressive, faster, and can leap 1.8m (6ft) into the air. Similarly, zebras are more aggressive than horses, and have better peripheral vision, which makes them almost impossible to catch with a rope. Gazelles have a tendency to panic, and are likely to batter themselves to death when placed in an enclosure.

HOW ANIMALS CHANGED

Animals separated from their natural environment began to change as farmers bred from specimens that met their needs. Because people selected smaller animals that were easier to manage, domesticated cattle became smaller than their wild ancestor, the aurochs. Evolution by natural selection also played a part – adaptations for survival in the wild, such as intelligence and long horns, were no longer necessary. Domesticated animals did not have to fear predators or search for new sources of food, and so their brains reduced in size.

In the wild, male mammals are much larger than females because they have to compete with other males for mates. This competition ended in captivity, because breeding was controlled by humans. As a result, male cattle, sheep, and goats became the same size as the females, aswell as losing their long horns.

The willingness of these animals to become domesticated ultimately ensured their evolutionary success. There are now 1.4 billion cattle on the planet – but their wild ancestor, the aurochs, became extinct during the 17th century.

> **DOMESTICABLE** ANIMALS ARE **ALL ALIKE**; EVERY UNDOMESTICABLE ANIMAL IS **UNDOMESTICABLE IN ITS OWN WAY**
>
> **Jared Diamond**, American scientist, 1937–, *Guns, Germs and Steel*

▶ **Wild at heart**
Bees are semi-domesticated. Through selective breeding, humans modified bee behaviour, making them less likely to sting and swarm than wild bees. Although managed by humans, bees still forage for their food and retain the ability to survive in the wild.

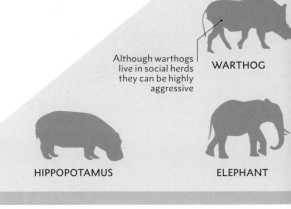

Although warthogs live in social herds they can be highly aggressive

WARTHOG

HIPPOPOTAMUS

ELEPHANT

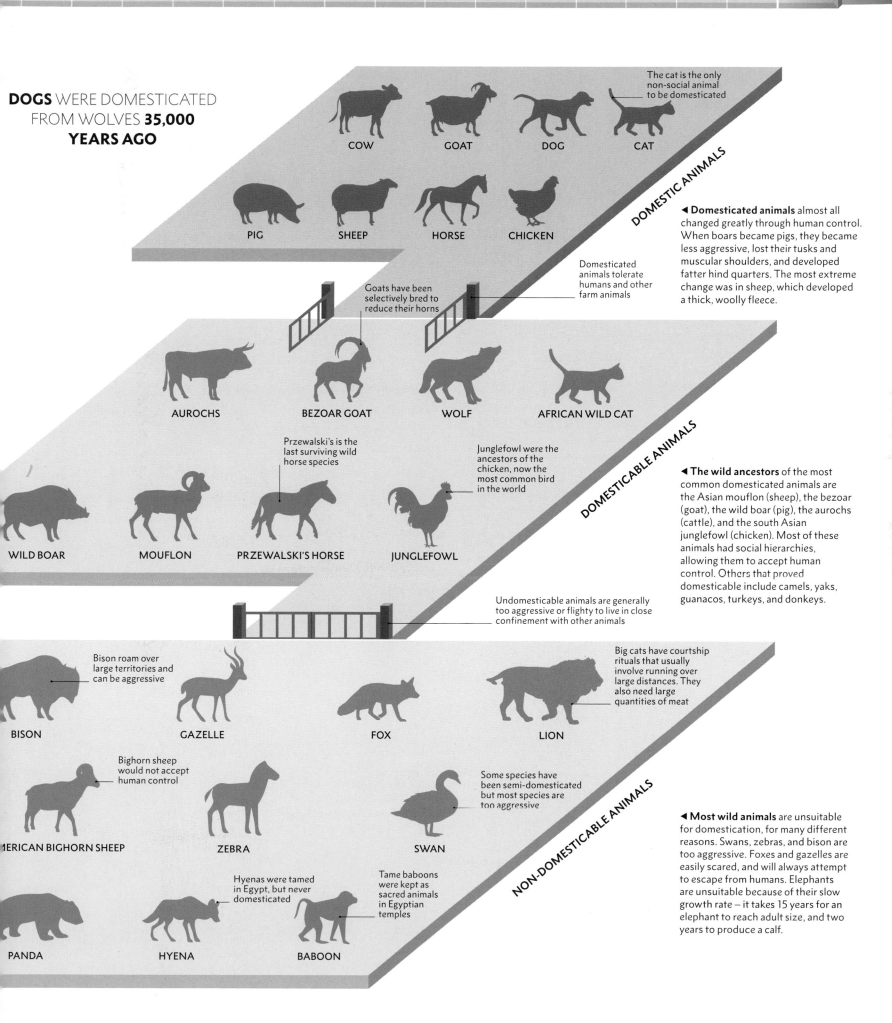

DOGS WERE DOMESTICATED FROM WOLVES **35,000 YEARS AGO**

DOMESTIC ANIMALS

COW · GOAT · DOG · CAT

The cat is the only non-social animal to be domesticated

PIG · SHEEP · HORSE · CHICKEN

◄ **Domesticated animals** almost all changed greatly through human control. When boars became pigs, they became less aggressive, lost their tusks and muscular shoulders, and developed fatter hind quarters. The most extreme change was in sheep, which developed a thick, woolly fleece.

Goats have been selectively bred to reduce their horns

Domesticated animals tolerate humans and other farm animals

DOMESTICABLE ANIMALS

AUROCHS · BEZOAR GOAT · WOLF · AFRICAN WILD CAT

Przewalski's is the last surviving wild horse species

Junglefowl were the ancestors of the chicken, now the most common bird in the world

WILD BOAR · MOUFLON · PRZEWALSKI'S HORSE · JUNGLEFOWL

◄ **The wild ancestors** of the most common domesticated animals are the Asian mouflon (sheep), the bezoar (goat), the wild boar (pig), the aurochs (cattle), and the south Asian junglefowl (chicken). Most of these animals had social hierarchies, allowing them to accept human control. Others that proved domesticable include camels, yaks, guanacos, turkeys, and donkeys.

Undomesticable animals are generally too aggressive or flighty to live in close confinement with other animals

NON-DOMESTICABLE ANIMALS

Bison roam over large territories and can be aggressive

Big cats have courtship rituals that usually involve running over large distances. They also need large quantities of meat

BISON · GAZELLE · FOX · LION

Bighorn sheep would not accept human control

Some species have been semi-domesticated but most species are too aggressive

AMERICAN BIGHORN SHEEP · ZEBRA · SWAN

◄ **Most wild animals** are unsuitable for domestication, for many different reasons. Swans, zebras, and bison are too aggressive. Foxes and gazelles are easily scared, and will always attempt to escape from humans. Elephants are unsuitable because of their slow growth rate – it takes 15 years for an elephant to reach adult size, and two years to produce a calf.

Hyenas were tamed in Egypt, but never domesticated

Tame baboons were kept as sacred animals in Egyptian temples

PANDA · HYENA · BABOON

Maize transformed farming in eastern North America when it arrived from Mesoamerica in *c.*2000 BCE.

FARMING
SPREADS

After its original adoption in several areas of the planet, farming spread in all directions. The new way of life expanded much more rapidly in Eurasia than in the Americas, due to the different shapes of each landmass.

Agriculture spread in two ways. The most common was where farmers were forced to leave their homeland due to the pressures of a rising population and competition over land. Moving on, they took their animals and crops with them. The second, less usual, was for hunter-gatherers to partly adopt the new way of life. As they came into contact with farmers, some hunter-gatherers acquired domesticated cattle, sheep, and goats, and so became herders.

The differing rates of spread were determined by the continents' axes. While Eurasia stretches east to west, the Americas stretch north to south. It was much easier for farmers to move their crops and livestock within the same latitude, because they found similar climactic conditions, seasonality, day lengths, pests, and diseases. But for crops to move from one latitude to another – as maize did in the Americas – the plant had to evolve to suit different conditions.

> ## WHY SHOULD WE PLANT WHEN THERE ARE SO MANY MONGONGO NUTS IN THE WORLD?

African Kalahari bushman, quoted by Richard Lee, *What Hunters Do for a Living*

With nutritious crops like maize and beans arriving from Mesoamerica, farming continued to spread through North America

EASTERN NORTH AMERICA
2000–1000 BCE

MESOAMERICA
3000–2000 BCE

AMERICAS

Squashes, pumpkins, and other members of the gourd family were grown in eastern North America before maize and beans.

WEST AFRICA
3000–2000 BCE

Farming in Amazonia may have originated here, or spread here from the Andes

AMAZONIA
3000–2000 BCE

In Africa, farming may have begun in any of three sub-Saharan regions

ANDES
3000–2000 BCE

Potatoes and quinoa were grown in the Andes

▲ **How agriculture spread from 9000–1000 BCE**
This map shows how farming spread, rapidly along the east-west axis of Eurasia and more slowly along north-south axes in the Americas and Africa. There is still uncertainty about exactly where in sub-Saharan Africa farming was first adopted.

KEY
➡ Spread of farming
➡ Continental axis direction
▮ Earliest farming regions, Americas
▮ Earliest farming regions, Eurasia
▮ Earliest farming regions, Africa
▮ Earliest farming regions, China
▮ Earliest farming regions, Australasia

Wheat, evolved from wild grasses in the Fertile Crescent over 11,000 years ago, is the earliest crop to be domesticated (see p.237).

Rice, today one of the world's most common staples, spread throughout Asia, reaching Europe during antiquity and the Americas at the time of European colonization.

EURASIA

FERTILE CRESCENT
9000 BCE

Farming spread most rapidly from the Fertile Crescent

CHINA (YELLOW RIVER BASIN) 7000 BCE

Millet and rice farming spread from China's Yellow and Yangtze River Valleys

CHINA (YANGTZE RIVER BASIN) 7000 BCE

SAHEL 3000–2000 BCE

ETHIOPIA 3000–2000 BCE

AFRICA

Ethiopian farmers adopted aniamls from the north, including camels, domesticated in southern Arabia

Taro spread from Southeast Asia to Oceania and New Guinea, where both its root and its leaves remain popular food staples.

NEW GUINEA
7000–4000 BCE

When Asian pigs reached New Guinea, farming became much more productive

Sorghum, a gluten-free cereal rich in nutrients, was first domesticated in Africa, possibly in Ethiopia, around 5,000 years ago.

MEASURING **TIME**

 Aztec calendar stone
This carved stone from the late 15th or early 16th century shows cosmic history as understood by the Aztecs of Mexico.

Agriculture gave a new importance to keeping track of time, since farmers needed to know when to plough, sow, and gather the harvest. With the rise of states, calendars became a means of social control, regulating work and coordinating the activities of large populations.

Hunter-gatherers knew about time passing because of seasonal changes, including the migrations of animals, birds, and fish, and the autumn appearance of fruits and nuts. They could see the passage of time in the sky, evidenced by the Moon's phases, the Sun's daily journey, and the regular reappearance of constellations, such as the Pleiades and Orion, throughout the year.

CONTROL BY CALENDAR

Agriculture requires long-term planning, so early farmers built on their astronomical knowledge to invent the first calendars. In the northern hemisphere, where people were especially aware of the Sun's seasonal movements, standing stones were used to track the progress of the year from where it rose and set on the horizon. Stonehenge in England, for example, was aligned with the midwinter Sun.

There was also a religious motivation in the creation of written calendars. Often the work of priests – who had the time and skills to make astronomical observations – such calendars were made for the regulation of

festivals and for divination. The ability to predict eclipses was a particularly good way to keep the populace in line at key moments. Written calendars later came to be used for more mundane things – when to collect taxes, when to go to war, and to establish the sailing season for merchant ships.

THE WORKING WEEK

Different cultures developed differing understandings of the passage of time. Mesoamericans, such as the Aztecs, saw time as a cyclical pattern of recurring events, in which the world was regularly destroyed and recreated.

Early societies devised a cycle of work days and rest days. The week was ten days long in China and Egypt, and seven in Mesopotamia. The day was divided into hours measured by clocks, the earliest types being water clocks and sundials. As societies grew more complex, people's lives were increasingly ruled by calendars and clocks, which measured human, social time rather than the cycles of nature.

Solar disc decorated with motifs and patterns on both sides

The model is made of bronze; only one side of the disc is gilded

▼ **Sun chariot**
This Danish model, from around 1400 BCE, imagines the Sun's journey through the sky as made by horse and chariot. Markings on the Sun's disc have led one archaeologist to suggest that it may have functioned as a calendar.

Symbols around the edge of the stone represent aspects of the heavens, including stars, the Sun's rays, and the planet Venus

▲ **Observing the heavens**
This curved structure was built in the 1420s as part of Sultan Ulugh Beg's Samarkand observatory. It allowed his astronomers to calculate when sunrise and sunset would fall each day, as well as the length of a year.

In the centre is the face of Tonatiuh, the fifth and present sun god

Each square around the face represents a previous era and sun, named after Jaguar, Wind, Rain, and Water

The fifth and current era and sun are represented by the shape of the frame enclosing the central signs

This circle shows the 20 signs used to name the Aztec days

> ## THE GODS **CONFOUND THE MAN** WHO FIRST FOUND OUT **HOW TO DISTINGUISH HOURS**.
>
> **Aulus Gellius**, Roman author, c.125–185 CE, *Attic Nights*

NEW USES FOR **ANIMALS**

Animals were first domesticated to provide a ready source of meat and hides. Later, farmers discovered that animals could also be used as a renewable resource, to provide milk, wool, and power. This new way of using animals is known as the secondary products revolution.

The first secondary product was milk. The earliest evidence, from the 7th millennium BCE, is pottery found in Turkey containing traces of milk. At the time, adults – unlike babies – lacked the enzyme needed to break down lactose, the main sugar in milk. But early farmers were able to reduce lactose levels by fermenting heated milk, making yoghurt and cheese. Fermentation was also the best way to preserve and store milk. Around 5500 BCE, people in Central Europe developed lactose tolerance. They were able to digest milk, giving them a rich new source of protein. Lactose tolerance spread across Europe and also appeared later in West Africa and parts of Asia. Today, about a third of humanity can drink milk.

Another new product that came into use around this time was sheep's wool, which was spun and woven into textiles. Farmers in western Asia selected animals with the best quality hair for breeding. As a result, sheep developed thick woolly fleeces between 7000 BCE and 5000 BCE.

POWER AND MOTION

The most important secondary product was animal power, which gave humans their first new source of energy since the control of fire. Around 4500 BCE, donkeys were domesticated as pack animals. Later, people in western Asia harnessed oxen to pull loads, at first on simple sleds. Then, in about 3500 BCE, the plough was invented and wheels – devised for turning clay pots – were fitted to sleds to make carts. Horses were also domesticated around this time.

Riding horses gave humans their first fast mode of transport. Horses and carts enabled people to move with their grazing animals and survive on Eurasia's grassy steppes – an unsuitable environment for growing crops.

▶ **Pulling power**
Wheeled carts spread so quickly across Eurasia that it is difficult to know exactly where they originated. This 4,000-year-old pottery model of an ox cart comes from the Indus civilization of India.

THE... REVOLUTION TURNED **DOMESTICATED HERBIVORES** INTO **EFFICIENT MACHINES** FOR TRANSFORMING **GRASS INTO ENERGY** USABLE BY HUMANS.

David Christian, Big History historian, 1946–, *Maps of Time*

Milking time
Early milking scenes often show calves.
In the early days of dairying, the calf's presence
was needed to make the cow release her milk.
This 7th-century CE carving is from a cave
temple in Tamil Nadu, India.

INNOVATIONS
INCREASE YIELDS

Larger, settled populations inevitably needed to produce more food. Farmers began to innovate and develop new agricultural methods, such as ploughing and the use of fertilizers. These new technologies enabled farmers to intensify production and increase yields.

With a pair of oxen and a plough, one man could prepare a whole field for planting in much less time than it took a team of workers with digging sticks. Ploughs made it possible to farm in heavier soils, greatly increasing the area of land available for cultivation. Ploughing is also an efficient way of removing weeds.

The plough was an adaptation of the digging stick, allowing it to be dragged continuously through the ground. It may have been invented in Mesopotamia, where images of ploughs have been found dating from the 4th millennium BCE. The earliest type was the scratch plough, or ard, which had a wooden tip (share) that could cut only a shallow furrow. To plough efficiently with an ard, farmers had to cross-plough, going over the field twice, with the second ploughing at right angles to the first. Later improvements included metal-tipped shares and a blade called the coulter, which sliced the soil in front of the share.

In the 1st century BCE, the Chinese further refined the plough with the addition of the mouldboard – a curved blade that turned over the soil, burying weeds and bringing nutrients to the surface. Use of this plough was carried west across Eurasia, reaching Europe by the 7th century CE. Thanks to the mouldboard, farmers no longer had to cross-plough. This doubled the amount of land a plough team could prepare.

Ploughs could only be used where there were suitable draught animals, such as oxen, water buffalo, horses, mules, and camels.

The plough was never invented in the Americas, where there were no domesticated animals strong enough to pull such a device.

IMPROVING THE SOIL
One great advantage of the use of draught animals is that their dung enriches the soil. American farmers, who did not have draught animals, found other kinds of fertilizer. The Incas of Peru collected vast amounts of seabird droppings (guano), which they spread on their fields. Guano is an ideal fertilizer because it is rich in nitrogen, potassium, and phosphate – all vital nutrients for growing plants. In ancient China, farmers used human manure (nightsoil), collected from towns at night.

UNEXPECTED CONSEQUENCES
Agricultural intensification had its problems as well as its benefits. Despite better harvests, which sparked increases in the population, food remained scarce for most people. Intensive irrigation and farming fields without a fallow period eventually impoverished the soil. Communities regularly faced shortages and periodic famines, which led to malnourishment, disease, and shorter lifespans. Scarcity also brought social disorder and led to war, mass migration, and cultural disruption.

OX PLOUGHS COULD NOT BE USED IN **SUB-SAHARAN AFRICA**, BECAUSE CATTLE WERE VULNERABLE TO **TRYPANOSOMIASIS**, A DEADLY DISEASE PASSED ON BY THE **TSETSE FLY**

Wooden handle, which the farmer used to steer the plough

▶ **Early plough**
This model of a farmer using an ard, or scratch plough, comes from an Egyptian tomb of c.2000 BCE. The Nile floods deposited nutrients on the surface, so the plough did not need to turn over the soil, merely break it up for sowing.

Wooden share cut a shallow furrow through the soil

> **GET TWO OXEN**, BULLS OF NINE YEARS. THEIR STRENGTH IS UNSPENT AND THEY ARE **BEST FOR WORK**. THEY **WILL NOT FIGHT** IN THE FURROW AND **BREAK THE PLOUGH**.

Hesiod, Greek poet, c.700 BCE, *Works and Days*

▲ **Cutting-edge technology**
The Egyptians harvested grain using wooden scythes set with flint teeth, cutting off the ears and leaving the stalks standing for livestock to feed on. The quest for higher yields led to the need for more manpower and, in some places, slave labour.

A wooden cross-piece called a yoke linked the oxen to the plough

Draft pole or beam

Oxen not only pulled the plough but also trampled the grain seed into the soil. After the harvest, they were used to tread the kernels out of their husks

SURPLUS BECOMES POWER

Once farmers learned to grow surplus food, they needed ways to store it for future use. Granaries built to store surplus grain were central to the creation of early states: these surpluses became a form of wealth that were taxed by rulers and used for trade or to reward loyal subjects.

To store grain, it must be protected from rodents and pests, and kept dry so that it does not rot or germinate. Many societies across Africa and Eurasia built granaries with raised floors, which deterred rodents and let air circulate underneath. Egypt's arid climate meant that raised floors were not necessary there. The Inca of Peru sited granaries on steep hillsides, exposed to the drying effects of mountain winds.

Large states needed ways to measure and record their grain supplies, which required an unprecedented level of organization and central control. In Egypt, this was done by measuring grain by volume, based on the *hekat*, a small barrel holding 4.8 litres (1.1 gallons). The *hekat* was the standard measuring unit used throughout the Eastern Mediterranean from 1500 BCE to 700 BCE.

The Chinese measured grain by weight, with the basic unit being the amount one man could carry on a shoulder pole. In China, archaeologists have found hundreds of vast underground grain silos dating from the Sui and Tang dynasties (581–907 CE). The walls of these state granaries bear inscriptions recording the variety, quantity, and source of the stored grain, and the date of its storage.

GRAIN AND STATE POWER

State granaries enabled rulers to feed not only their armies but also the workers who toiled on great building projects, such as the pyramids of Egypt and the Great Wall of China. Granaries also provided vital famine relief in years with a bad harvest. Rulers knew that the grain supply was vital to maintain the good will of the people. Roman emperors gave a monthly ration of free grain to the citizens of their capital city, which was distributed from the Temple of Ceres, goddess of grain. It was imported in great ships from Sicily and Egypt, which the emperor maintained as his personal estate.

Workers using measuring barrels

▶ **Counting the grain**
This model, found in an Egyptian tomb, shows sacks of grain being brought into a granary. On the right, workers use barrels to measure the amount of grain, while two shaven-headed scribes record the harvest in ledgers.

I HAVE **HEAPED GRAIN** IN THE GRANARIES FOR THE PEOPLE. **IN ORDER THAT THEY MIGHT EAT** IN THE SEVEN YEARS OF EMPTY HUSKS, I HAVE COLLECTED GRAIN **FOR THE PEOPLE**.

Epic of Gilgamesh, *c.*2000 BCE

Traditional granaries
The Dogon people of Mali still live in an agricultural society. They store millet in tall granaries, built from clay and raised on rocks, with thatched roofs that protect them during the rainy season.

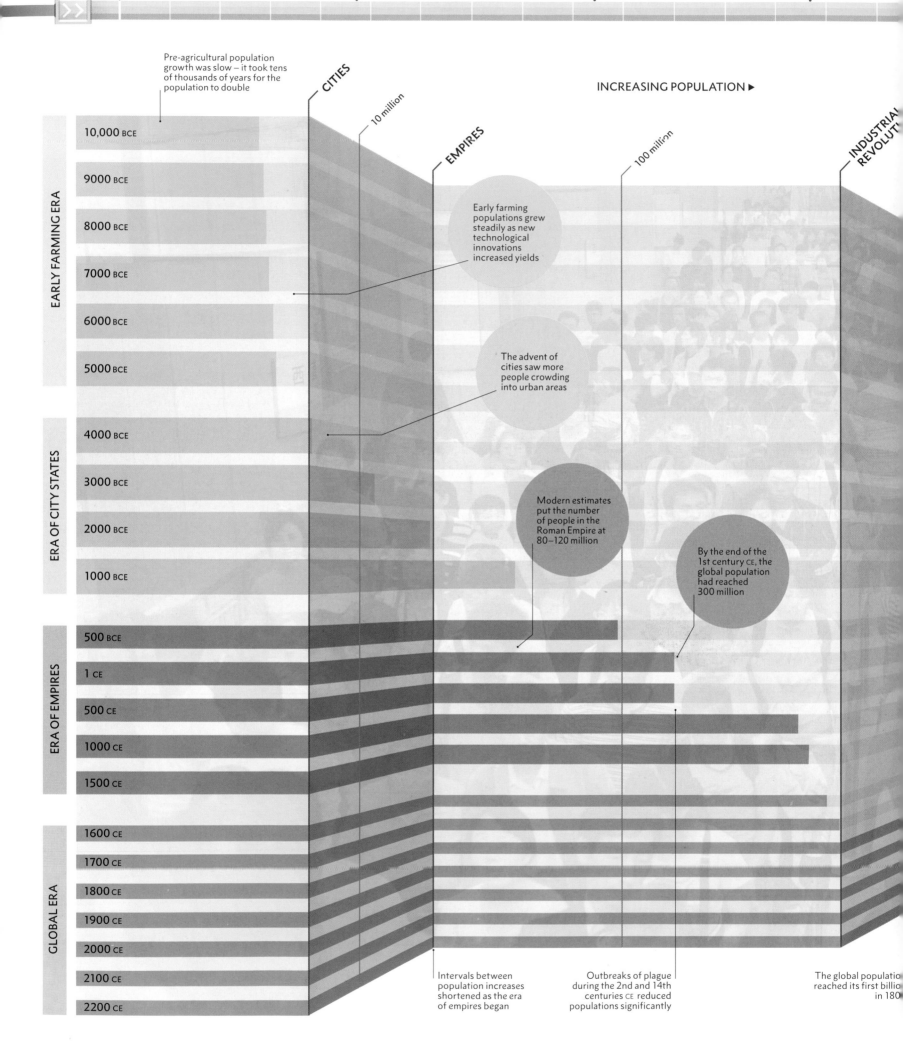

Pre-agricultural population growth was slow – it took tens of thousands of years for the population to double

CITIES

EMPIRES

INCREASING POPULATION ▶

INDUSTRIAL REVOLUT

10 million

100 million

EARLY FARMING ERA

10,000 BCE
9000 BCE
8000 BCE
7000 BCE
6000 BCE
5000 BCE

ERA OF CITY STATES

4000 BCE
3000 BCE
2000 BCE
1000 BCE

ERA OF EMPIRES

500 BCE
1 CE
500 CE
1000 CE
1500 CE

GLOBAL ERA

1600 CE
1700 CE
1800 CE
1900 CE
2000 CE
2100 CE
2200 CE

Early farming populations grew steadily as new technological innovations increased yields

The advent of cities saw more people crowding into urban areas

Modern estimates put the number of people in the Roman Empire at 80–120 million

By the end of the 1st century CE, the global population had reached 300 million

Intervals between population increases shortened as the era of empires began

Outbreaks of plague during the 2nd and 14th centuries CE reduced populations significantly

The global populatio reached its first billio in 180

IN 2015, THE ANNUAL HUMAN BIRTH RATE WAS MORE THAN TWICE THE DEATH RATE

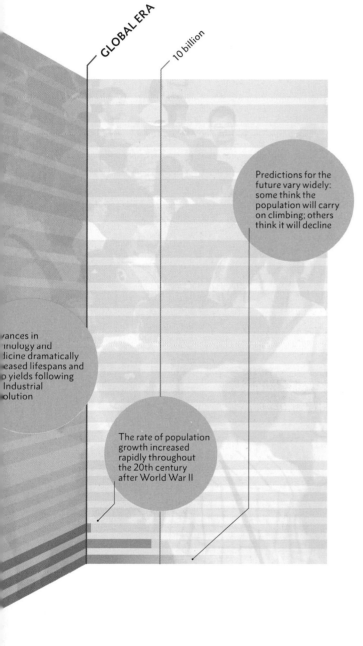

GLOBAL ERA

10 billion

Predictions for the future vary widely: some think the population will carry on climbing; others think it will decline

...vances in ...nology and ...dicine dramatically ...eased lifespans and ...p yields following ...Industrial ...olution

The rate of population growth increased rapidly throughout the 20th century after World War II

▲ **Population growth**
Human numbers grew slowly up to 1700 CE. From around 1750 through to present day, population growth has been rapid, thanks to farming innovations, industrial production, and the spread of more productive food crops, such as manioc and maize, following the Columbian Exchange (pp.296–297).

POPULATION
STARTS TO RISE

The switch to agriculture and the creation of food surpluses led to population growth: even early farming could support 50 to 100 times more people than hunting and gathering. Agricultural innovations, such as the plough and irrigation, accelerated the increase in population.

There are many different estimates for early world populations, ranging from 2–10 million in 10,000 BCE to 50–115 million in 1000 BCE. Whatever the true figures, there is consensus that the period saw a dramatic increase in the global population as a result of farming. As large human populations spread, living in ever denser settlements, they became vulnerable to disease and periodic famine. In two periods populations fell significantly as a result of famine and plague: in the Roman Empire during the 2nd century CE and in 14th-century Eurasia.

Changes in population growth are often attributed to "Malthusian cycles". In the 18th century, economist Thomas Malthus argued that human populations always rise faster than the food supply, which results in

famine and decline. Malthusian cycles often began with a new innovation: for example, improved horse collars in Europe allowed animals to pull ploughs that cut deeper soils, and thus improving productivity. As agricultural innovations spread, the population rose, which led to larger areas being farmed. Periods of growth stimulated commercial activity and encouraged towns to expand – and their populations needed to be supplied with food. Larger populations exchanged more ideas and innovations, but ultimately in the agrarian era population growth would outpace the rate of change and was followed by a Malthusian crash.

NEW FOODS
The spread of new food crops could also stimulate population growth. In the 11th century CE, China adopted a new variety of early-ripening rice from Champa, Vietnam, which could produce up to three harvests a year. This drought-resistant crop could be grown on higher ground, doubling the area available for rice cultivation. This enabled the population of China to double from the 10th–11th centuries. During the 16th century, the introduction of American maize and potatoes – which could be grown at even higher altitudes than rice – led to further population growth in China.

◄ **Around one in every five** people on Earth is Chinese. There are as many people in China today as there were in the whole world just 150 years ago. India is predicted to displace China as the most populous country in around 2050.

THE RAGING **MONSTER UPON THE LAND** IS **POPULATION GROWTH**.

E.O. Wilson, American biologist, 1929–, *The Diversity of Life*

THE FENTON **VASE**

Pottery is one of archaeology's greatest resources, as it survives in the ground when organic materials decay, providing invaluable clues to the cultures and technologies of ancient civilizations.

This beautifully decorated ceramic pot, discovered in Guatemala in 1904, provides a fascinating glimpse into the life and times of the Maya, a pre-Columbian civilization of Mesoamerica. The Maya occupied much of southeastern Mexico and northern Central America, and this vase dates from 600–800 CE. Like many Mayan vases, it was placed in the burial of a noble and depicts a scene from court life – here, the offering of a tribute – providing invaluable evidence of ritual, belief, and the daily life of the elite.

Dating pottery has become increasingly sophisticated. In the late 19th century, archaeologist Flinders Petrie used different styles of Egyptian pottery to invent sequence dating. He recorded the various styles of pot and arranged them in order according to the depths at which they were discovered. Sequence dating is still used to date archaeological sites.

Pots can now be dated scientifically using a technique that exploits the property of clay to absorb and trap electrons. If the clay is heated in a lab, the electrons are released as light. Measuring how much light is released indicates when the pot was fired. The Maya probably sourced the clays for their pots from river valleys, as their descendants do today. Chemical analysis of the clays used provides a "chemical fingerprint", which helps to identify where the clay was sourced.

The distribution of a particular style of pot can also provide clues to trade or migration. One group of Neolithic peoples, who moved into western Europe between 2800 and 1800 BCE, made a distinctive style of pot known as the bell beaker, so archaeologists refer to them as the Beaker people. The beakers found at burial sites around Europe have revealed how extensively the Beaker people travelled.

The lord's name and titles written in glyphs

Ancient writing

Mayan vases often include vital information in the form of hieroglyphs, a sophisticated writing system that was unique in Mesoamerica. Sets of glyphs used within a scene on a pot record the names and titles of the key individuals portrayed. Some pots also have text around the rims, to dedicate the vessels and list their contents.

Kneeling noble presents a Spondylus seashell

Basket piled high with maize cakes

Elaborate headdress of lord marks his rank

Glyphs in panels identify figures shown in scene

The entire scene depicted on the Fenton Vase reveals a lord seated in a palace throne room receiving tribute from Mayan nobles, whose status is indicated by their ornate turbans. The five figures are individually named by the glyphs in the panels beside them. The lord points at a basket filled with tamales (maize pancakes) on top of bolts of cloth. Behind him, a scribe records the details of the tribute.

Scribe records the exchange in a screenfold book

Figures wear jewellery, elaborate clothing, and turbans decorated with flowers

Red slip used to paint details

How was it made?

The first pots were made by coiling strips of clay, or beating clay into slabs. Then, around 3400 BCE, the potter's wheel was invented in Mesopotamia. Early wheels were turned slowly by hand, but later, the foot-operated kick wheel made it possible to "throw" pots quickly, enabling potters to produce ceramics on a large scale. Thereafter, pottery became a specialized craft, usually practised by men. The Fenton Vase would have been made by hand, probably using the coil technique, as the potter's wheel was unknown in pre-Columbian America.

Ancient Egyptian at potter's wheel

Making a mark

The Maya decorated their pots with coloured clay slips, fine mixtures of clays and minerals that fuse to a pot when it is fired. Black and red slips were used on the Fenton Vase. The earliest designs on pots such as this European bell beaker were made using incised marks.

Bell beaker

Food from the past

Pots often contain microscopic traces of the food kept within them, providing information about what people ate in the past. Scrapings from Mayan pots such as the Fenton Vase show that they were used to hold chocolate. The 4,000-year-old bowl of noodles shown below was found in China in 2005. Analysis of the noodles' starch grains revealed that they were made of millet.

The world's oldest noodles

EARLY SETTLEMENTS

As agriculture became more productive, people began to live in more dense, permanent settlements. Alongside farming, they developed impressive crafts, and created regional trade networks.

The oldest and largest early settlement was Catal Höyük in Central Turkey, which lasted from around 7300 to 5600 BCE. It covered 13 hectares (32 acres) and had a population of several thousand people. Catal Höyük was the world's first true town. Another early town was 'Ain Ghazal in Jordan, founded around 7200 BCE. 'Ain Ghazal was slightly smaller than Catal Höyük.

LIFE IN THE FIRST TOWNS

The people of these early towns were farmers, who kept large herds – sheep at Catal Höyük, and goats at 'Ain Ghazal. Both towns grew wheat, barley, peas, and lentils. They also hunted local wild animals, including aurochs (wild cattle), deer, and gazelles.

These first towns may have been quite isolated except for their trading routes. We do not know if they had any contact with neighbouring hunter-gatherer bands, if these existed. As trade developed, it prompted the development of new crafts and skills. Vital new technology – ploughs, wheels, bronze tools – would later emerge from the specialist artisans living in towns.

The first experiments in urban living, these towns developed in different ways. Buildings in each were rectangular, and densely packed together. 'Ain Ghazal had courtyards and narrow lanes between the houses, which were entered through doorways. By contrast, at Catal Höyük, the houses were built against each other without passageways. They were entered through rooftop openings, reached by ladders.

Houses at 'Ain Ghazal vary considerably in size, which suggests that some of its inhabitants were wealthier than others. However, at Catal Höyük, there is no evidence of different classes: there were no high-status homes, public buildings, or even public open spaces. People here seem to have lived lives of equality.

> ## THE **QUALITY AND REFINEMENT** OF NEARLY EVERYTHING MADE HERE **IS WITHOUT PARALLEL** IN THE CONTEMPORARY NEAR EAST.

James Mellaart, British archaeologist, 1925–2012

This 16cm-high (6½in) clay figure, found at Catal Höyük, depicts a woman who is flanked by two leopards

Figure is thought to represent a mother goddess, who controlled the fertility of the earth

STONE GODDESS

Strong, colourful textiles were woven on looms

Wild plants, such as fruit trees, provided an additional source of food

Graves for the dead under house floors. Bodies were exposed to vultures and then the skeletons were buried

DECORATED INTERIORS

House walls were plastered with white clay and then painted with geometric patterns or images of hunting scenes

▶ **Bone tools** used for sewing and weaving provide evidence of textile making at Catal Höyük. Patterned pottery seals have also been found, which may have been used to print patterns on fabrics or on people's skin for decoration.

BONE TOOLS USED FOR MAKING TEXTILES   POTTERY SEAL

Entrances to houses offered ventilation. They may have been covered by woven awnings to keep off the sun

Domesticated sheep were sent out to graze during the day

House roofs acted as the town streets and thoroughfares

Wooden beams supported a reed and mud roof

Windows were thought to have been set high in the walls

Walls were made with mud dug from nearby marshes. This was moulded into bricks, which were dried and hardened by the sun

Roof made of dried reeds

Pens for oxen and other tamed cattle

Many houses had a shrine, some featuring the horns of a wild aurochs, which showed the growing importance of religion

▲ **Inside Catal Höyük**
Catal Höyük was filled with hundreds of houses packed together like cells in a beehive. House sizes varied but averaged 4 x 5m (13 x 16ft). The houses were built to different heights, which allowed people to have small windows at the tops of their walls. The town had no purpose-built defences, although the outermost houses had thicker perimeter walls.

▶ **Social hierarchy in ancient Egypt**
Egyptian society, as in many states, resembled a
pyramid, with the king at the top and different
ranks beneath. There have been many other types
of social pyramid. In the states of medieval Europe
and Japan, warriors became the dominant class.
Merchants were powerful in the Indus civilization,
but had a lowly position in Imperial China. Some
societies, such as the Roman Empire, depended on
the mass use of slaves, who were people with no
rights and were regarded as property.

SLAVES WERE AT THE
BOTTOM OF ANY **SOCIETY** IN
WHICH THEY WERE FOUND

The pharaoh (king) was
seen as a living god, whose
presence was believed to
ensure the harmonious
working of society

PHARAOH

The vizier, or
chief minister,
oversaw the
day-to-day
government

VIZIER

Egyptian nobles had
senior positions as
regional governors,
chief priests, and
military commanders

NOBLES

Scribes usually came from
the upper classes and were
highly educated

SCRIBES

Merchants created
wealth by exchanging
Egyptian products – such
as grain – for goods from
foreign lands, like ebony
and leopard skins

MERCHANTS

Craftsmen were valued
for their specialist skills,
such as metalworking,
making pottery, and
stonemasonry

CRAFTSMEN

society. When there was
no farm work to be done,
they were conscripted
onto building projects

FARMERS

SOCIETY GETS ORGANIZED

As the population increased, humans had to learn, for the first time, to live in peace alongside large numbers of strangers. There were new forms of social organization, ultimately leading to the creation of the state, with a king at the top presiding over a hierarchy of different classes.

▲ **Mother and child**
Between 100 BCE and 250 CE, the Jalisco people of Mexico made many pottery figures of mothers with babies, reflecting women's primary role in their society.

Hunter-gatherers lived in small bands of 25 to 60 individuals who were related through family and marriage ties. Bands were egalitarian: there were no leaders, although certain members were highly respected because of their wisdom or skill at hunting or gathering. Men and women were also equal, with each contributing food supplies, the men hunting and the women gathering.

With the advent of agriculture, people settled down in larger groups, coming together as tribes. A tribe is a group of up to a few thousand, often united by a belief in their descent from a shared ancestor. Early tribal societies remained egalitarian and decisions were made communally. Many tribes had a "big man" whose opinion was valued, but his status came through force of personality rather than inheritance.

Once a population reached several thousand, people had to live alongside others to whom they were not related. Powerful chieftains kept the peace, claiming a monopoly on the right to use force. Tribal members paid tribute to the chief, who redistributed it to his followers. This led to the emergence of different classes. Kinship was still important, but the chieftain's own lineage came to be seen as superior.

THE FIRST STATES

States emerged once populations exceeded 20,000 people – too great a number for kinship to play a role. State organization resembled a pyramid, with an all-powerful ruler at the top and a hierarchy of classes below, including priests and administrators. The largest class of all was made up of peasant farmers. They were at the bottom of the pyramid, even though it was their hard work that created the surpluses on which the whole system was based.

Meticulous record-keeping was essential for the state to function. Royal scribes were rewarded with wealth and power

Egyptian craftsmen had their own hierarchies, with royal artisans having a much higher social status than ordinary craftsmen

> **SOCIETY HAS ARISEN** OUT OF THE **WORKS OF PEACE**: THE ESSENCE OF **SOCIETY IS PEACEMAKING**.
>
> **Ludwig von Mises**, Austrian economist, 1881–1973

PATRIARCHY EMERGES

After people switched from hunting and gathering to farming, women gradually lost their equality within the tribe and came under male control – a system known as patriarchy. Men now supplied the food or income, while women were tied to the home, giving birth and caring for children. Many states prevented women from owning property and placed them under the legal control of husbands or fathers. In some societies, men were allowed to take multiple wives. Sons were preferred over daughters, and there was infanticide of female babies.

War captives
This Mayan wall painting of *c.*790 CE shows King Chan Muwan of Bonampak, in the centre, triumphing over captured warriors from a rival city. The captives, stripped of their high-status clothing, have had their fingernails torn out as a demonstration of his superiority and power.

RULERS
EMERGE

As societies grew larger, power began to shift from consensual kinship relationships to top-down, coercive rule. The new rulers, called chieftains or kings, backed up their position with armed force, which they used to exact tribute from their subjects.

Rulers were able to achieve their positions of power by redistributing the tribute they received. They armed and rewarded elite groups, creating a class of warriors or nobles, while disarming the mass of people.

Why did the majority of people allow a small minority to rule over them? To begin with, there may have been a consensual element, as people willingly gave up power in exchange for organization, security, and protection. Alternatively, the process may simply have been imposed on them from above by forceful and ruthless individuals.

All over the world, rulers found similar ways to display their power. They sat on raised seats (thrones), wore tall headdresses, and held ornamental staffs called sceptres. The Egyptian pharaohs carried a shepherd's crook and a flail, symbolizing the king's protective and coercive role as the "shepherd" of his people.

Success in war was also a sign that rulers had the support of the gods. In public art, kings had themselves depicted triumphing over enemies, who were often shown naked to emphasize their powerlessness.

DIVINE BACKING

Royal authority was usually justified by supernatural claims, in which the ruler's well-being was portrayed as essential to society. Egyptian pharaohs, for example, were said be the earthly embodiment of the sky god Horus, Chinese emperors claimed to have the "Mandate of Heaven", and Mayan kings claimed descent from divine ancestors, who were believed to retain power over the living. Subjects who approached kings were expected to adopt submissive postures, such as bowing or prostrating themselves.

Polynesian chieftains were surrounded by religious taboos that forbade their subjects from even touching their shadow. To do this would be to damage the chieftain's sacred power, or *mana*. As the chief's *mana* was vital to maintain the ritual security of the community, such actions were thought to place the entire population at risk.

▼ **King's coffin**
The coffin of Pharaoh Tutankhamun (c.1327 BCE) is covered with symbols of the king's royal authority and divine status. It was made of gold, which was seen as the flesh of the gods, and inlaid with blue enamel.

The cobra and the vulture represent the pharaoh's supreme power and authority over the Upper and Lower Kingdoms of Egypt

Striped linen headdress (*nemes*) was only worn by the pharaoh

Crook signifies pharaoh as a shepherd, or protector

Ceremonial false beard was a symbol of divinity

Flail, a whip used to goad livestock, shows the pharaoh's power to punish

LAW, ORDER, AND JUSTICE

Large, complex societies need an objective set of rules to govern conduct and resolve disputes peacefully. The earliest law codes were compiled by rulers as a means of social control. Later, an ethical sense developed, based on the idea that justice should be equally available to everyone.

The rise in populations following the introduction of agriculture led to many more opportunities for disputes. Unlike hunter-gatherers, who had no sense of private ownership, farmers quarrelled over land, property, water-rights, inheritance, and many other matters.

Before the rule of law developed, it was the family or kinship group's responsibility to avenge wrongs against individual members. Failure to avenge a wrong, such as a killing, brought dishonour on the whole kinship group. This could set in motion a cycle of violence, a blood feud, that might last for generations. Blood feuds have been common in societies throughout history, and they form the subject of Greek myths, Icelandic sagas, and Japanese samurai tales.

ROYAL CODES

As states emerged, rulers were quick to assume a monopoly of the right to use violence. To resolve disputes peacefully and prevent feuds, they compiled lists of punishments for crimes, or compensations to be paid by perpetrators to victims.

▶ **Mark of proof**
Evidence has become important to provide a basis for provable fact. Today's evidence law is influenced by Roman legal practices. In early times, evidence was primarily oral, occasionally written, and only rarely physical.

The earliest surviving law code is that of the Sumerian city of Ur-Nammu, of *c.*2100 BCE. It lists various compensation sums for a wide range of specific injuries. For example, "If a man has cut off another man's foot, he is to pay ten shekels of silver."

The most famous early law code of all is that of Hammurabi, king of Babylon from 1792–50 BCE. He had 282 decrees inscribed on a 2.25m (7ft 5 in) high cone-shaped stele – a stone pillar – set up in the centre of Babylon for all to see. Hammurabi's Law Code is best known for "If a man put out the eye of another man, his eye shall be put out."

At the top of the stele, Hammurabi declared that he had been commanded by the gods "to bring about the rule of righteousness in the land, to destroy the wicked and the evil-doers; so that the strong should not harm the weak." He suggested that any man who felt wronged should go to the stele and have its laws read out: "Let him see the law which applies to him, and let his heart be at rest."

For kings like Hammurabi, dispensing justice was a way of winning popularity. When they were not fighting wars or performing religious ceremonies, many ancient rulers spent much of their time listening to appeals and judging disputes.

According to his biographer, Plutarch, King Demetrius I of Macedon was once on a journey when an old woman approached him and asked for an audience. The king

> **LAW IS THE KING** OF ALL THINGS, BOTH **DIVINE AND HUMAN**.

Chrysippus, Greek philosopher, *c.*279–206 BCE, *On Law*

answered that he was too busy, at which she shouted, "Then don't be king!" Stung by the rebuke, he stopped and spent the next few days giving audiences to all who asked for them, beginning with the old woman. Plutarch concludes, "And indeed there is nothing that becomes a king so much as the task of dispensing justice."

DIVINE LAWS

The emergence of moral religions brought a new attitude to law, with many crimes or transgressions now being seen as offences against God rather than against society or individuals. The Hebrew Torah (Law) is a collection of instructions for every aspect of life, which Jews believe were handed to Moses by God. The most important of these instructions were the Ten Commandments, which were inscribed on stone tablets and kept in the central shrine of the Jewish Temple in Jerusalem.

Islamic Sharia law is a similar set of commandments for every aspect of life. Sharia is based on the Koran, traditions about the Prophet Muhammad, and fatwas – rulings – by Islamic scholars. Sharia means "the clear path" in Arabic. In some Muslim countries, Sharia Law has continued the ancient tradition of "an eye for an eye". In 2009, an Iranian Sharia court offered a woman, blinded

good example of proper behaviour by those in authority. He said, "To govern simply by law, and to create order by means of punishments, will make people try to avoid the punishment but have no sense of shame. To govern by virtue, and create order by the rules of propriety, will not only give them the sense of shame, but moreover they will become good."

The Legalists rejected Confucianism. They viewed people as innately greedy, self-interested, and lazy, and they advocated controlling behaviour through strict laws and harsh punishments. Legalism was adopted by the state of Qin in the 4th century BCE. Lord Shang, the chief minister of Qin, wrote, "Those who do not carry out the king's law are guilty of death and should not be pardoned, but their punishment should be extended to their family for three generations." Lord Shang eventually fell out of favour and suffered under his own harsh laws. In 338 BCE, he was torn apart by five chariots and his whole family was killed.

The Han dynasty succeeded the Qin. The Han Emperor Wu (ruled 141–87 BCE) combined Confucianism and Legalism. Confucianism, with its emphasis on moral behaviour and filial duty, became the state philosophy. Yet it was backed up by strict Legalist punishments. This was summed up by the saying "Confucian on the outside, Legalism within." Legalism has been at the core of the Chinese system ever since.

ROMAN LAW

The Romans were the first people to treat law as a science, with jurists analyzing the principles underlying laws and their application. Roman jurists argued that the spirit or intent behind a law was more important than its precise wording. Another principle was that the accused should be given the benefit of the doubt.

Over centuries, a mass of Roman laws and legal commentaries, often contradictory, built up, which lawyers and magistrates were expected to study. This was reduced to a manageable form in 528–33 CE by the Emperor Justinian, who commissioned a team of experts to collect all the existing Roman laws in one volume – the *Corpus Juris Civilis* (Body of Civil Law). They created a second work, the *Digest*, by editing the legal commentaries to remove repetitions and contradictions. Justinian's Law Code spread to the West where, from the 11th century,

> # "JUSTICE IS A CONSTANT, UNFAILING DISPOSITION TO GIVE EVERYONE HIS LEGAL DUE.

Ulpian, jurist quoted in Justinian's *Digest*, c.533 CE

in an acid attack, the opportunity to pour acid into the eyes of her attacker. She chose to pardon him, saying, "I knew I would have suffered and burned twice had I done that."

CHINESE PHILOSOPHIES

In China, from the 6th century BCE, two very different approaches to law developed, based on contrasting views of human nature. The philosopher Confucius argued that people will behave well if they are set a

Legalism enabled the kings of Qin to create an authoritarian state and then conquer the other kingdoms. In 221 BCE, the unification of China was completed by the First Emperor, who imposed Legalism on the whole country. All Chinese families were organized into mutual responsibility groups, in which each member would be punished for crimes committed by another. Confucian books were banned. The First Emperor's rule proved so harsh that the Qin dynasty survived for only four years after his death in 210 BCE.

the *Digest* was used to educate generations of lawyers. The Code itself influenced many later ones, including the French Napoleonic Code of 1804. In his 1951 book, *Natural Law: An Introduction to Legal Philosophy*, the Italian author Alessandro d'Entreves declared, "Next to the Bible, no book has left a deeper mark upon the history of mankind than the *Corpus Juris Civilis*."

THE **WRITTEN** WORD

With the spread of farming and trade, the need to keep accurate records led several early civilizations to invent writing systems. Writing was soon put to other uses, including setting down laws, composing religious texts, chronicling events, spreading scientific ideas, and creating literature.

Writing began around 3300 BCE in Egypt and Mesopotamia as a way to store vital information. Initially it only benefited the ruling classes, as the first systems used so many signs that only a small elite group, the scribes, could master them.

The Phoenician invention of an alphabet, using less than 30 signs to represent sounds, helped to extend literacy beyond just the scribal classes. In the 1st millennium BCE, the alphabet was spread throughout the Mediterranean by Phoenician traders, and then adapted by the Greeks and Romans. Writing was increasingly used for everyday purposes, such as composing letters, making shopping lists, and labelling possessions to indicate ownership.

Books were a valuable tool for collective learning: knowledge could be shared between cultures, and passed down to future generations. They were collected in ancient libraries, the most renowned being the Great Library of Alexandria in Egypt, which was a major centre of Greek learning from the 3rd century BCE. One of its chief librarians was the mathematician Eratosthenes, who accurately calculated Earth's circumference in around 200 BCE.

That we know about Eratosthenes today is due to the preservation of Greek and

Medieval books were prized for their decoration, so they survived long after the Latin language in which they were written had fallen out of use

> WE MUST... THANK **OUR PREDECESSORS**, BECAUSE THEY DID NOT LET ALL GO IN JEALOUS SILENCE, BUT **PROVIDED A RECORD** IN WRITING **OF THEIR IDEAS OF EVERY KIND**.

Vitruvius, Roman architect, c.80–15 BCE, *On Architecture*

▶ In loving memory
The invention of writing allowed people's names to live on after their death. This funeral stele (memorial stone) from Yemen bears an inscription in the Old South Arabian alphabet, which was used from the 9th century BCE to the 6th century CE.

Latin books through the Middle Ages by the Roman Catholic Church and the Byzantine Empire, and also by Islamic scholars, who translated them into Arabic.

Printing with moveable type, which allowed books to be cheaply mass produced, marked the next great advance in the rise of literacy. The first European printed book was Johannes Gutenberg's Bible, printed in 1455 CE. By 1500, presses in Europe were turning out 10–20 million volumes a year, and 35,000 different books were in print.

▶ A beautiful read
Until the coming of printing, only the wealthy could afford books, which were designed to be admired as objects of beauty as well as read. This 15th-century hand-written prayer book, or "book of hours", is in Latin, which limited its readership.

Ornate initial capitals announced text divisions or highlighted important sections of a work

Pictures were an aid to literacy, helping the reader to understand the text

Upper and lower case lettering only emerged in the 8th century CE

The text was hand written before the page was illustrated

Egyptian Hieroglyphs, a system based on picture signs, were first used about 3300 BCE.

AFRICA

3300 BCE

Papyrus, an early form of paper, was developed about 3000 BCE in Egypt.

The Indus people invent a script in 2600 BCE that is still undeciphered. There are around 400 signs, which are read right to left.

EAST ASIA

The earliest-surviving Chinese writing dates from 250C BCE.

The Akkadians of Mesopotamia in 2350 BCE simplified cuneiform, reducing the number of signs to about 600.

2220 BCE

EUROPE

WEST ASIA

Sumerian cuneiform is developed about 3200 BCE. It is another system based on picture signs.

The Minoans in Crete invent the "Linear A" system in 1900 BCE. It is inspired by trade with Egypt and is mainly used to keep accounts.

The Rosetta Stone is carved in 196 BCE in Egypt, with inscriptions in Hieroglyphs, Demotic, and Greek, making it possible to later decipher Egyptian scripts.

Parchment is developed in Pergamon, Ancient Greece, in the 2nd century BCE. Both sides can be used for writing – unlike leather – and it can be reused by scraping off old text.

Mayan writing system develops in 300 BCE, in Mesoamerica, with signs standing for syllables as well as ideas.

The Ancient Library of Alexandria is built in Egypt around the 3rd century BCE.

Brahmi script is developed in India in the 4th century BCE. It is an "abugida" system that uses consonant signs with vowel notation.

1500 BCE

The Mycenaeans adapt Linear A in 1450 BCE to create Linear B, the earliest form of Greek.

The Proto-Sinaitic (also called Canaanite) alphabet is developed in Canaan or Sinai between 1850 and 1650 BCE.

AMERICAS

Phoenicians simplify the Proto-Sinaitic alphabet about 1200 BCE, and spread its use around the eastern Mediterranean. It has 22 signs, all standing for consonants.

Ugaritic script, a cuneiform system, is developed in western Syria in 1300 BCE.

In Egypt, hieroglyphics are simplified in 650 BCE to create a new script, Demotic, designed for writing on papyrus.

Greeks invent a true alphabet in 800 BCE, based on the Phoenician system, with added letters for vowels.

In Italy, the Greek alphabet is adapted in 650 BCE to write Etruscan and Latin – two different systems. The Latin alphabet is the one we still use today.

900 BCE

In Ireland, Ogham writing – made in stone – featuring straight marks develops around the 4th century CE.

The Chinese invent printing on paper using carved woodblocks in the 1st century CE.

The last-known hieroglyphic inscriptions are made in 394 CE, in an Egyptian temple.

Japanese scribes adapt the Chinese script in the 5th century CE, and also invent two syllabic systems (hiragana and katakana) – giving Japan three writing systems.

The Romans create the codex in the 1st century CE. It is the first book with separate pages, which is more convenient to read than a scroll.

Literacy starts to be encouraged in Benedictine monasteries in the 5th century CE, leading to the creation of scriptoriums to copy books. Monasteries begin lending to each other, which increases collective learning.

The Cathach of St Columba is the first document to show a large capital letter at the start of each psalm, followed by decreasing-size letters to regular small capitals, in 610 CE. This is the start of writing in uppercase and lowercase.

Monasteries in England and Ireland begin producing illuminated manuscripts – featuring elaborate decorations and illustrations – from the 7th century CE.

Carolingian script is developed in western Europe in the 8th century. It introduces spacing between words, and produces some of the most clear and legible documents in the history of writing.

The Islamic Golden Age begins around 786 CE, when scholars gather in the court of Harun al-Rashid to translate classical texts into Arabic, thus preserving them.

The first moveable-type printing press is created by German publisher Johannes Gutenberg in 1440 CE. It allows books to be mass-produced, making them affordable, and spreading literacy.

The Yongle Encyclopedia is completed in China in 1408 CE. It is the world's largest encyclopedia until Wikipedia, comprising 11,095 volumes and copies of 7,000 texts.

1CE

1000CE

1600CE

TIMELINES

WRITING DEVELOPS

Writing emerged when the earliest civilizations began to use pictographs to keep economic records. Sumerian and Egyptian pictographs could stand for words, ideas, and sounds.

Different styles of writing evolved to suit the materials used. Sumerian cuneiform used simple wedge shapes, because it was written by pushing a pointed stylus into soft clay. The flowing appearance of Chinese writing arose because it was originally painted on bamboo strips with a brush. Alphabets were created when the eastern neighbours of the Egyptians adapted around 30 hieroglyphs, using them to represent sounds. The earliest alphabets only contained signs for consonants. Later, the Greeks added vowel signs, too.

Writing systems can be difficult to date because it depends on the accidental survival of ancient texts. While Sumerian clay tablets have survived for millennia, early Chinese writing, on bamboo, has been lost.

▼ **Irrigating the fields**
This reconstruction shows a typical farming village, with its irrigation system, in southern Mesopotamia. It is based on archaeological evidence, such as dried up irrigation canals, and Mesopotamian texts, including instructions for irrigating fields.

Canal at a higher level

Sluice gates

Tapered bank to control water flow

Water regulators controlled the water supply from the canal

WATER REGULATOR

Reeds were harvested for roofing and weaving into baskets

Reed fishing boat

Vegetable and salad crops required plenty of fresh water

W... provi... groundwa... in times... droug...

Mesopotamian rivers carried a lot of silt and often changed course

Fruit trees, such as apples, olives, date palms, and pomegranates, were grown closest to the canal

Tre... pro... sha... cro...

Dyke held back floodwaters and prevented deposition of silt into canal

Peas and chickpea... fixed nitrogen in the soil

Shaduf

Small footbridge

Reservoir stored water for emergencies

Weir maintained upstream water level of canal

Animals provided a secondary income from their products

Date palm

Cattle ploughing field ready for planting

Fields were allowed to fall fallow in alternate years to reduce salinization

Pigs in village compound were fed on scraps

Livestock fertilized fallow fields and acted as insurance against drought – farmers could revert to nomadism

VILLAGE

Canal entrance could be blocked with mud to prevent flooding

DESERT

Marginal fields

Wheat is sensitive to salt, so it was grown as close to the main canal as possible

Flax was grown to make linen

Salt-resistant barley was grown in the areas near the marshes

Irrigation channels needed regular dredging to prevent silt blocking them

Cross section to show gradient

The plains of Mesopotamia were very flat, making them prone to waterlogging and salinization

Marshes were used as game reserves for waterfowl and wild boar

Canal ebbs into marshland

A shaduf was a long, pivoting pole with a bucket on one end and a weight on the other, used for lifting water from canals and wells

DYKE

SHADUF LIFTING SYSTEM

Bucket was lowered and filled by pulling on a rope

DESERT

WATERING THE DESERT

The ability to transfer water from rivers to fields and store it in reservoirs for later use allowed farmers to grow crops beyond the limits of rain-fed agriculture, and even transform desert into fertile land.

Irrigation was very labour intensive, and called for large-scale social cooperation. The first civilizations – Egypt, Mesopotamia, the Indus, and China – all developed extensive irrigation systems. Egypt and Mesopotamia had low rainfall, but benefited from major rivers that flooded every year, depositing nutient-rich silt on the surrounding fields. In Mesopotamia, where the river flooded at the wrong time of year to grow crops, the water had to be diverted and stored for later use.

DYKES AND CANALS

To divert and control the water, people dug wide canals alongside the rivers. They used the excavated soil to build dykes, which protected their fields and villages from flooding. From the larger canals, smaller channels ran downhill into reservoirs and fields. Weirs and regulators allowed them to adjust the flow from the canals into the channels.

One problem with irrigation is that when water evaporates it leaves behind salt, which builds up in the soil, reducing its fertility. The Mesopotamians dealt with this by leaving fields fallow to recover, and by growing barley, which is more salt resistant than other crops, but overly salty fields were eventually abandoned.

Irrigation demanded a huge amount of work, maintaining dykes and removing silt from the canals. Despite this, the system proved so productive that, in the 4th millennium BCE, the first city-states grew out of these busy and prosperous agricultural towns.

Farmer stood here and walked on the rim

▲ Paddle wheel
Farmers in China lifted water onto their fields using the paddle wheel. The operator stood on the wheel and used the tread of his feet to make it turn and scoop up water.

Turning the screw drew water up the tube

▲ Archimedes' screw
This hand-operated pump consisted of a rotating metal screw inside an angled tube. It was said to have been invented by the Greek scientist Archimedes in the 3rd century BCE.

A canal around the city carried water from the river to fields inland

Livestock

The city was surrounded by huge areas of irrigated farmland

Canal

Palaces also housed craft workshops, food stores, and ceremonial courtyards

Gate

Fortress

Fast roads linked Ur to other city states

Street

Royal palace

Temple and treasury

Priestesses' palace

Some houses had an open courtyard and a domestic chapel

Temple

North harbour

Courtyard

Temple

Canal

Ur was an important Sumerian centre for goods imported and exported by sea and river

Royal mausoleums where kings and queens were buried with their treasures

West harbour

The river flooded each spring, depositing nutrient-rich silt on the land

Ziggurat was the highest point in the city. It supported a temple for the patron god of the city. The people of Ur brought their agricultural surplus here

Buildings were made of sun-baked bricks. They didn't last, so they were demolished and rebuilt

Sacred quarter – walled precinct in northern half of city

High defensive outer wall

EUPHRATES RIVER

UR

▲ Location of Ur
Ur was once a major port close to the mouth of the Euphrates on the Persian Gulf. The coastline has since shifted and the site lies far inland, in what is now Iraq.

Palm tree

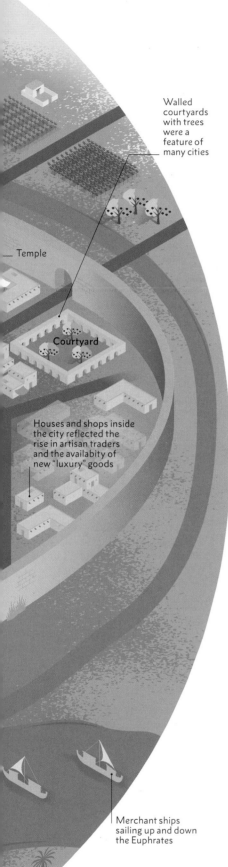

Walled courtyards with trees were a feature of many cities

Temple

Courtyard

Houses and shops inside the city reflected the rise in artisan traders and the availability of new "luxury" goods

Merchant ships sailing up and down the Euphrates

▲ The city of Ur
Ur was built on the eastern bank of the Euphrates. This trading hub was a wealthy city with palaces, courtyards, temples, market-places, and many mud-brick houses, where ordinary people lived.

CITY STATES EMERGE

Around 3500 BCE, farming villages and towns along the Tigris and Euphrates rivers, in southern Mesopotamia, were transformed into the world's first cities. In seven other places worldwide, cities emerged independently and human history entered a new era: an age of agrarian civilizations.

The first cities were more than just the large villages of the early agrarian era, which consisted of similar, self-sufficient households. These cities saw humanized environments emerge with new forms of hierarchy and complexity. One factor that led to the emergence of cities was rapid population growth, the result of increases in productivity, after collective learning led to the invention of new technologies.

region of Sumer lacked raw materials, and the need for resources led to the development of long-distance trading networks. Sumerian cities exchanged pottery and grain for tin and copper from Anatolia and gold from Egypt.

By 3000 BCE, there were a dozen Sumerian cities including Uruk, Ur, and Lagash, each with a population of between 50,000 and 80,000 people. Cities were complex economic structures that required

> THIS IS THE **WALL OF URUK**, WHICH **NO CITY** ON EARTH **CAN EQUAL**. SEE HOW **ITS RAMPARTS GLEAM LIKE COPPER** IN THE SUN.
>
> *Epic of Gilgamesh, c.2000 BCE*

Uruk was the first of several cities that appeared in southern Mesopotamia, or Sumer. The area was surrounded by desert, which led to the development of settlements with irrigation systems. This innovation made it possible to support a larger population: these cities attracted settlers from more arid parts of the region, and became important centres of exchange. The

new forms of social organization: kings and priestly elites emerged and specialized occupations developed. This led to the creation of states with political, social, and economic hierarchies. During a period of extraordinary invention, the elements of what we call civilization were born: kingship, social hierarchy, monumental architecture, tax collecting, law codes, and literature.

◄ Centre point
Sumerian cities were dominated by tall mud-brick temples called ziggurats, which could be seen for miles around. The size of the temple displayed the importance of the local god and the wealth and power of the city that built it. This ziggurat, at Ur, has been partially reconstructed.

FARMING IMPACTS THE **ENVIRONMENT**

When farmers reshaped the landscape to make it favourable for growing food, there were unforeseen consequences. Deforestation, the removal of tree cover, caused soil erosion and the loss of woodland species, while irrigation gradually turned the soil so salty that it could not sustain crops.

The pollen record shows a massive loss of forests across Eurasia as a result of farming. Forests were cut down to provide timber, charcoal for iron working, and arable and grazing land. The Mediterranean lost its deciduous forests, leaving thin soils only suitable for olive trees. In China, felling the trees of the Loess Plateau allowed mineral-rich soil to be washed into the Yellow River, giving its waters their distinctive hue.

Deforestation has a disastrous impact in arid lands, where trees have adapted to the low rainfall by growing deep roots. Between 200 and 400 CE in southern Peru, the Nazca people removed all the local huarango trees. The huarango has the deepest root system of any tree, which helps to maintain the soil's fertility and moisture levels. Pollen samples reveal that the trees were replaced by cotton and corn. Without the anchoring huarango roots, Nazca fields were devastated by soil erosion from high desert winds and seasonal flooding. The land became unsuitable for agriculture, much of it turning to desert. Salinization – the deposition of mineral salts when irrigation water evaporates from fields – also helped to hasten the end of the Nazca culture. The salts accumulate at the soil's surface, making it toxic to most plants. By 500 CE, only salt-tolerant weeds grew on what was once productive Nazca farmland.

Other American cultures induced similar crises. The Maya, for example, were forced to abandon their cities and pyramids after over-intensive use of water and land.

EASTER ISLAND

When Polynesians arrived at Easter Island (Rapa Nui) in the Pacific, in about 1200, it was covered with a thick palm forest. Pollen studies tell us that by 1650 the last trees had been cleared by slash-and-burn farming. Without wood, the islanders could no longer build boats to fish. They managed to survive the loss of the trees by scattering rocks over half of their island. Called lithic mulching, this system reduces evaporation and soil erosion, and helps replace lost nutrients.

▶ **Planting techniques**
The deforestation of Easter Island by the mid-17th century resulted in wind-lashed, infertile fields. The islanders responded by building thousands of planting enclosures called *manavai*. These circular stone walls preserve moisture in the soil and protect young plants from high winds as well as grazing cattle.

Stripped bare
An aerial view of part of Easter Island shows signs of the massive erosion caused by the loss of its palm trees over three centuries ago. The nutrients in the soil were washed away by heavy rainfall and not replaced, which led to a loss of plant and animal diversity.

BELIEF SYSTEMS

Humans have long believed in the supernatural, but these beliefs have altered over time in response to changing lifestyles. As hunter-gatherers became farmers, beliefs shifted from animism to the worship of ancestors and new gods. Later, as societies grew larger and more complex, universal faiths were established, most of them monotheistic.

The earliest religion we know of is animism or shamanism, which is still practised by modern hunter-gatherers. This is based on the belief that people, animals, and forces of nature all have spirits, which can be contacted through ceremonies. Bad weather, sickness, or an unsuccessful hunt can all be explained by displeased spirits. Religious specialists, called shamans, enter a trance state to contact the spirits, and then perform rituals to appease them.

With the shift to farming and settled communities, there was a new focus on the

---

I BELIEVE IN THE **FUNDAMENTAL TRUTH OF ALL GREAT RELIGIONS** OF THE WORLD.

"

Mahatma Gandhi, Indian independence leader, 1869–1948

---

worship of the ancestors – the spirits of the dead, who were thought to watch over the living. In many farming communities, people even kept the bodies of the dead in their houses and made offerings to them. The earliest religious structures are great tombs, megaliths, and passage graves, often built on hilltops. The local people's claim to the land they farmed would have been strengthened by the visible presence of their ancestors in the landscape.

Farmers also worshipped the Earth, or Great Mother, because it produced new life, and the Sun, on which they depended for a good harvest. The Incas of Peru called their sun god Inti and the Earth goddess Pachamama, meaning "World Mother". Farmers in the Andes still perform rituals for Pachamama before the sowing season.

It was widely believed that the favour of supernatural forces could be won by offering gifts, called sacrifices. People in Bronze Age

Europe threw precious bronze swords and shields into lakes and rivers, which were seen as portals to the spirit world. The more precious the offering, the more effective it would be. Humans were killed as sacrifices in many cultures, including Bronze and Iron Age Europe and Mesoamerica.

A FAMILY OF GODS

Over time, natural forces and abstract ideas were personified, and families of gods emerged. The Indo-Europeans were pastoralists who, from around 4000 BCE, migrated across western Eurasia, spreading the family of languages. They carried with them the worship of a sky and thunder god, called Dyaus Pita in India, Zeus in Greece, and Jupiter in the Roman Empire. He was the head and king of a family of gods.

The rise of states went hand-in-hand with organized religions, and with temples and priests dedicated to local patron gods. State religions provided a new common bond, uniting large numbers of people who were not tied by kinship. This benefited rulers by creating an ideological framework for the transfer of wealth from the masses to elites. Farmers were expected to bring tribute to offer to the gods at their local temple.

Just as hierarchical state systems emerged, gods also came to be ranked in terms of seniority. Kings justified their rule by claiming to have a unique relationship to the gods, and would intercede on behalf of the people to obtain successful harvests.

Polytheistic religion was inclusive and always open to new gods. The Romans thought that the more gods they could call on, the safer their empire would be. Visitors to other cities were happy to take part in ceremonies honouring local gods without feeling disloyal to their own deities. Polytheistic gods also had no concern with morality. The gods in Homer's *Iliad*, which was the closest thing that the Greeks had to a sacred text, behave just as badly as the human protagonists.

The question of what people believed was unimportant; some Greek philosophers even questioned whether gods existed. Around 580 BCE, the philosopher Xenophanes stated that humans create gods in their own image: "Ethiopians say the their gods are flat-nosed and dark, Thracians that theirs are blue-eyed and red-haired. If oxen and horses had hands and were able to draw, horses would draw the shapes of gods to look like horses and oxen to look like oxen."

UNIVERSAL RELIGIONS

A major shift took place with the rise of universal religions offering moral teaching, emotional fulfilment, and salvation. The most important were Zoroastrianism in India, Buddhism in India, Confucianism in China, and Judaism, Christianity, and Islam in the Mediterranean world. These were all founded by male teachers, who were thought by their followers to be divinely inspired.

Universal religions first appeared in the 1st millennium BCE, after the emergence of great empires and the rise of urban life. They were a response to the human need to

---

THE **CHRISTIAN BIBLE** IS THE WORLD'S **BEST-SELLING BOOK**

---

find meaning in a world of increasing social complexity. Historians of religion call this period the Axial Age, because it was the time when most of today's religions and philosophies emerged.

In the Americas, there was no Axial Age and no universal religion, perhaps because urban living developed much later than in Eurasia and there was no long-distance trade network that allowed ideas to spread.

> ## "CONCERNING **THE GODS**, I HAVE **NO MEANS OF KNOWING** WHETHER THEY **EXIST OR NOT**.
>
> **Protagoras**, Greek philosopher, c.485–415 BCE
> *On the Gods*

ONE GOD

Most universal religions were monotheistic, based on the worship of a single, all-powerful God whose primary concern was human behaviour. Religions that addressed moral actions were of use to states in enforcing conformity, enabling rulers to claim that the social order was divinely inspired. Religion offered those who suffered in this life the consolation of an afterlife, and a promised reward in paradise made people willing to sacrifice their own lives for the greater good. This willingness among individuals to sacrifice themselves made the state more successful in warfare.

Universal religions flourished when they were adopted by empires. Christianity and Zoroastrianism became the state religions of the Roman Empire and Persian Empire respectively, and Confucianism became the state philosophy of China. The new religions spread widely thanks to the Eurasian trade networks. From its Indian birthplace, Buddhism was carried east along the Silk Road to China, Japan, and Southeast Asia. Islam spread even further, thanks to its control of the Mediterranean hub region. In the century after the Prophet Muhammad's death, in 632 CE, Muslim armies conquered many lands and established an empire that stretched from Spain to India. Missionaries and merchants went on to carry Islam around the Indian Ocean.

STRONG BELIEFS

Unlike the polytheistic religions, the universal monotheistic faiths placed great importance on beliefs. The problem was that they offered different interpretations of what people should believe. This clash of belief systems caused tensions between nations and cultures. For the first time, people went to war over religion.

The major conflict was between Islam and Christianity. As a result of inter-faith wars, the Eurasian trade network became

> ## IN 2010, **ISLAM** HAD **1.6 BILLION** FOLLOWERS, A **QUARTER OF THE WORLD'S POPULATION**

divided into rival blocs, with Christian Europe cut off by the Islamic Ottoman Empire from the Silk Route to China. This led, in the 15th century, to the Age of Exploration, when Christopher Columbus and other European explorers set off to discover new maritime routes to the East.

In this way, religion acted as a major trigger for globalization – the linking up of the entire world by European Christian nations as they travelled, traded, and conquered in the name of faith.

◀ **Face of the god**
The elephant-headed Ganesh is one of the best-known and most-popular deities in the Hindu pantheon. Known as the Remover of Obstacles, he is the god of wisdom and learning.

Lord of the dead
This reconstruction of the Lord of Sipán's tomb shows his richly dressed body in the centre, with four people around him. His male attendants had had their feet cut off, perhaps to prevent them from deserting their posts.

GRAVE **GOODS**

People have long believed that death is followed by an afterlife: the practice of burying the dead with items that would be useful in the next life goes back more than 30,000 years. The coming of agriculture and the rise of civilization saw a huge increase in grave goods.

Through grave offerings, we can trace the rise of different social classes. The graves of the first farmers, who were buried with simple pots or joints of meat, show no signs of social distinction. By the Bronze Age (c.3000 BCE), chieftains had emerged, buried under large grave mounds with rich treasures.

Grave goods tell us a lot about daily life and beliefs in the past because they include items considered important or valuable at the time. High-status grave goods – evidence of technology – include Iron Age British and Chinese chariots and complete Anglo-Saxon and Viking ships. They also provide evidence of long-distance trade. The 7th century Anglo-Saxon king buried in his ship at Sutton Hoo in England had silver bowls and spoons that had been brought all the way from Constantinople in the Roman Empire (now Istanbul, Turkey).

The absence of grave goods is also significant. It provides evidence of a changed view of the afterlife, spread by new religions. The change is most obvious in late Roman cemeteries, which pagans – buried with grave goods – shared with Christians, who were buried without offerings and with their feet pointing east, towards Jerusalem.

ROYAL GRAVES

The most elaborate offerings come from royal graves, such as that of the Moche Lord of Sipán, on the north coast of Peru. He was buried in around 300 CE with 451 precious objects, made from gold, silver, and feathers.

Sharing his tomb were three women, two men, a child, two llamas, and a dog. They were probably sacrificed to accompany their lord in the afterlife.

Human sacrifice was also practised in the royal tombs of early China, Egypt, and Mesopotamia. As the custom died out, models were used as substitutes for real humans. In Egypt, wooden servants performed work on behalf of the living, while in China, the First Emperor, Qin Shi Huang (259–210 BCE), was buried with a complete terracotta army to defend him from the angry ghosts of the people he had killed during his reign.

◄ **Terracotta guardian**
This kneeling warrior is one of 7,000 life-size figures buried to guard the tomb of China's First Emperor. The position of his hands suggests that he held a crossbow.

> MEMBERS OF THE **KING'S HOUSEHOLD** ARE **BURIED BESIDE HIM**... ALL OF THEM STRANGLED. **HORSES** ARE BURIED TOO, AND **GOLD CUPS** AND **OTHER TREASURES**.

Herodotus, Greek historian, describing the funeral of a Scythian king, c.484–425 CE

CLOTHING
SHOWS STATUS

The production of textiles dates back to the early days of agriculture, when skills from basket weaving were first applied to plant and animal fibres. As textile production developed, fabric became a highly tradeable commodity, and clothing became a new way to demonstrate social rank.

Clouds represent the celestial realm, signifying rain, luck, and never-ending fortune

Textiles were invented independently in several parts of the world, using various materials. The earliest textiles, from about 7000 BCE, were linen made from fibres of the flax plant, which was domesticated in the Near East, and cotton, domesticated in India. Later there was wool, which came from sheep in Eurasia and from alpacas and llamas in South America. The main fabrics in Mesoamerica were cotton and ayaté, made from the maguey plant.

MAKING FABRICS

Weaving began with the development of the loom, a device designed to keep warp (lengthwise) threads tight while weft (cross) threads are woven between them. In the Americas, this was achieved by attaching the loom to the weaver's back. Eurasian weavers used an upright wooden frame with weights tied to the warp threads.

Textiles were coloured with dyes from plants, minerals, insects, and shellfish. The ancient world's most expensive dye was purple, produced from the *Murex* sea snail in the eastern Mediterranean. This dye was so highly prized that the people who traded in it came to be called Phoenicians, meaning "purple people" in Greek.

STATUS AND SILK

Clothing became an important way for people to display status. In both Egypt and Mesopotamia, linen, which is lighter and smoother than wool, was a high-status material worn by the wealthy. Many societies had laws governing the clothes people were allowed to wear. In Tudor England, members of the royal family alone could wear cloth of gold. In China, only the emperor and his closest relatives were allowed to wear bright yellow.

Silk was the most sought-after textile because of its lustre, softness, smoothness, and isothermal properties, which made it cool in summer and warm in winter. It was made in China before 4000 BCE from cocoons of the *Bombyx mori* moth, the world's only fully domesticated insect. Through selective breeding the moths lost their ability to fly and the legs of the larvae shrank so that they could not crawl away from the trays on which they were kept.

EVEN MEN HAVE NOT BEEN ASHAMED TO ADOPT **SILK CLOTHING IN SUMMER** BECAUSE OF ITS LIGHTNESS.

Pliny the Elder, Roman scholar, 23–79 CE, *Natural History*

◀ **Chinese silk**
This early 12th-century Chinese painting shows women ironing silk. This fabric was so valued that the overland route from Asia to Europe along which it was traded became known as the Silk Road. Until the 6th century CE, China maintained a monopoly in silk production by making it a capital crime to export silkworms or cocoons. The painting itself was made on a sheet of silk.

Red and blue are lucky colours

◀ Dragon lord
This embroidered yellow silk robe from the 18th century was worn by the Chinese emperor on festive occasions. The colour and symbols shown on it were reserved for imperial use.

Flaming pearl is one of the Eight Treasures (pearls of wisdom), which stand for perfection and enlightenment

Dragon is a symbol of good fortune and an emblem of rank and high power. Five-clawed dragons show that wearer is an emperor – lower ranks have three or four claws

Nine dragons appear in total, as nine is the number reserved for the emperor

Dragon flies from the waves to the heavens, bringing rain and fertility

Hem of robe represents the sea

Copper is first extracted from its ores by heating over a fire (smelting) in Western Europe and East Asia c.5000 BCE. The metal is poured into moulds to make tools.

5000 BCE

Metal foundries process gold, copper, lead, zinc, tin, and iron at Metsamor, Armenia, from 5000 BCE.

Death mask of Tutankhamun is made using techniques purifying gold from ores, which emerged in Egypt c.1327 BCE.

6000 BCE

1 FIRST METALS

Metalworking began in the Fertile Crescent, in the Middle East, c.7000 BCE, with people in farming communities making jewellery from naturally occurring nuggets of gold, copper, and lead. These soft metals could be worked without using heat, although too much hammering would make them brittle.

Tin bronzes are made at Pločnik, Serbia, c.4500 BCE. Knowledge of the process is lost when the Vinča culture from the region dies out.

7000 BCE

PURE METALS

World's oldest known gold treasure, c.4600–4200 BCE, is found buried with the dead in a cemetery in Varna, Bulgaria.

4000 BCE

Tuyere pipes, depicted here in a 15th century BCE painting, are used to increase the temperature in a crucible while smelting copper, from c.4000 BCE.

TIMELINES

USING **METALS**

The invention of metallurgy was one of the most important technological advances in history. Metal tools can be moulded, hammered into new shapes, and resharpened when they grow blunt.

Copper is cast, using the lost-wax process, in what is now Israel c.3700 BCE.

Metallurgy developed in stages, as Eurasian people gradually learned how to work harder metals. The earliest metal was copper, which is a soft metal, so tools needed regular resharpening. Later, people learned how to make bronze by adding a small amount of tin to copper. This produced a harder metal suitable for swords, spears, and shields. Copper and tin are both scarce metals, so bronze was mainly used by the elite.

Iron was the last metal to be worked, because it requires very high temperatures to smelt. Yet the use of iron, to make high-status weapons and low-status tools and nails, would change the lives of everyone across Afro-Eurasia.

Bronze is made by the Sumerians in Western Asia c.3500 BCE. Gold and silver, as native metals, are also exploited in the region.

BRONZE

2 BRONZE BEGINS

Bronze is a mixture of copper and another metal, usually tin. Since copper and tin ores are rarely found together, tin bronzes are evidence of trade. Most archaeologists date the start of the Bronze Age to c.3500 BCE, but there is evidence that tin bronze was being worked in Serbia 1,000 years before that.

Bronze casts are used to make weapons c.3100 BCE, though these are too expensive to be used by anyone but the elite.

Two forms of bronze are in use: "classic bronze" for casting, and "mild bronze" for sheet metalwork and armour c.3000–2100 BCE.

3000 BCE

Bronze spearhead

1000 BCE

Iron working reaches western Europe c.800 BCE. The European Iron Age brings increased warfare, reflected in the building of hill forts and defences.

Wootz steel, an alloy of iron with carbon, is invented in southern India c.550 BCE and is exported to the West.

The blast furnace, for making cast iron, is invented in China c.500 BCE. It is centuries before the technology is matched in Europe.

Lead smelting takes place in the Roman Empire (c.366 BCE–36 CE), contributing to early global pollution.

Damascus steel swords are made by eastern Mediterranean metalworkers c.330 BCE, using imported Wootz steel from India. Knowledge of their sword-making technique is later lost.

Soldering is invented by Chavín metalworkers in Peru c.330 BCE. They also invent tumbaga, an alloy of gold with copper, which is used to make beautiful artworks.

Gold tumbaga pectoral

100 CE

Carbon steel is first created by the Haya people of Tanzania c.100 CE, centuries before its production in Central Europe.

IRON

IRON SHIFT

[Da]tes given for the start [of] the Iron Age vary, but [iro]n objects found in [In]dia and evidence of [st]eel manufacturing in [A]natolia, Turkey, date [ba]ck to 1800 BCE. Iron [is] an abundant metal, [bu]t it requires high [te]mperatures to smelt. It [is] possible that disruption [of] the tin trade forced [th]e shift in use from [br]onze to cheaper iron.

Bronze objects from the Chinese Shang dynasty become more decorative (c.1500 BCE).

Shang dynasty taotie (bronze animal mask)

Worked gold necklace, c.2000 BCE, is found in a grave near Lake Titicaca, Peru. The metal is made from a naturally occurring nugget, cold-hammered into shape.

Ironwork spreads across western Asia and the Mediterranean, 1200–1100 BCE, where this Greek vase depicting a smith at a forge was later painted in the 6th century BCE.

European sword-makers develop stronger swords by welding together successive layers of iron with added carbon, or by beating out thin iron strips and welding them together, 700–800 CE.

European iron sword

[Sil]ver starts to be [mine]d and smelted [in Ana]tolia, Turkey, [300]0–2500 BCE.

Gold and silver are among the materials used to make *The Ram in the Thicket* statuette, from Ur, Iraq, c.2550 BCE.

The Ram in the Thicket statuette

Western Mediterranean countries initially make bronze with arsenic, but poisoning forces them to switch to using tin, which is more expensive.

Bronze knife, c.2700 BCE, found at Dongxiang, provides the earliest evidence for bronze-making in China.

English iron foundries convert cheap coal to coke and use it instead of charcoal in the 1600s, to produce cast iron.

Bessemer process for making steel, invented in the 19th century, has its roots in East Asia c.1200 BCE.

1000 CE

Gunpowder weapons, including the "flying-cloud thunderclap eruptor", a cast-iron cannon, are invented in China c.1200 CE.

Cast iron is developed in Europe during the 1400s. Because it is strong and can be cast into tube shapes, it finds an immediate use in the manufacture of artillery.

Cast-iron late 17th-century 3-pounder gun

Health issues

Ötzi suffered with arthritis, from a life of hard physical work. He was also infested with intestinal whipworms, from drinking dirty water, which would have given him stomach pains and diarrhoea, and he may have had Lyme disease – a bacterial infection caused by tick bites. Growth patterns in his one surviving fingernail show that Ötzi had been seriously ill three times during the last year of his life.

Unhealed knife wound on right hand, between thumb and index finger

Although all Ötzi's fingernails dropped off after death, one was found when his body was recovered

Ötzi's body was naturally preserved by freeze-drying. It is unaltered by burial rites or other post-death interventions

Comfortable shoes

The outer covering of Ötzi's shoes was made of deerskin. Inside was a woven-grass netting that held an insulating layer of hay in place. Both parts were fastened by leather straps to a bearskin sole. The shoes would have been warm and comfortable, but they were not waterproof.

Leather straps

Inner shoe

Goat leather loincloth was fastened with a belt

▶ A museum reconstruction allows us to visualize what Ötzi may have looked like. He was short in stature and had a wiry, but strong, frame. He lacked a twelfth pair of ribs and had no wisdom teeth.

Ötzi reconstructed

Pollen from the hop hornbeam tree found in his body shows that Ötzi died in spring or early summer

Analysis of Otzi's stomach showed that his last meal was meat from a wild goat called an ibex

ÖTZI THE **ICEMAN**

In 1991, a naturally mummified man was found in the Ötzal Alps, between Austria and Italy. Nicknamed Ötzi, items found with him tell us that he lived and died around 5,300 years ago.

Ötzi's body, discovered with 70 items of clothing and equipment, gives us a unique and detailed snapshot of one individual who lived and died during the Copper Age (c.4500–3500 BCE), when metal tools were first used in Europe.

Although he belonged to a farming community, Ötzi was also a hunter. The copper axe he carried was a symbol of the status he held in his community. Ötzi had the typical health problems of early farming peoples, including bad teeth and arthritis.

Ötzi's clothing, made from the hides of domesticated goats alongside wild deerskin and bearskin, consisted of a loincloth, a belt

with a tool pouch, leggings, shoes, a coat, and a cap. The clothes were infested with fleas. He may have used a piece of grass matting to shelter from the rain.

Ötzi died violently. Not long before his death he had fought off an attacker who had wounded him in the hand with a knife. Ötzi escaped but was later killed when an arrow struck him in the back. His body was quickly covered by snow and ice, which protected it from decomposition.

Tools and equipment

Ötzi was well equipped to survive long periods away from home. For hunting he carried a longbow made from springy yew, with 14 flint-headed arrows, and a string net for catching birds and rabbits. He had a copper-headed axe, for felling trees, and a flint-bladed dagger. His kit also included flints for making fire and fungi with medicinal properties.

Flint-bladed dagger

Tree bark sheath

Body art or pain relief?

Ötzi had 61 tattoos, mostly crosses and lines. They were made not by needles but by fine cuts to the skin, into which soot was rubbed. The tattoos are on areas of the body where Ötzi would have suffered from arthritic pain. They may have been done as pain relief, like acupuncture. Ötzi is the world's oldest tattooed mummy.

Cross behind right knee

Three lines on inner right ankle

Ötzi's teeth were badly worn. His diet, which was high in cereals, gave him gum disease and tooth decay

Ötzi originally had brown hair, but it all fell out while he was in the ice. Particles of copper in his hair suggest he may have been a coppersmith

A wound to the back of the head was caused by a fall or an assault

As well as long head hairs, shorter, curly hairs were also found at the site, indicating that Ötzi probably had a beard

8000 BCE | AGRICULTURE EMERGES   6000 BCE | FIRST CITIES FORM   4000 BCE | WRITING DEVELOPS   3100 BCE | FIRST CIVILIZATIONS EMERGE

CONFLICT
LEADS TO **WAR**

For most of human history the population was small enough to avoid inter-communal violence on any great scale. Warfare began as populations rose and demand increased for land and resources. As communities grew larger, conflicts became ever more deadly.

The earliest evidence of targeted collective violence comes from a cemetery in Egypt, where archaeologists discovered 24 skeletons of hunter-gatherers who had been killed by flint arrowheads around 13,000 years ago.

The birth of agriculture led to a steep rise in violent conflict. Farmers had land, goods, and livestock to protect, and they were vulnerable to attack. Groups competed over resources, with conflict intensifying when harvests were poor. Evidence of early massacres comes from three mass graves found in Germany, from around 5000 BCE, where the dead were slain with stone adzes.

THE FIRST ARMIES

The formation of states led to the creation of armies and the development of new military technologies. These technologies included the chariot, used by elite warriors across Bronze Age Eurasia, and the composite bow, which combined horn and wood to make a small weapon of great power. After the domestication of the horse had opened up the steppes of Asia to nomadic pastoralists, swift-moving tribes of mounted nomads armed with these bows became a constant threat to the settled civilizations of China and western Eurasia.

Western literature begins with Homer's *Iliad*, a poem glorifying heroic warriors. In many cultures, warriors were considered superior to all other classes, with farmers at the bottom of the social hierarchy. Yet waging war was only possible thanks to the work of farmers, who grew the crops that armies depended on. Military campaigns had to be planned to coincide with the period when crops were available to feed the troops.

The Eurasian trade network allowed military innovations to spread widely. Gunpowder weapons, invented in China in the 13th century, reached the west in the 15th century. Gunpowder ended the elite status of warriors. European knights and Japanese samurai were both vulnerable to guns fired by conscripted peasant soldiers – for so long their social inferiors.

The wings flapped as the warrior moved

▶ **Dressed to impress**
High-ranking Celtic warriors wore helmets for display rather than protection. This 4th-century BCE bronze helmet from Romania has a huge bird of prey as its crest.

> **WAR – I KNOW IT WELL**, AND THE **BUTCHERY OF MEN**... IN CLOSE FIGHTING, I KNOW **ALL THE STEPS** OF THE **WAR GOD'S DEADLY DANCE**.

Homer, Greek poet, c.800–700 BCE, *Iliad*

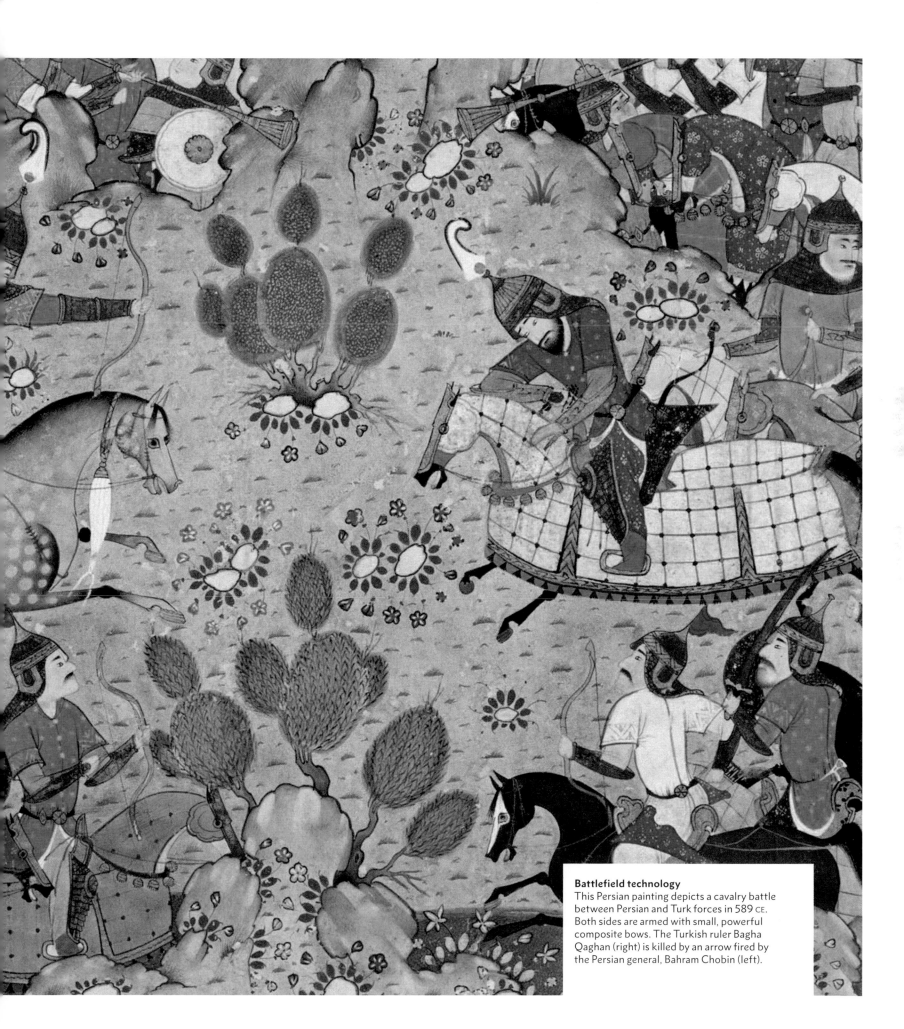

Battlefield technology
This Persian painting depicts a cavalry battle
between Persian and Turk forces in 589 CE.
Both sides are armed with small, powerful
composite bows. The Turkish ruler Bagha
Qaghan (right) is killed by an arrow fired by
the Persian general, Bahram Chobin (left).

Edge of the empire
Hadrian's Wall, built by the Romans across northern Britain in 122 CE, was both a defensive barrier and a means of controlling the population on either side. It split the territory of the local Brigantes tribe in two, and was used to monitor, and tax, movement from one side to the other.

AGE OF
EMPIRES

Empires arose as states expanded out of their own regions, conquering other areas to acquire more resources. In the process, rulers had to work out how to keep a diverse range of conquered subjects under control, exact tribute, and govern far-flung lands.

The simplest form of empire is one based on indirect rule. In the 15th century CE, the Aztecs conquered a huge empire that stretched from the Pacific to the Gulf of Mexico, but they did not directly rule any of its peoples. Instead, the conquered cities were expected to send annual tributes of

same languages (Latin and Greek), clothing, and gods throughout its territories. Men in places as distant as Egypt and northern Britain wore the Roman toga.

The Romans also offered stable rule, known as the *Pax Romana* (Roman Peace), which encouraged trade. They linked the

> " LET US PRAY THAT ALL **THE GODS** AND THEIR CHILDREN GRANT THAT **THIS EMPIRE** AND THIS CITY **FLOURISH FOREVER**. "
>
> **Aelius Aristides**, Greek rhetorician and Roman citizen, 117–181 CE, *The Roman Oration*

luxury goods – including textiles, jade, and feathers – to the Aztec capital, Tenochtitlan. The disadvantage was that their subjects resented Aztec rule and, when the chance came, rebelled against it.

Other empires were able to enforce direct rule by installing governors in conquered cities. In the 540s BCE, Cyrus the Great, founder of the Persian Empire, created 26 satrapies – local governorships. The Persian Empire was diverse and multicultural: stone reliefs show people from all over the empire, in their distinctive dress, bringing tribute to the Great King. The weakness of this system was that the conquered had no reason to remain loyal to Persia, and satraps were able to create independent power bases.

THE ROMAN EMPIRE

The most effective and long-lasting empire was that of the Romans, whose innovation was to open up citizenship to new conquests. Elites were offered the chance to become Roman, with all the rights and privileges that entailed. Unlike the Persian Empire, Rome offered a shared culture, with the

lands of their empire with a vast network of roads and rid the Mediterranean of piracy. The rich empire was also a market for goods from distant lands, including silk from China, Baltic amber, and Indian spices.

Although the Roman Empire finally fell, it left a lasting legacy in the form of roads, towns, literature, architecture, and a template for effective imperial governance that would inspire nations and rulers for millennia.

▼ The Oxus Chariot
The Persian Empire was the first to use a road system as a means of governance and communication. Satraps and messengers could travel quickly on the royal roads, in chariots similar to the one depicted by this tiny gold model.

HOW EMPIRES
RISE AND FALL

Throughout history, hundreds of empires have risen and fallen, often following a similar lifespan – a period of vigorous growth, followed by a decline. Some empires fragmented into smaller states. Others were conquered by new rising empires.

Empires were hard to sustain. Armies had to be funded and maintained. As long as an empire was expanding, the expense could be met by new conquests. However, once it reached its largest size, this had to be done by taxing the population. Empires were vulnerable to external enemies and internal conflict, as well as environmental factors, such as famine and disease.

The earliest empire we know of is that of Sargon of Akkad, who conquered all of Mesopotamia around 2300 BCE. He pulled down the fortifications of conquered cities and installed his sons as governors. The Akkadian Empire broke up around 2150 BCE after a series of rebellions and foreign invasions. Although Sargon's empire fell, he had set an example that many later Mesopotamian rulers attempted to match.

LASTING LEGACIES

The most successful conqueror was Alexander the Great (356–323 BCE), whose empire stretched from Egypt to Afghanistan. Although his empire did not survive his death, Alexander's astonishing conquests inspired both the Romans and Chandragupta Maurya,

◄ **Early emperor**
This bronze head is thought to be Sargon of Akkad. He was admired by the Mesopotamian conquerors who followed him.

founder of India's first empire. Greek ideas, art, and culture greatly influenced the Romans. Meanwhile, more than two hundred theories have been put forward to explain why the Roman Empire "fell". Today, historians tend to describe its end as a gradual transformation rather than a sudden collapse. What is more interesting, perhaps, is the fact that while central rule ended, the Roman Empire, like Sargon's and Alexander's, left a lasting legacy, through collective learning. By 1300 CE, universities that were founded in many European cities introduced Greco-Roman ideas to European intellectual life. And the Roman legal system, reorganized by Emperor Justinian, is still the basis of legal systems in most of Europe today.

► **Rise and fall of empires**
Throughout history, empires across every part of the globe have grown and then collapsed, all folllowing a similar process with these common elements contributing to their rise and decline.

Conquers other states
with power vacuums and valuable economic assets

Well-governed, strong city state reaches the limits of its growth and resources

ANY **KING** WHO WANTS TO **CALL HIMSELF MY EQUAL,** WHEREVER I WENT [CONQUERED], **LET HIM GO**.

Sargon of Akkad, Emperor of the Akkadian Empire, d.2215 BCE

Fall of the Persian Empire
This ivory shows Alexander the Great's defeat of the Persian King Darius, at the Battle of Gaugamela in 331 BCE.

PEAK OF EMPIRE

Cultural unification strengthens the imperial structure

Wealth of empire starts to fall: population is taxed more to compensate

Population increases and becomes wealthier

Infighting and corruption in state and provinces

Difficulties keeping or developing new territory; weak rulers lose their grip on government

...ay for larger ...y to hold and ...ase territory

Increase in revenue from taxes, tribute, and trade

Tax revenues decline: it is hard to pay army, and inflation sets in

Disease epidemics reduce population

Army develops loyalty to local generals or paymasters

Farmers look to local landowners rather than the state for protection

...ernment imposes ...trol and structure, ...creates political ...ility

Safety within empire declines: factions and civil wars increase

Revolutions or opportunist invaders topple empire

New empire begins

▶ Qianlong coin
This coin of China's Qianlong Emperor (ruled 1736–95) follows the model of the First Emperor's coinage. It has a powerful symbolic design, asserting the emperor's universal authority. The coin was minted in denominations of 1 and 10.

Characters around the hole are read in this order: top, bottom, right, then left. The top and bottom characters together give the emperor's title, Qianlong

Side characters (read right to left) mean "circulating treasure", signifying that the coin should circulate freely

Circle represents the dome of the heavens above the world, which is symbolized by the central square hole

Coin is made from copper alloy cast in a mould

▶ Replicated designs
These coins show how the idea of money spread across Europe. At left is a gold Greek coin issued by Philip of Macedon (ruled 359–336 BCE). Philip's coin was copied by the Parisii, a Celtic tribe of northwest Europe. On later Parisii coin designs, the imagery became less realistic.

Head of Apollo

Stylized horse

Abstract design

4th century BCE
Greek coin (front)

4th century BCE
Greek coin (back)

1st century BCE
Parisii coin (front)

1st century BCE
Parisii coin (back)

Later Parisii coin (front)

Later Parisii coin (back)

MAKING MONEY

Money is a symbolic token of value, used as a means of exchange. At first, items that had local significance, such as cowrie shells, feathers, textiles, or cacao beans, were used as tokens. These were replaced by more valuable metals, which greatly improved trade between regions.

The earliest form of trade was bartering. The problem with bartering is that both sides in the exchange must have something of equivalent value that the other wants. To solve the problem, the earliest civilizations invented money.

Currencies that were used for trade over wider areas used metals, especially gold, silver, and bronze. Gold and silver are most valued because of their scarcity, beauty, durability, and the effort needed to extract them. At first, weighed silver was used as a currency. Then, in the 1st millennium BCE, as the Eurasian trade network expanded, states began to issue coins – metal tokens stamped with their values.

The first true coins were made in Lydia, in what is now Turkey, around 600 BCE. From Lydia, coinage spread to Greece. Each Greek state minted its own coins, usually decorated with an image of a patron god or the god's sacred animal.

The act of issuing coins was an assertion of political authority and the right to rule. Rulers realized that they could use coins to promote their public image and spread ideas or information widely and quickly. Roman coins combined a portrait of the reigning emperor with news of his achievements – for example, a military victory or the building of a new temple. Similarly, Islamic caliphs issued coins bearing religious inscriptions, such as: "In the name of God, Muhammad is the messenger of God."

COINS AS EVIDENCE

The distribution of coinage is evidence of the new trade networks, and the spread of ideas, across Eurasia. Roman coins found as far away as Afghanistan and India bear witness to the trade in spices from the East.

A decline in the quality of coinage is an indication of an empire in economic trouble. The Roman Antonianus was a silver coin, first issued in 215 CE. Over time, its silver content was reduced; by the 270s, it was only silver-coated copper. This led to inflation as traders raised prices in response to what they perceived as a less valuable currency.

CHINESE COINS

Coins, in the form of miniature cast-bronze tools, became widespread in China during the Warring States period (475–221 BCE). The northern and eastern states shaped their coins like knives, while the central states modelled theirs on spades.

After uniting China in 221 BCE, the First Emperor introduced a uniform circular copper coin. It had a square hole in the centre so that coins could be strung together. Copper is not as valuable as bronze, but the intrinsic value of the material from which the coins were made no longer mattered, because everyone in China was using the same monetary system. The important factor was that the right to mint coins was a monopoly held by the imperial government.

As trade increased, so did the demand for money. Around 900 CE, Chinese merchants, who wanted to avoid carrying around thousands of coins, started trading receipts from shops where they had left money or goods. The government then granted a monopoly to certain shops, giving them the right to issue the receipts. In the 1120s, the government took over the system, and issued the world's first paper money.

One length of rope

One measure of wheat

A jar of oil

A small measure of grain

One garment

MESOPOTAMIAN COUNTING TOKENS

◀ **Symbolic worth**
These clay tokens were used by early Mesopotamian merchants to keep their accounts. Different-shaped tokens stood for different goods. The tokens were often passed between merchants as bills of trade in clay "envelopes" that recorded how many tokens were inside.

> ❝ WITH THIS **PAPER-MONEY** THEY CAN **BUY WHAT THEY LIKE** ANYWHERE **OVER THE EMPIRE**, WHILST IT IS ALSO VASTLY **LIGHTER TO CARRY** ABOUT ON THEIR **JOURNEYS**. ❞
>
> **Marco Polo**, Venetian merchant, c.1254–1324, *The Travels*

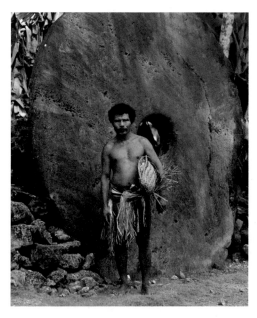

◀ **Stone money**
On the island of Yap in Micronesia huge discs carved from limestone are a traditional form of currency (*rai*). The discs were quarried on the islands of Pulau and Guam and towed on rafts to Yap. A stone's value depends on its size, workmanship, and history – especially how difficult or dangerous it was to transport to Yap. Ownership is recorded orally, and the stones often remain in situ despite changing hands.

The Triumph of Death
Following the Black Death, The Triumph of Death became a popular subject in European art. This wall painting from Sicily, painted in the 1440s, shows Death as a skeleton riding a horse, shooting down all classes, including emperors, nobles, and churchmen, with a bow and arrow.

UNHEALTHY
DEVELOPMENTS

Farming could support many more people than hunting and gathering, but the move to a limited diet proved to be a less healthy way to live. As the population rose, and communities became denser and more widely connected, diseases spread rapidly and with devastating effect.

The skeletons of early farmers reveal problems caused by the new way of life. Grain-based diets caused scurvy and rickets from a lack of vitamins C and D. Farmers also suffered injuries caused by hard, repetitive work. Female skeletons from the first farming site, Abu Hureyra in Syria, show damaged lower backs and knees, and deformed big toes, all caused by long hours kneeling to grind grain.

Periodic famine was an inadvertent consequence of agriculture. People had replaced their broad hunter-gatherer diet with a smaller number of crops and animals, all of which could fail due to climate, disease, or pests. In Egypt, farming depended on the annual flooding of the Nile, which usually reached 8m (26ft) high. A 7m (23ft) flood would result in a poor harvest, but anything less would lead to famine. Repeated failures led to the collapse of some civilizations.

DEADLY DISEASES

Close proximity made it easier for bacteria and viruses to change their host species from domesticated animals to humans. Measles, for example, evolved from the rinderpest virus, a deadly disease in cattle. Diseases could be passed on by direct contact with animals, or transmitted by blood-sucking insects, such as fleas and lice. The most devastating was bubonic plague, caused by the *Yersinia pestis* bacterium, passed from rats to fleas to humans. The worst outbreak – the 14th-century Black Death – began in Asia and was then carried west along trade routes, killing one-third of Europe's population.

Hunter-gatherers rarely had contact with rats, but human settlements, with all their rubbish, made an ideal habitat for rodents. Drinking water sources were often contaminated with human and animal faeces. Roundworm infections, and two deadly bacterial diseases – cholera and typhoid, both caused by sewage-polluted water – were common occurrences. Even something as simple as an infected cut could prove fatal before the advent of modern medicine.

◀ **Plague carrier**
Bubonic plague is an ancient disease of rodents, but humans caught it only after they began to settle in large communities. This 20 million-year-old flea, preserved in amber, carries plague bacteria in its mouthparts.

> **GREAT PITS WERE DUG** AND PILED DEEP WITH **HUGE HEAPS** OF THE **DEAD**... AND I, AGNOLO DI TURA, **BURIED** MY FIVE CHILDREN **WITH MY OWN HANDS**.
>
> **Agnolo di Tura**, Italian merchant and chronicler, c.1347

TRADE NETWORKS
DEVELOP

As agrarian civilizations grew, they were linked together in vast interconnected networks, where goods, languages, technology, microbes, and genes were all exchanged. The most important exchange network of the Agrarian Era is known today as the Silk Roads.

The treeless steppes stretch for 4,800km (3,000 miles) from eastern Europe to the borders of China. For the last 6,000 years, the steppes have been home to nomadic pastoralists. Mounted on horses or camels, these people were constantly on the move in search of fresh pastures for their animal herds. The extreme mobility of the steppe nomads enabled the creation of the Silk Roads. This collection of routes spanned the steppes of Eurasia. During the Agrarian era, they connected the entire Afro-Eurasian world zone. Other world zones had early exchange networks, such as the American trade networks of the Andes mountains and Mesoamerica, but they were smaller and less varied than the Silk Roads. While warfare played a role in connecting different civilizations, the most influential networks were built through trade.

THE SILK ROADS

The Silk Roads included land routes across China, Central Asia, and the Mediterranean and also trade that took place by sea. By the first major period of Silk Roads trade, from 50 BCE to 250 CE, small early agrarian civilizations had been consolidated into vast and powerful empires, enabling large-scale exchanges. The four ruling dynasties – the Roman, Parthian, Kushan, and Han empires – constucted road networks that connected their territories. Technological advances in metallurgy and transport, intensified agricultural production, and the emergence of coinage all contributed to conditions in Afro-Eurasia that allowed for unprecedented levels of material and cultural exchange. Meanwhile, large and powerful

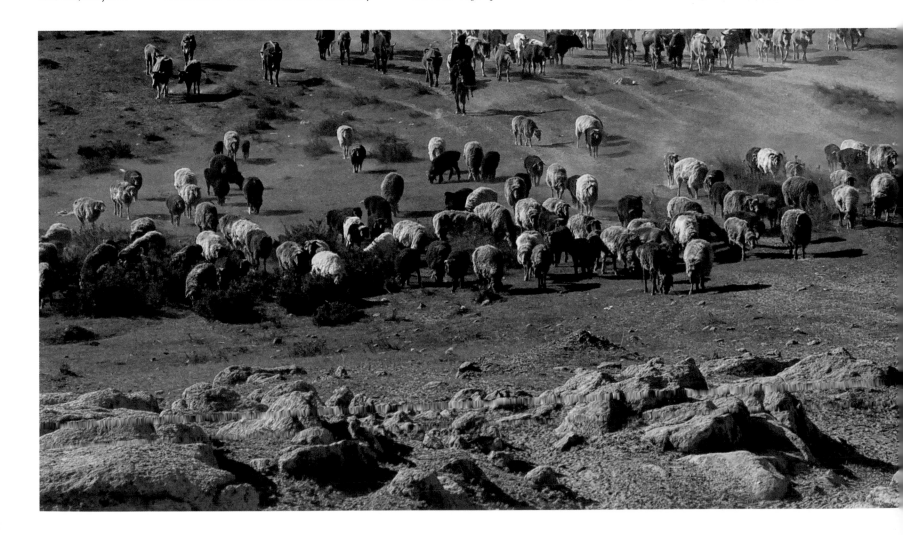

▼ **In search of pasture**
Modern Kazakh nomads, riding horses and using camels to carry their belongings, herd their flocks on the Altai Plain of China, which was part of the Silk Roads. Their way of life has changed very little in 6,000 years.

nomadic communities had appeared across the harsh interior of Inner Eurasia. They helped to link up the different civilizations, and travellers relied on these nomadic people once the Silk Roads formed.

Long-distance trade between China and the Mediterranean flourished from around 200 BCE, following the Han dynasty's expansion into Central Asia. Merchants crossed the steppes and deserts, carrying Chinese silk, jade, and bronze, Roman glass, Arabian incense, and Indian spices. Control of the trade brought great wealth to oasis towns in the deserts, and to the cities of Northern Persia and Afghanistan.

Even more important were the ideas and religions, including Buddhism and Islam, that were carried along the Silk Roads. In the 550s CE, monks from the Byzantine Empire reached China, where they managed to smuggle silkworm eggs back to the West, allowing the Byzantines to begin silk manufacture and breaking China's long-held monopoly of this sought-after fabric.

The Silk Roads also made it easy for disease to spread. During the 2nd and 3rd centuries CE, there were deadly epidemics of the same diseases in both Han China and the Roman Empire. Over time, this exchange of microbes allowed the peoples of Afro-Eurasia to build up resistance to diseases.

All these different types of exchange resulted in Afro-Eurasia having common technologies, artistic styles, cultures, and religions. Through these exchanges, the Silk Roads encouraged higher levels of collective learning, which contributed to growth, and innovation.

◄ **On horseback**
Polo, invented in Central or South Asia, spread all the way to China along the Silk Road. This pottery Tang dynasty burial figure (618–907 CE) features one of the much-prized "heavenly horses", which were traded along the Silk Road.

THEY HAD **BROUGHT THE EGGS** TO **BYZANTIUM**… THE METHOD HAVING BEEN LEARNED, THUS **BEGAN** THE ART OF **MAKING SILK**… IN THE **ROMAN EMPIRE**.

Procopius of Caesarea, Roman historian (c.500–560), on the spread of silk production

EAST
MEETS WEST

Until 1492, people in the "Old World" of Afro-Eurasia and the "New World" of the Americas were each unaware that the other existed. European explorers brought the two worlds together, leading to the "Columbian Exchange": a transfer of people, animals, crops, diseases, and technology.

BETWEEN 1492 AND 1650 UP TO **90 PER CENT** OF THE **NATIVE AMERICAN POPULATION** WAS **WIPED OUT** BY **EPIDEMICS**

WESTERN HEMISPHERE

NORTH AMERICA

Manioc
South American manioc resists drought and pests, and thrives even in poor soils. It spread around the tropical regions of the world, where it now provides a basic diet for over half a billion people.

◄ The New World
European explorers arrived in the Americas and began to extensively colonize the entire region after 1492. They returned to the Old World with crops and animals from the Americas that often became desirable luxuries in Europe.

Spanish conquistador Hernán Cortés took control of the Aztec Kingdom in 1521

Tobacco
From the early 1600s, tobacco was an important cash crop for the European settlers of North America. It was exported to Europe and spread quickly across Afro-Eurasia.

In 1500, a fleet led by Portuguese navigator Pedro Álvares Cabral landed in Brazil and took possession of the land, claiming it for his country

SOUTH AMERICA

Chilli
American chillies were easy to grow and spread rapidly across Eurasia. They were carried by Portuguese traders to Africa, India, and Southeast Asia, where they added flavour and spice to local diets.

Spanish conquistador Francisco Pizarro conquered the Inca Empire in 1533

European explorers made full use of their superior technology – horse-riding, guns, and steel weapons – to conquer the peoples of the New World, and the diseases they carried with them also helped. The Columbian Exchange transformed life across the world. Everywhere, people benefited from new foods, resulting in global population growth for the next two centuries. Crops and animals spread, along with improved agrarian techniques and new organizational methods. The power of governments was enhanced and they began to expand their territories to increase their populations and revenues, resulting in an increase in human control of the land.

New global exchange networks emerged, and the cultural impact of the Columbian Exchange was felt most profoundly in two regions: the Americas and Europe. In the Americas, it devastated cultural and political traditions: American languages died out, as people learned to speak European languages. But Europe lay at the heart of the newly created global exchange network, and flows of new information had the greatest impact here. Surprisingly, this did little to increase rates of innovation. In 1700, the world was still traditional, but the scale at which existing ideas, goods, people, crops, and diseases were exchanged had increased, paving the way for a spectacular burst of innovation in the late 18th century.

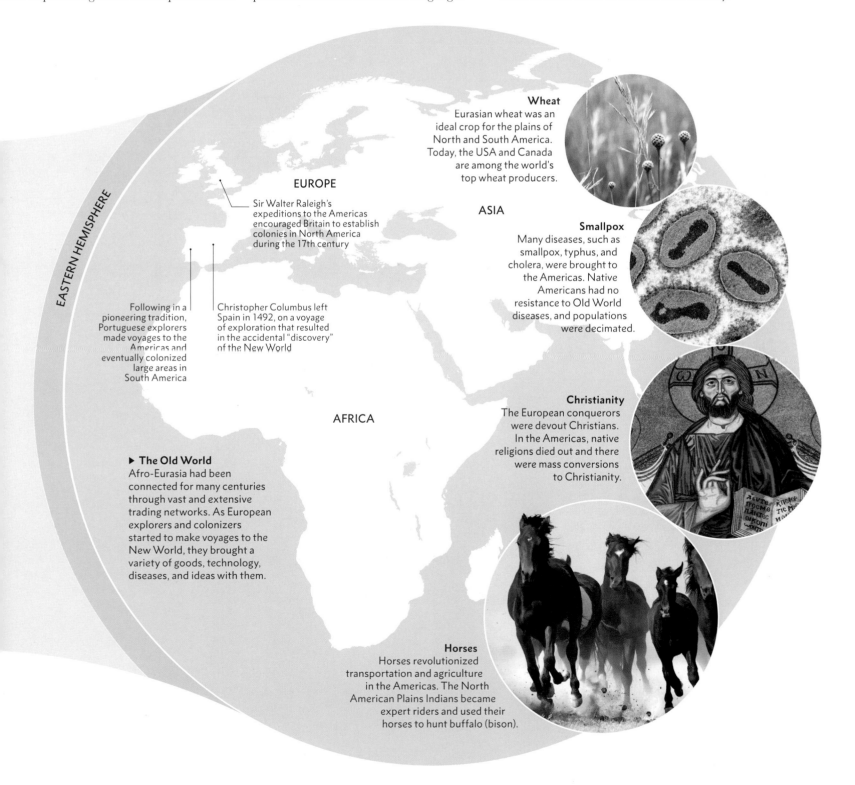

EASTERN HEMISPHERE

EUROPE

Sir Walter Raleigh's expeditions to the Americas encouraged Britain to establish colonies in North America during the 17th century

Following in a pioneering tradition, Portuguese explorers made voyages to the Americas and eventually colonized large areas in South America

Christopher Columbus left Spain in 1492, on a voyage of exploration that resulted in the accidental "discovery" of the New World

ASIA

AFRICA

▶ **The Old World**
Afro-Eurasia had been connected for many centuries through vast and extensive trading networks. As European explorers and colonizers started to make voyages to the New World, they brought a variety of goods, technology, diseases, and ideas with them.

Wheat
Eurasian wheat was an ideal crop for the plains of North and South America. Today, the USA and Canada are among the world's top wheat producers.

Smallpox
Many diseases, such as smallpox, typhus, and cholera, were brought to the Americas. Native Americans had no resistance to Old World diseases, and populations were decimated.

Christianity
The European conquerors were devout Christians. In the Americas, native religions died out and there were mass conversions to Christianity.

Horses
Horses revolutionized transportation and agriculture in the Americas. The North American Plains Indians became expert riders and used their horses to hunt buffalo (bison).

TRADE GOES GLOBAL

From the late 15th century, the world became globally connected for the first time, as European ships traversed the oceans, creating a worldwide system of maritime trade. Most important was the linking of Eurasia and the Americas, but the effects of globalization were felt worldwide.

Globalization began in 1492, when Christopher Columbus sailed west across the Atlantic, hoping to reach Asia. Instead, he found the Americas, "a New World" whose existence had not even been suspected in Eurasia. Six years later, a Portuguese fleet under Vasco da Gama sailed south and east to India. Then, in 1519–22, the Spanish expedition of Ferdinand Magellan sailed all the way around the world. Soon the English, French, and Dutch were also making long-distance voyages.

EUROPEAN MOTIVATION

Why was it Europeans rather than other peoples who connected the globe? Europe was at the wrong end of the Eurasian trade network, far from the source of spices and silks, and cut off from the overland route by the rise of the hostile Ottoman Empire. So Europeans, all too aware of their exclusion, set about creating technology – including

ships, navigational devices, and maps – to bring the spices within reach. In this, the countries of northwest Europe had an advantage over Mediterranean nations, since their coasts faced out into the Atlantic.

Europe was then a continent divided by rivalry and conflict. This spurred European countries to conquer lands overseas in search of riches to fund their frequent wars.

While China, too, had the technology to explore new lands, the country was unified and there was no incentive to investigate the wider world. There was one brief period of exploration in the early 1400s, when fleets of junks sailed as far as Africa, but the purpose was to display Chinese power rather than to discover new sources of wealth. After 1433, when the emperor called an end to these expeditions, China became inward looking.

There were no long-distance trade routes in the Americas; the Aztecs of Mexico and Incas of Peru were not even aware of each

> ◄ **The world on an egg**
> Made in Europe around 1500, this is the earliest known globe to depict the New World. It was carved on two half ostrich eggs from Africa – further evidence of global connections.

Asia with the Indian Ocean

There are 71 place names. On the east coast of Asia (not visible here) is written *Hic sunt dracones*, meaning "Here are dragons"

Africa

Madagascar

OLD WORLD

> "
> **WORLD TRADE** [DATES] FROM THE 16TH CENTURY ... FROM THEN ON THE **MODERN HISTORY OF CAPITAL** STARTS TO UNFOLD.
> "
>
> **Karl Marx**, German scholar, 1818–1883, *Das Kapital*

"Isabel" is La Isabella, Columbus's settlement in what is now the Dominican Republic

South America, labelled "Mundus Novus" (New World)

Terra Sanctae Crucis ("Land of the Holy Cross")

NEW WORLD

other's existence. As a result, the peoples of the Americas had no idea that other lands were worth exploring and no reason to build ocean-going ships.

THE NEW GLOBAL NETWORK

As a result of new global connections, the focus of trade networks shifted. Northwest Europe, formerly at the margins of the Eurasian network, became the centre of a rapidly expanding new global network. This is why four of the most widely spoken languages today are English, Spanish, Portuguese, and French. The previously important trading hubs of southern Europe, such as Venice, went into long-term decline.

European economies changed, as wealth poured in from the Americas and other lands. Power shifted from landholding aristocrats to merchants, marking the birth of what would become modern capitalism.

◀ **Portuguese trade**
In 1543, the first Portuguese ships, sailing from Goa, India, reached Japan. They exchanged Chinese silks and porcelain and Indian cloth for Japanese metalwork and artwork. This Japanese painting shows a Portuguese carrack, a type of large merchant ship.

SOUTH AMERICAN SILVER

In 1545, the Spaniards discovered a mountain of silver ore at Potosi in Bolivia. This was the biggest source of silver ever found. By 1660, about 60,000 tonnes of silver had been shipped to Spain, tripling the amount of the metal in Europe.

Silver, sought after by Asian merchants, soon became the foundation of the world economy. Much of it found its way to China, where it was used to buy silks and porcelain. Spanish galleons, sailing from Mexico, carried the silver across the Pacific to the Philippines. Portuguese ships also went east, using New World silver to buy cotton and spices in India, and porcelain and silks in China, which they then traded in Japan.

The flood of silver from America caused widespread inflation in Europe and beyond. Through trade, Spanish silver coins reached the Ottoman Empire, rendering the local coinage, with its lower silver content, less valuable. Government officials and soldiers found they could no longer live on their pay.

Despite the flow of silver from the Americas, the Spanish crown, constantly engaged in wars, was always in debt. The wealth ended up in the hands of foreign bankers who serviced the royal debt.

DESTRUCTIVE IMPACT

Globalization also spread Eurasian diseases throughout the world. Their impact on the indigenous peoples of the Americas, Australia, and the Pacific Islands was especially devastating.

At first, mines and farms in the Americas were worked by Native Americans, but so many perished as a result of ill treatment and introduced diseases that a new source of labour was required. From 1534, Europeans began to transport African slaves – who had a resistance to Old World diseases – to the Americas. Over the next 350 years, 12–25 million Africans crossed the Atlantic, chained in the holds of slave ships.

The impact of globalization on the environment was also catastrophic. The introduction of sheep to Australia and goats to the Pacific Islands, for example, resulted in widespread deforestation and the extinction of many species of native wildlife.

◀ **Spanish silver**
Famous for their consistent weight and purity, Spanish silver coins set a standard against which other coins were measured.

THRESHOLD

INDUSTRY **RISES**

Spurred on by the need to feed and care for a growing population, humans unlock a new source of energy from the Earth – fossil fuels. These power the rise of industry and consumerism, creating a new world order in which humans become a dominant force for change on Earth.

GOLDILOCKS CONDITIONS

In large, diverse, interconnected societies, collective learning is a powerful force. The journey to our highly complex modern world began in the 18th century, when new global connections enriched existing networks of exchange. The pace of change started to accelerate — as did the human capacity to control the biosphere.

Expanding networks of exchange and trend to globalization

Innovative, problem-solving skills

Rapid acceleration in collective learning

What changed?
Extensive access to new sources of energy – first coal, then oil and natural gas. These fossil fuels replaced wind, water, human, and animal power, leading to the production and use of energy on a new scale.

Agricultural revolution
Commercial methods begin to transform farming, as new technology and innovations increase the carrying capacity of the land and use less human labour. Redundant farm workers take up crafts and gravitate to urban centres, creating a potential industrial workforce.

Population growth
Efficient farming techniques allow food production to soar and support larger populations of potential factory workers.

Mechanization
Wind, water, and animal power are used to drive machinery that can grind grain, pump water, and transport goods faster and more efficiently than humans alone. Entrepreneurs – especially in the textile trade – look for ways to replace hand tools and human labour with mechanical production methods.

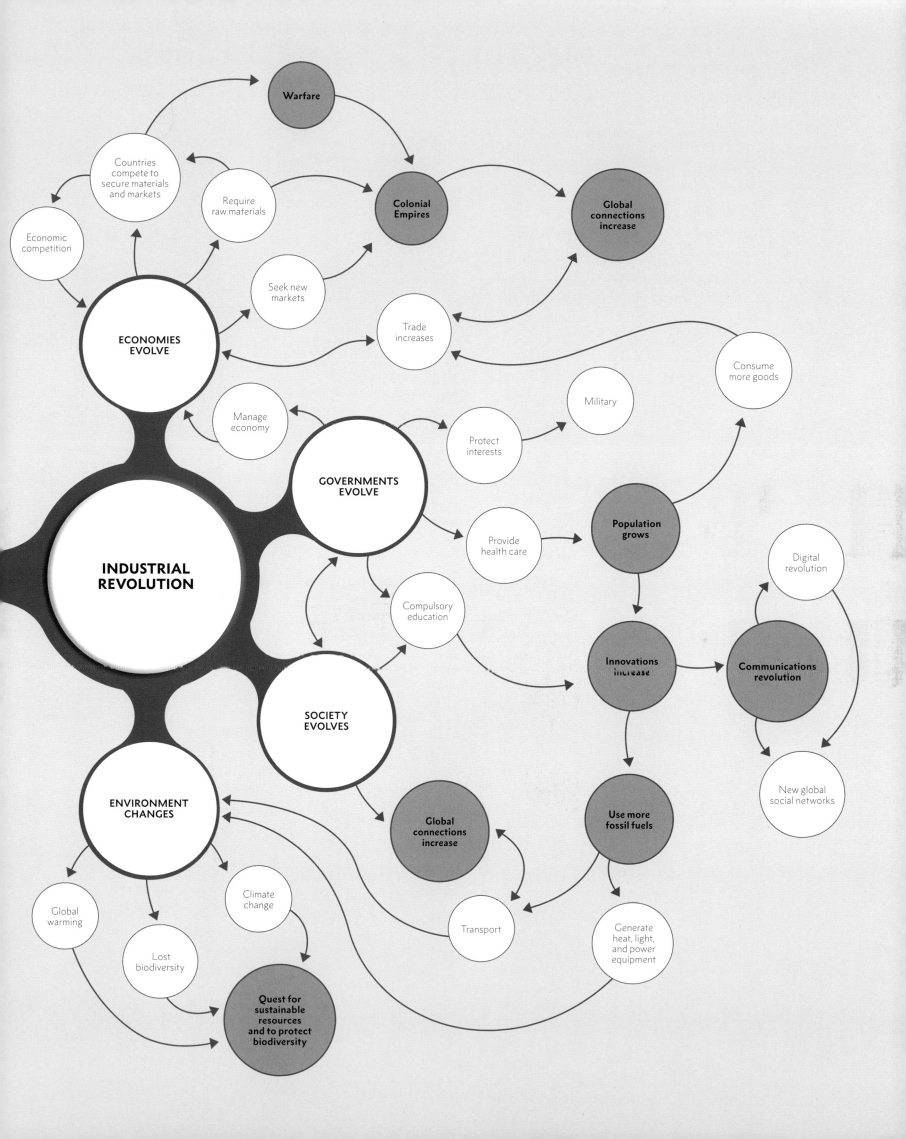

Warfare

Countries compete to secure materials and markets

Require raw materials

Colonial Empires

Global connections increase

Economic competition

ECONOMIES EVOLVE

Seek new markets

Trade increases

Consume more goods

Manage economy

Protect interests

Military

GOVERNMENTS EVOLVE

Provide health care

Population grows

Digital revolution

Compulsory education

Innovations increase

Communications revolution

INDUSTRIAL REVOLUTION

SOCIETY EVOLVES

New global social networks

Global connections increase

Use more fossil fuels

ENVIRONMENT CHANGES

Climate change

Transport

Generate heat, light, and power equipment

Global warming

Lost biodiversity

Quest for sustainable resources and to protect biodiversity

THE INDUSTRIAL **REVOLUTION**

In the mid-18th century, after hundreds of years of slow development, a series of innovations in Britain began a process that would change the world forever. This process is now known as the industrial revolution.

The industrial revolution transformed agrarian societies that discovered how to use fossil fuels like coal to replace human and animal power in manufacturing, communication, and transportation. It began in Britain, when several factors – both global and local – ushered in an era of relatively fast technological change.

WHY THERE, WHY THEN?

Britain's industrialization followed a period of rapid population growth in Europe. Innovations in agriculture, such as the horse-drawn seed drill and the adoption of modern farming methods, had combined to increase the carrying capacity of the land, fuelling population growth (see pp.252–53). It was also a time of social change: with landowners able to produce twice as much food using less labour, many agricultural workers moved to the cities or took up crafts. Landowners no longer took tribute from their peasants, who became wage earners. For the first time, the structure of society

commercial projects and rewarded innovation, as part of an intellectual climate known as the enlightenment.

Most of Britain's national income came from commerce, which was protected by a strong army and navy, and provided the essential capital needed for industrialization. London was an important trade hub; at the centre of an international trade network connecting Europe and the Americas, Britain was perfectly placed to benefit from new inventions as a result of collective learning.

In theory, with its large population, China could have industrialized at any point from the 11th century, when it developed an iron and steel industry, powered by coal. But its coalfields were located in the unstable north of the country, far from the economic centres, which had moved south after the Mongol invasions in the 13th century. The political climate was also unfavourable: the Confucian ideals promoted by the government emphasized stability, and industrialization was seen as disruptive.

[THE INDUSTRIAL REVOLUTION] WAS PROBABLY THE MOST IMPORTANT EVENT IN **WORLD HISTORY... SINCE THE INVENTION** OF **AGRICULTURE** AND **CITIES**.

Eric Hobsbawm, British historian, 1917–2012

began to change from an agrarian society to a commercialized one.

This was a significant change. Rates of innovation are slower when social and ideological conditions offer no incentives to innovate, and the political climate played a part in that too. During the 18th century, Europe's absolute monarchies stifled innovation, but Britain had a parliamentary monarchy with a government that supported

A GROWING PROBLEM

Britain's population doubled between 1750 and 1800. This led to a shortage of wood, so coal was increasingly used as a source of fuel. As the shortage became acute, demand for coal rose. Britain had abundant reserves, but they were underground and difficult to access. This created a need to innovate; Britain had all the necessary conditions for innovation to thrive – and thrive it did.

Working from home
Agricultural workers freed up to work in cottage industries, such as textiles, boosted the economy, trade, and exports, helping to pave the way for industrialization.

▼ **Workings of a coal mine**

As Britain began to industrialize, more coal was needed to fuel steam engines and furnaces. As a result, coal production increased, mines got deeper, and the industry became more dangerous.

Horse-drawn carts were used for delivery of wood and other materials and the transportation of coal

Coal for collection

Brick chimney

Steam engine house

Steam engine also powered winches to transport miners up and down one shaft and bring coal up to the surface

Hot air rising from the upcast had a lower density than the cold air in the nearby downcast shaft. The difference in air pressures pushed fresh cold air down the downcast

Large piles of wood support mine shafts and tunnels

Wooden platform for simple pulley system

Upcast shaft was lined with wood

Workers were winched down to the pit bottom in large wicker corf

Workers transported coal from small coal seams to the main shaft

Hot air rose up the upcast shaft, drawing poisonous and highly combustible gases from the mine up the shaft to the surface

Coal was hoisted up to the pit surface

Water pump pipe extracted water from below ground. Miners sometimes worked up to their waists in water, and mines were prone to flooding

Coal supply for furnace

Furnace burned coal to ventilate the mine, removing poisonous gases, and reducing the chance of explosions

Worker shovelled coal into furnace

Cold air pushed down the downcast shaft ventilated the mine

Horse-drawn coal corves on wooden wagons were taken to down a shaft

IN **1700** BRITAIN PRODUCED **2.54 MILLION TONNES** OF COAL. IN **1900** IT PRODUCED **224 MILLION TONNES**

Young boys called trappers were in charge of opening and closing doors that controlled ventilation and the flow of air around the mine

Miners and their families lived in tiny cramped cottages near the mine

Coal shovelled into boiler to power engine

Boiler

Winding and pumping engine

Spoil tip, the waste rock removed during mining

Coal supply

By the late 18th century, the purpose of the steam engine was twofold: both to pump water from the mine, and also to move the baskets that lowered the miners and to remove the coal. This required giving the steam engine rotary motion.

Worker in a shallow coal seam

Hurriers, often women or young children, transported coal away from the pit face. Smaller seams with height restrictions did not have tracks or horses

Main coal seam

Hewers, usually adult men, chipped at coal from the pit face using pick axes. Davy lamps provided illumination

Wooden props prevented the roof from collapsing over areas from which coal had been excavated

Coal was loaded onto corves on shallow wooden carts with iron wheels and pushed along major coal seams

Entire families were encouraged to work in mines, until the 1842 Mines Act prohibited the employment of children under 10. Men would typically hew the coal from the rockface and the women and children would haul it to the surface.

COAL FUELS INDUSTRY

Access to large reserves of coal was the breakthrough that fuelled the machines of industry and set the modern age alight. Coal was the first of several fossil fuels used to power the industrial world.

The history of coal is far older than the mines of 18th-century Europe. It was used in China as early as 1000 BCE to heat homes, smelt copper, and fuel blast furnaces to create iron; by the 11th century CE, the Song Dynasty relied on coal to produce the iron needed to make weapons and armour. In Britain, coal was used as fuel from the 2nd century CE, when the Romans mined coal near the surface to heat their forts, fuel furnaces, and burn sacrifices at altars in honour of their gods. After the Romans departed in the 5th century, the use of coal declined. For most people, wood was a far more accessible source of fuel, but from the 13th century sea coal – an abundant resource that washed up on the beaches of northeast England – was collected and distributed by boat.

Fuel was needed for industrialization, and in Britain coal deposits were fortuitously located in thick seams, albeit deep underground. However, early mining was hazardous: pits continually filled with water, and horsepower removed it too slowly. The steam engine, invented by Thomas Newcomen and developed by James Watt, was the breakthrough that made it possible to effectively pump water out of mines and access more coal at greater depths.

◄ Screening coal Women and children sorted the coal and separated it into different groups based on size. The sorted coal was washed and dried, before being transported from the mine.

STEAM POWER
DRIVES CHANGE

Developed in the 18th century to pump floodwater from mines, the steam engine was the defining invention of the industrial age. Fuelled by the newly available coal, steam engines replaced human, animal, and water power and led to the rise of factories, railways, and steamships.

In 1712, British ironmonger and engineer Thomas Newcomen invented a steam engine that could pump water with the power of twenty horses from mines deep underground. This made it possible to mine to greater depths and unlock the seemingly endless supply of British coal. Newcomen's machine became so popular that by 1755 his engines were installed in France, Belgium, Germany, Hungary, Sweden, and the United States. However, Newcomen's engine was large, inefficient, and consumed enormous quantities of coal: without improvements it could operate only in coal mines. In 1765, inventor James Watt realized a lot of coal and steam was going to waste in Newcomen's machine and built an engine with a separate condenser to eliminate this wastage.

▲ Powering industry
Watt's improvements to the Newcomen engine enabled it to power factory machinery, leading to the rise of mass-production.

RISE OF THE FACTORY SYSTEM

Although mining engines relied on an up-and-down motion, the industrialist Matthew Boulton recognized the potential of Watt's improved design to be adapted to the rotary motion needed to drive factory machinery. Boulton was the owner of Birmingham's Soho manufactory, which produced small metal trinkets and toys. Like many industrialists of the time, Boulton relied on a waterwheel to power his machinery, and when a drought left the river bed dry, production came to a halt.

▼ Driving change
Railways carried passengers, raw materials, and manufactured goods. Steam locomotives provided cheap transportation that encouraged further industrialization.

Boulton gave Watt the tools and engineers to build a prototype, and in 1776, Watt's steam engine was invented, releasing manufacturing from the constraints of natural power. It produced the same amount of power as the Newcomen engine on a quarter of the fuel, and could be installed anywhere. Soho became the first steam-powered factory in the world and its employees began toiling on production lines in the new mass-production of goods. Steam engines enabled the growth of a new mode of production: the factory system.

The shift to machine-based manufacturing began with the textile industries in Britain, the United States, and Japan. Steam power transformed the industry and the mass-production of textiles transformed the British economy. Attaching a steam engine to spinning and weaving machines allowed cotton textiles to be produced at unprecedented speeds. By 1850, Britain was using 10 times more cotton than in 1800, and textiles became cheap and widely available. The demand for more American cotton kept the country's slave plantations in business.

THE SPREAD OF STEAM
Steam engines made it possible to work and produce goods without being reliant on proximity to waterways. Towns sprang up around steam-powered factories at the turn of the century. To supply these towns

with the necessary amounts of coal, raw materials, and goods for market, new transport links were created: turnpike roads, canals, and then railways.

Railways were part of a second wave of industrialization that was made possible through the mass-manufacture of iron. British engineer Abraham Darby learned how to smelt iron by burning coke in the early 18th century, and Britain's iron production rapidly increased thanks to the new availability of coal. The marriage of iron and smaller, high-pressure steam engines allowed for the manufacture of steam locomotives and tracks to run them along. During the 19th century, new railway lines joined up other industrializing nations too. Iron, coal, and railways became the central symbols of the industrial revolutions in Germany, Belgium, France, and the United States. Railways were another example of the incessant drive in the industrial age to improve existing technologies.

Introducing a turbine system to the steam engine allowed the technology to power ships. The introduction of a screw-propeller, which was more efficient than the earlier paddle wheels, enabled a more consistent propulsion. By 1840, steamships were making trips across the Atlantic to transport goods and people. By the end of the 19th century, the ironclad warship, a steam-propelled vessel protected by iron or steel plates, showed that the power of steam could also be used as a weapon.

▲ **Women weavers**
The power loom was gradually adopted in textile factories. When it became more efficient, women and children could operate the equipment and replaced men as weavers.

THOSE WHO ADMIRE **MODERN CIVILIZATION** USUALLY **IDENTIFY IT** WITH THE **STEAM ENGINE** AND THE ELECTRIC TELEGRAPH.

George Bernard Shaw, Irish playwright and political activist, 1856–1950

▲ **Shipping lines**
The Royal Netherland Steamship company transported goods, passengers, and mail between Europe and the Dutch East Indies.

Coal

EFFICIENT TRANSPORT NETWORKS
Getting raw materials to factories and finished goods to market was an essential aspect of industrialization. Turnpike roads were followed by canals and later railways. Steam ships enabled fast transport across the Atlantic.

SOURCE OF ENERGY
Countries industrialized by harnessing an energy source: water, coal, oil, or gas. Coal was the main energy of the Industrial Revolution, used in steam engines, iron-producing blast-furnaces, and as fuel.

TECHNOLOGICAL ADVANCES
Improvements in steam power technology were constantly made, leading to locomotives and steam ships. Coal-burning steam engines still power the world by producing much of its electricity.

Oil

A WORKFORCE
Population growth created by innovations in agriculture led to the specialization of labour: artisans, craftsmen, weavers, and wage workers were no longer tied to rural areas and could migrate to cities to find work in factories.

Steam engine

INNOVATIVE MINDSET
New machinery, such as the water frame, cotton gin, and spinning jenny, allowed goods to be mass-produced. Large machines powered by steam engines led to the rise of the factory system.

THE PROCESS OF
INDUSTRIALIZATION

FREEDOM TO EXCHANGE IDEAS
The exchange of ideas between innovators and industrialists led to the creation of new technologies, such as the steam engine. Industrial espionage and expanding trade routes enabled these technologies to spread.

As the first country to undergo an industrial revolution, Britain provided a template that other nations could follow. Each country took a unique path, but they all shared common factors.

Industrialization transformed agrarian economies. It produced a series of technological innovations that increased the use of natural resources and led to the mass production of manufactured goods. Access to new energy unlocked a chain of innovation; the invention of machines that increased production but required less human energy to operate allowed work to be organized differently in factories, which led to increased specialization and division of labour. As science was increasingly applied to industry, new materials like iron contributed to developments in transport and communication infrastructures.

Eventually, industrialization resulted in political, social, and economic change as trade expanded, economies grew, governments responded to the needs of the new industrialized societies, and new cities and empires emerged.

Iron

STRONG TRADE LINKS
Industry created wealth: governments and industrialists provided the capital. New domestic and international markets were opened to provide raw materials and buyers for the finished products.

INGREDIENTS FOR INDUSTRIALIZATION

◄ How industrialization works
Industrialization was a process that transformed agricultural societies and economies. Spurred on by new inventions and technologies, it resulted in vast social and political changes, new economic doctrines, and the creation of powerful industrial empires.

GROWTH OF CITIES
Cities sprang up around industrial centres. Mass-urbanization often led to overcrowding, squalor, and the spread of disease. Industrial cities were dirty, and provided little sanitation or running water for working-class inhabitants.

POLITICAL PARTNERSHIPS
Revolution, the rise of the middle classes, and political and social reforms led to new social contracts between governments and their citizens, the creation of the modern state, and the rise of democracy.

SOCIAL REFORMS
In the 19th century, governments began to act to improve the lives of their citizens, introducing laws to control working hours and child labour; compulsory public education; health systems; and instigating sanitation projects to clean up cities.

MONEY MANAGERS
Industrial governments began to manage markets. Financial institutions were created to control and accumulate wealth, including banks, stock markets, and insurance agencies.

POWERFUL MILITARIES
Industrial wealth enabled governments to create militaries large enough to compete with other industrialized nations. These militaries were sometimes also used to control vast colonial empires.

MILITARY TECHNOLOGY
Building strong militaries was a major concern of industrial powers. Military technology, such as machine guns, gave governments control over markets and encouraged some unindustrialized nations to open to trade.

NEW PRODUCTION METHODS
Factories housing the new industrial machines mass-produced goods. There were cial consequences, as workers toiled for long hours, in terrible conditions and with very little pay.

NEW IDEOLOGIES
As governments of industrial countries adopted the institutions of the modern state, concepts of nationalism and imperialism developed. Inherent in imperialist doctrine were the ideals of supremacy over peoples and nations of the unindustrialized world.

CONSUMER CULTURE
The availability of luxury products at low cost, an influx of foreign goods through new trade networks, and higher wages led to the rise of the middle classes. The consumer revolution created capital that could be re-invested.

COLONIAL STRENGTH
Industrial powers used their strong armies and navies to colonize parts of the world rich in the raw materials needed for their factory-made products, in a practice known as imperialism.

ECONOMIC STRENGTH
Industrialization drove consumer capitalism, which created wealth. It resulted in a growing divide between rich and poor citizens, and an even larger division between industrialized and unindustrialized countries.

REASONS TO CONTINUE INNOVATING

NEW INFRASTRUCTURE AND INSTITUTIONS

SOCIAL, POLITICAL, AND ECONOMIC CHANGE

1 CHANGE BEGINS

British inventors and innovators lead the way, mechanizing the textile industry and introducing the factory system. Using raw materials from the overseas colonies and the newly mechanized factory processes to mass-produce cheaper goods, Britain begins to dominate world trade.

Steam engine is developed by James Watt, 1765. It is more efficient than the Newcomen engine (1712) and able to power machines, leading to the rise of the factory system.

Soho Manufactory opens, 1766. It pioneers mass production of a range of metal and glass goods using steam power.

Cromford Mill, in Derbyshire, built in 1771, is the first water-powered cotton-spinning mill. The system is adopted by other industrializing countries.

Spinning jenny, invented in 1765, lowers the cost of yarn and helps meet demand from weavers.

Water frame, a spinning machine powered by water and invented by Richard Arkwright, in 1769, requires less skill to operate.

Adam Smith's The Wealth of Nations is published in 1776. It expounds a new economic theory for the industrial age, advocating free trade (trade without restrictions).

Flying Shuttle (patented 1733) is more widely adopted by textile manufacturers c.1753, doubling the output of individual weavers.

GREAT BRITAIN

1750

Bridgewater Canal opens, 1761. It is entirely man-made and revolutionizes transport in Britain.

World's first cast iron bridge is constructed by Abraham Darby III over the Severn River, Shropshire in 1779. It becomes known across the world as a symbol of the Industrial Revolution.

Spinning mule, 1779, combines the spinning jenny with the water frame and fully automates the weaving process, which leads to expansion of the textiles industry.

Puddling furnace, invented by Henry Cort in 1783, increases wrought iron production by 400 per cent in 20 years.

Threshing machine, invented in 1786, increases efficiency in farming.

TIMELINES

INDUSTRY GOES GLOBAL

Britain's early industrialization gave the country a new economic might and an ability to exploit its position on a global scale. Other countries soon tried to emulate its success.

Industrialization arose in Britain as the result of a combination of unique and unplanned forces, but it could be replicated by other countries, where it was implemented by strong governments or by entrepeneurs. The new industrial societies developed in their own way, each with distinctive features, but they all descended from the British predecessor and shared common elements, such as the importance of coal, iron, steel, and the textiles industry.

Britain tried to protect her advantage by preventing new technology and skilled workers from leaving, but countries determined to compete smuggled out machinery, sent spies to learn British secrets, and bribed entrepreneurs to set up factories abroad. The first countries to industrialize were the ones that were geographically or culturally similar to Britain: Belgium, France, and Prussia were next to develop railways and factories essential for industrialization.

Coal gas first used by William Murdock to light his home in 1792. Eventually coal gas replaces candles and oil lamps and is used to light up streets, houses, and factories.

Cotton gin, invented by Eli Witney, 1793, efficiently separates cotton seeds from fibre; production – and demand for slave labour – soars.

Cotton gin

Richard Trevithick uses steam locomotive to transport coal, 1804, and paves the way for a new era of fast, efficient transport.

USA

BELGIUM

European Industrial Revolution begins in 1799 when Englishman William Cockerill contravenes British law to build spinning machines in Belgium.

1800

North River Steamboat, 1807, connects New York with Albany via the Hudson River. First commercial use of steam for river transport.

James Young begins distilling oil in 1848, to produce petroleum, paraffin, and kerosene for use in lamps and for lubricating machinery.

1850

The commercial American oil industry is born when Edwin Drake strikes oil in Titusville, Pennsylvania in 1859. By the end of the 19th century oil is a major fossil fuel used to power engines.

Pneumatic tyre created by Robert Thompson, 1845, makes travel more comfortable.

USS Princeton, 1843, was the first screw-propelled warship powered by steam.

Mass manufacture of weapons is introduced to Europe by German steelworker Alfred Krupp in 1847 after he constructs the first steel-cast cannon.

American steam-powered warships arrive in Tokyo Bay in 1853 and use force to open Japan to trade with industrial nations.

Bessemer process, 1856 enables the mass-production of steel, which reduces the cost and allows it to be used for large-scale engineering work.

Four railways built in France by British engineer Thomas Brassey in 1841. France develops a railway system, which is essential for industrialization.

Launch of SS Great Western, 1837, the first paddle steamship to cross the Atlantic. Steam ships revolutionize the transportation of goods and people.

Siemens-Martin process improves steel production and makes it cheaper, 1865.

JAPAN

First rotating electric motor created by Moritz von Jacobi, 1834. Four years later, his improved design was strong enough to power a boat.

PRUSSIA

Rapid industrialization of Japan instituted by the Meiji government in 1868.

French textile factories open in Rouen, Lille, and Mühlhausen, 1830, and the textile industry drives industrialization.

3 INDUSTRIAL WORLD

Driven by the desire to compete, Japan and Russia industrialize against a background of domestic social and political upheaval. European powers also compete to secure raw materials in the scramble for Africa.

Rail engineer Horatio Allen ships America's first steam locomotive from England, 1829.

Gatling gun first used in the American Civil War, in 1860, is intended to reduce deaths from war-time disease.

Pennsylvania steelworks built by Scotsman Andrew Carnegie in 1875. It utilizes the Bessemer system, and the American steel industry greatly expands.

FRANCE

First passenger train runs from Stockton to Darlington, 1825.

Benz automobile

First automobile is patented by Karl Benz in 1886. It is powered by the internal combustion engine, which runs on the newly available fossil fuel – oil.

2 THE REVOLUTION SPREADS

Political revolutions in 1830 and 1848 cause social upheaval but spread liberal ideas and new innovations across Europe. The USA also starts to industrialize, capitalizing on the rich natural resources of her newly acquired territories, and the pace of change accelerates after the American Civil War ends in 1865.

William Cockerill imports a Watt steam engine to Liège, 1813. Steam power transforms the Belgian coal, iron, and textile industries.

Richmond Union Passenger Railway opens in Virginia, in 1888. It is the first successful large electric street railway system.

Trans-Siberian railway constructed 1891–1916 opens up vast areas of Russia to industrialization.

RUSSIA

1900

GOVERNMENTS EVOLVE

Governments soon realized that industrialization could increase their country's wealth – and it changed the way they ruled. They began to work in partnership with industry, and this ushered in a new balance of power, as governments became managers of markets and citizens.

The process of industrialization saw the nature of government change. Structures that served agrarian civilizations either evolved or were replaced by new institutions that were developed to manage the wealth and power of industrial economies. As the first country to industrialize, the British government led the way in facilitating the creation of more wealth, cooperating with merchants and using its navy to protect their overseas interests. Successful commerce led to larger markets and even greater wealth, so the government began to encourage innovations to meet demand and increase output. Other countries observed that industrialization produced revenues that could be used to fund their militaries, and their governments also became increasingly concerned with trying to support industrialists, control the new economies, and manage the growing numbers of wage workers – all of which led to more bureaucracy and the creation of the modern state.

The way in which modern states evolved varied dramatically. France created a completely new bureaucracy after the social and political revolution of 1789 swept away the institutions associated with its *ancien régime*. Britain already had an established representative assembly and gradually developed other institutions over time. To ensure the loyalty of their citizens, leaders began to develop national ideologies, and, by 1914, the modern state had begun to shape the politics of countries around the world.

> ❝
> THE **SUBJECTS OF EVERY STATE** OUGHT TO **CONTRIBUTE TOWARDS** THE SUPPORT OF THE **GOVERNMENT** IN PROPORTION TO THEIR RESPECTIVE ABILITIES.
> ❞
>
> **Adam Smith**, Scottish philosopher and pioneer of the political economy, 1723–1790

▼ **Pressures of power**
Industrialization transformed society, distributing wealth far more broadly, and different groups began to make demands on goverments.

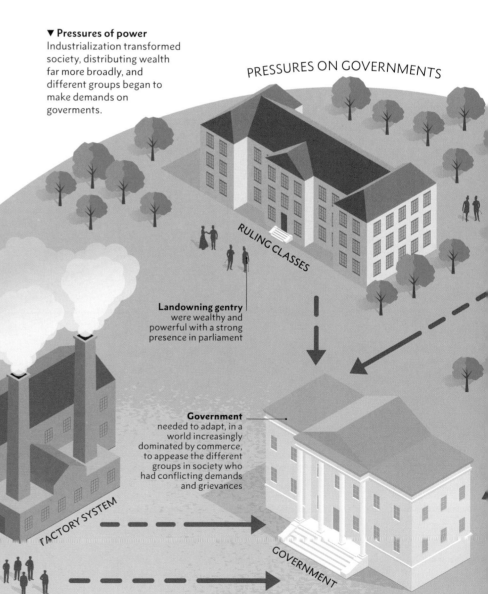

PRESSURES ON GOVERNMENTS

RULING CLASSES

Landowning gentry were wealthy and powerful with a strong presence in parliament

Government needed to adapt, in a world increasingly dominated by commerce, to appease the different groups in society who had conflicting demands and grievances

Industrialists gained enough wealth to demand more representation in government. They pressed for the adoption of free trade, so they could accumulate more wealth

Wage workers toiled in the new factories for long hours with little pay and sometimes in dangerous conditions. They attacked the industrial machines, and organized unions and strikes to campaign for better working conditions and wages

FACTORY SYSTEM

GOVERNMENT

▶ **The new establishment**
Governments were forced to adapt to manage the growing wealth and power of industrial economies. To do so, they increasingly developed the institutions of modern states: citizen armies, taxation, and services that included infrastructure, protection, education, and hospitals.

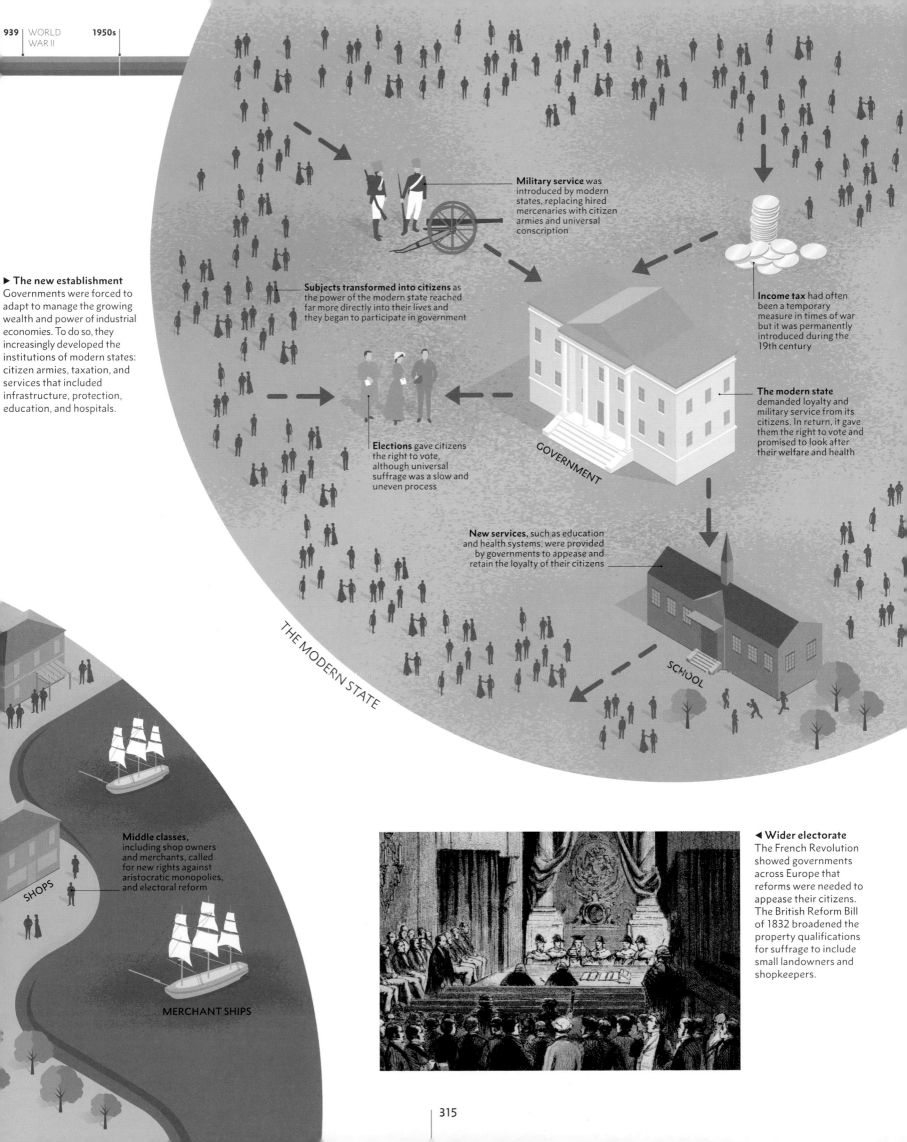

Military service was introduced by modern states, replacing hired mercenaries with citizen armies and universal conscription

Subjects transformed into citizens as the power of the modern state reached far more directly into their lives and they began to participate in government

Income tax had often been a temporary measure in times of war but it was permanently introduced during the 19th century

Elections gave citizens the right to vote, although universal suffrage was a slow and uneven process

The modern state demanded loyalty and military service from its citizens. In return, it gave them the right to vote and promised to look after their welfare and health

GOVERNMENT

New services, such as education and health systems, were provided by governments to appease and retain the loyalty of their citizens

THE MODERN STATE

SCHOOL

Middle classes, including shop owners and merchants, called for new rights against aristocratic monopolies, and electoral reform

SHOPS

MERCHANT SHIPS

◀ **Wider electorate**
The French Revolution showed governments across Europe that reforms were needed to appease their citizens. The British Reform Bill of 1832 broadened the property qualifications for suffrage to include small landowners and shopkeepers.

CONSUMERISM
TAKES OFF

Industrialization meant that land was no longer the only source of wealth. It became possible to generate wealth through manufacturing and trading goods. During the late 18th century, the middle classes grew, leading to a new emphasis on upward mobility and consumption.

▲ **Household items for everyone**
Expansion in the pottery industry increased consumer choice, and labourers who once ate from metal platters dined from Wedgwood porcelain.

▼ **Consumer culture**
With the advent of the department store, customers could buy an astonishing array of goods all in one place and shopping became a leisure activity.

Industrialization brought improvements in transport and manufacturing technology, which increased the availability of consumer products. This, combined with increased international trade, brought an unprecedented array of new goods to the domestic market. Rising prosperity and social mobility allowed the middle classes to increase their ranks and more people had a disposable income to spend. The middle classes were not a homogeneous group but a broad band of the population, which fell between the aristocracy and the workers. At the lower end were the shopkeepers and at the top were the capitalists who owned companies. They included businessmen and entrepreneurs, doctors, lawyers, and teachers. The emergent middle classes all shared a common interest in the expansion of the economy and held specific ideas about the role the government should play in its management. They wanted an economy unfettered by government restrictions, as they thought this was the best way to foster individual achievement. They also shared common values: they believed that through hard work and self-reliance it was possible to achieve economic success.

The notion of self-improvement was a key part of middle-class culture. As they rose up the social ladder, and in order to ensure the aristocracy no longer had an unfair advantage, the middle classes campaigned for electoral reform and free trade. These were seen as the necessary conditions to make it possible for anyone to succeed through their own efforts.

In Britain, the middle classes converted economic success into political power with the 1832 Reform Act, as a more aspirational society began to demand and expect more from the government.

CONSPICUOUS CONSUMPTION

The middle classes often aspired to the consumption patterns of the aristocracy. Clothing and household possessions were a way of communicating one's social position and by the end of the 18th century these status symbols were within the financial reach of many. The dizzying array of goods on offer included textiles, furniture, clothes, hats, china, books, jewellery, lace, perfume, and food. Middle-class wives filled their homes with new material possessions and purchased fashionable clothing to display their husbands' financial success.

Wages were high in 18th-century Western Europe, especially in Britain, which meant that even members of the lower classes could afford some of these consumer goods. Most 18th-century towns had taverns offering cheap meals, and coffee houses where coffee and chocolate could be consumed and ideas could be exchanged.

Greater purchasing power and a gradual fall in prices led to rising demand for new consumer products, which in turn fuelled the economies of industrializing countries. These commodities were made affordable by slave labour, with over 11 million slaves producing the goods that flowed into Europe's ports. These slaves were part of a system known as the "triangular trade": European merchants transported slaves from Africa to work on plantations in the Americas and the Caribbean, and then transported the commodities produced by the slaves back to Europe.

ADVERTISING AND ASPIRATIONS

English entrepreneur, Josiah Wedgwood, noticed the way aristocratic fashions slowly filtered down through society. He sold tea services to the British Queen, and his "Queen's Ware" became a must-have item among the middle classes. Wedgwood realized that he needed to convince consumers they wanted to buy his wares, and that consumers were primarily women. He opened a showroom where women were encouraged to meet, drink tea, and be shown his new ranges of china. His pottery reached every industrial market in Europe and North America. He is often considered the father of modern advertising. Wedgwood's marketing genius had a knock-on effect in London and then abroad, as retail outlets made products more easily available to the consumer. This was manifest in the growth of

Cocoa bean

◀ **Chocolate temptations**
Once the favoured drink of the aristocracy, chocolate became accessible to the general public, and manufacturers targeted women and children in advertising campaigns.

department stores, which opened in Paris in the 1830s, Russia in the 1850s, and Japan in the 1890s.

With the rapid growth of towns and cities, by the 19th century shopping had become an important cultural activity, as a shift in behaviour meant people began buying for fashion rather than necessity. Shop fronts displayed mirrors, bright lights, colourful signs and advertisements, and all of their products to entice shoppers inside. Many shops tried to appeal to the wealthier end of the market, but cheaper mass-manufactured goods and an abundance of food markets made shopping a cultural activity open to every class.

◀ **Luxury and slavery**
Imports of raw cotton, sugar, rum, and tobacco came from slave plantations in the Caribbean, where African slaves were the primary source of labour.

Popular catchcries of the American and French revolutions, the concepts of liberty, equality, and fraternity were drawn from 17th and 18th century Enlightenment ideals of reason, knowledge, and the freedom of people to improve their condition. The marriage between the philosophies of the Enlightenment and the actions of the revolutionaries launched a sea change in western politics. People began to demand freedom from the oppression of absolute monarchies and imperial overlords and wanted a new social contract in its place. On a practical level, this included greater representation in government and the right to own land, but it also brought about a general shift in consciousness. The existence of universal natural rights became part of a new, more empathetic world view, which fed into the development of the modern state.

EQUALITY AND **FREEDOM**

Revolutionary ideas promoting liberty, equality, and fraternity were introduced to the industrializing world in the late 18th century, after revolutions in France and America dismantled established aristocratic regimes. These ideas echoed through the politics of the 19th century and became central to modern beliefs about human rights.

INTERNATIONAL EXCHANGE

These principles were first asserted by Thomas Jefferson, a key figure in the American War of Independence and author of the 1776 Declaration of Independence. The Declaration stated that all men are born free, are equal before the law and have natural rights to property, life, and liberty – ideas that remain central tenets of democracy today. Democracy itself was not a new concept: it had been established in ancient Athens around the 5th century BCE, and was rediscovered during the Renaissance. The Athenian experience helped inspire revolutions against absolute monarchies, such as in France.

The Declaration of Independence – and the American revolution itself – was heavily influenced by international figures: English philosopher John Locke argued that legitimate governments needed the consent of the governed; writer and activist Thomas Paine advocated for the right to revolt against a government that did not protect its citizens' needs. They published their arguments in polemical pamphlets, distributed through a revolutionary exchange network, including men who

200 COPIES OF THE AMERICAN **DECLARATION** OF INDEPENDENCE WERE **PRINTED AND DISTRIBUTED**

had participated in both the American and the French revolutions, such as the Marquis de Lafayette – a French hero of the American war. This ensured that ideas, such as Paine's *Rights of Man* (1791), reached an international audience. The spread of ideas between America and France was the most important political exchange network of the time. America showed the world what was possible: many Frenchmen helped in its liberation from British rule and returned home influenced by what they had seen. After France's own uprising, the Marquis de Lafayette enlisted help from Thomas Jefferson – in Paris at the time – to pen the *Declaration of the Rights*

◀ **The gift of liberty**
The Statue of Liberty was built by a French architect as a gift to the United States from France. It became an icon of the United States and a symbol of freedom.

of Man and of the Citizen. The American and French revolutions revealed how powerful uncensored ideas could be.

The exchange of Enlightenment ideas was encouraged among the bourgeoisie, the middle class who led the French revolution. They were ambitious and well-read, schooled in the theories of Montesquieu, Rousseau, and Voltaire, the thinkers known as the "philosophes" who advocated the uncensored exchange of ideas and freedom of the press. The philosophes spread their views through the Republic of Letters, a community of European and American intellectuals who communicated through letters, essays, and published papers.

In the 17th and 18th centuries, Enlightenment thought led to a shift away from religious dogma towards scientific experiment and empirical modes of thought. Scientific progress and technological innovation helped incubate the industrial revolution in Britain. The exchange of broader Enlightenment ideas was encouraged among the middle classes of Europe through "societies of thought" such as reading rooms, coffee houses, Masonic lodges, and scientific academies. Coffee houses became famous meeting places for later revolutionaries such as Karl Marx and Friedrich Engels, key figures of the 1848 revolutions in Europe. They harnessed the power of the rotary press, invented in 1843, which enabled the mass-production of print books and newspapers. Marx's own newspaper, the *Rheinische Zeitung*, reported on the events of the 1848 uprisings, and helped to spread the revolutionary message to the masses.

THE LEGACY
The American, French, and other revolutions of the 19th century were all based on the Enlightenment idea that

humans have certain inalienable rights. The government's role would be to recognize and secure the rights and property of its citizens, and it would be formed by elected, tax-paying citizens. Women, slaves, and foreigners were not included. However, in the aftermath of the French revolution a new consciousness began to spread through Europe. Many people developed an empathy with the plight of others – progressive thinkers called for the reform of prisons, an end to harsh sentences, and the abolition of slavery. France was first to abolish slavery in 1794; Britain and America followed in 1807 and 1808, respectively. By 1842, the Atlantic slave trade was over.

The human rights ideal played an important role in Europe in 1820, 1830, and 1848 when revolutionary activity

10,000 AFRICAN SLAVES WERE **FREED** AFTER **THE FRENCH REVOLUTION**

broke out across the continent. Thinkers from both the right and the left, the two sides that defined modern politics, echoed the principles of the *Declaration of the Rights of Man and of the Citizen* and argued that the ideals of universal rights justified their political action. Crucially, the Declaration's clause that "the source of all sovereignty resides essentially in the nation" was evoked constantly during the rise of nationalism and the formation of the modern nation states of Europe.

A key principle of the *Declaration of the Rights of Man and of the Citizen*, that "all human beings are born free and equal in dignity and rights", spread widely

> TO **DENY PEOPLE** THEIR **HUMAN RIGHTS** IS TO **CHALLENGE** THEIR VERY **HUMANITY.**

Nelson Mandela, South African civil rights activist, 1918–2013

throughout the 19th century. Progressives across the world believed that the universal, equal, and natural human rights espoused in the Declaration would overturn all undemocratic forms of rule. Simon Bolivar (1783–1830), the liberator of Spanish Venezuela, Ecuador, Bolivia, Peru, and Columbia, openly admired the French Revolution. Hindu reformer Ram Mohun Roy (1772–1833) argued for freedom of speech and religion as natural rights in condemning India's caste system. And during the late 19th and 20th centuries, educated Asian and African leaders argued that European colonization contravened the human rights of the indigenous people. Eventually the principle became enshrined in the first article of the United Nations 1948 Universal Declaration of Human Rights, which set out to protect the fundamental rights to which all peoples – no matter where they come from – are inherently entitled.

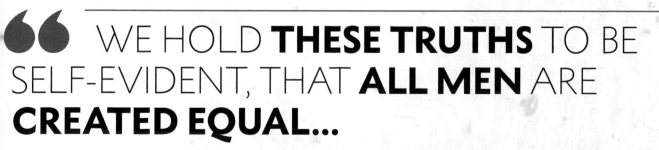
> WE HOLD **THESE TRUTHS** TO BE SELF-EVIDENT, THAT **ALL MEN** ARE **CREATED EQUAL...**

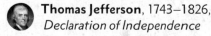
Thomas Jefferson, 1743–1826, *Declaration of Independence*

NATIONALISM
EMERGES

The second half of the 18th century was a period of immense revolution, in both social and political terms. These profound changes in the world order led to the formation of new nation states and a growing sense of nationalism, as countries began to assert their individuality.

The roots of modern nationalism can be traced back to the political philosophy of John Locke in 17th-century England, with its emphasis on the individual and his rights, and the human community. It was also influenced by the unprecedented social changes brought about by the industrial revolution and by the liberal ideals of the Enlightenment philosophers. Essentially, modern nationalism demanded loyalty to one's country and embodied a sense of common identity and history shared by rulers and citizens alike.

Unity under a free and equal democracy was central both to the liberal nationalism of the American War of Independence of 1776, and to the outbreak, in 1789, of the French Revolution, which paved the way for the modern nation state as a united community enjoying equal rights under a Constitution. The French revolutionaries introduced a centralized administrative bureaucracy with uniform laws, and established French as the common language of the land.

NEW NATION STATES

The growing sense of of nationalism in Europe sparked struggles for independence in Greece and Belgium (where there was a successful revolution against Dutch rule). In 1848, revolution once again erupted across Europe, as huge swathes of the populace vented their dissatisfaction, demanding national unification and constitutional reform. The Kingdom of Italy was finally created in 1861 and Germany in 1871, but these two unifications came at a cost. Absolute monarchies were re-established and liberal institutions such as the popular press were persecuted. A misplaced blend of nationalism and beliefs about racial superiority led European nations to colonize many countries in the late 19th century.

Culturally, nationalism often took the form of a celebration of a nation's history, culture, and achievements. Proud of their rapid modernization, the great industrial nations of the world hosted impressive international trade exhibitions to show off their latest manufacturing – the supreme expression of confidence in their nation.

▼ **Unifying force**
In 1871, Chancellor Otto von Bismarck finally achieved his aim of bringing 300 small kingdoms and principalities together to form a unified Germany.

LIEBIG COMPANY'S FLEISCH-EXTRACT UND-PEPTON.

Bismarck-
Kaiser-Proclamation zu Versailles, 18. Jan. 1871.

Siehe Rückseite

Gesetzl. geschützt.

PATRIOTISM IS WHEN **LOVE OF YOUR OWN PEOPLE** COMES FIRST; **NATIONALISM**, WHEN HATE FOR PEOPLE OTHER THAN YOUR OWN COMES FIRST.

Charles de Gaulle, former President of France, 1890–1970

Patriotic display
The Great Exhibition of 1851, in Britain, was the first international exhibition of manufactured products, as well as a display of national pride.

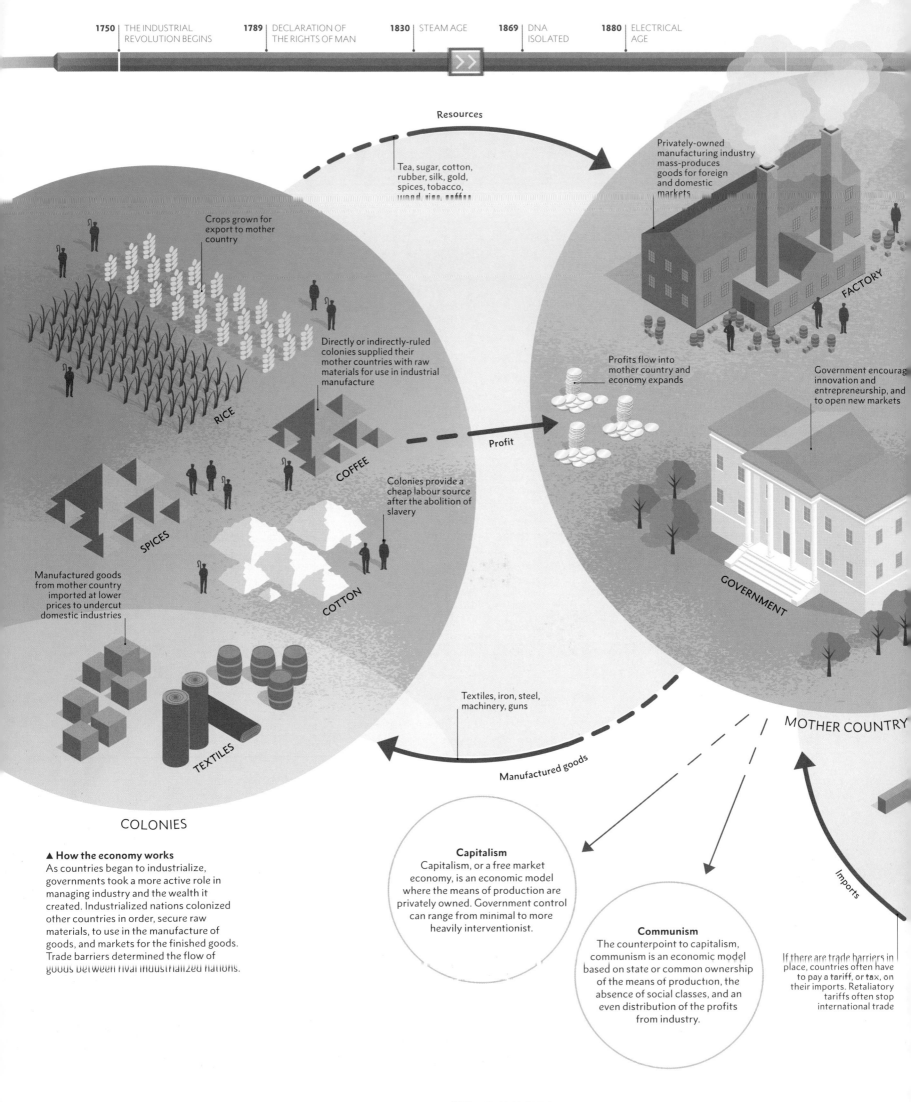

Resources

Tea, sugar, cotton, rubber, silk, gold, spices, tobacco, wood, rice, coffee,

Privately-owned manufacturing industry mass-produces goods for foreign and domestic markets

Crops grown for export to mother country

FACTORY

Directly or indirectly-ruled colonies supplied their mother countries with raw materials for use in industrial manufacture

Profits flow into mother country and economy expands

Government encourage innovation and entrepreneurship, and to open new markets

RICE

Profit

Colonies provide a cheap labour source after the abolition of slavery

COFFEE

GOVERNMENT

SPICES

Manufactured goods from mother country imported at lower prices to undercut domestic industries

COTTON

Textiles, iron, steel, machinery, guns

MOTHER COUNTRY

TEXTILES

Manufactured goods

COLONIES

Imports

▲ How the economy works
As countries began to industrialize, governments took a more active role in managing industry and the wealth it created. Industrialized nations colonized other countries in order, secure raw materials, to use in the manufacture of goods, and markets for the finished goods. Trade barriers determined the flow of goods between rival industrialized nations.

Capitalism
Capitalism, or a free market economy, is an economic model where the means of production are privately owned. Government control can range from minimal to more heavily interventionist.

Communism
The counterpoint to capitalism, communism is an economic model based on state or common ownership of the means of production, the absence of social classes, and an even distribution of the profits from industry.

If there are trade barriers in place, countries often have to pay a tariff, or tax, on their imports. Retaliatory tariffs often stop international trade

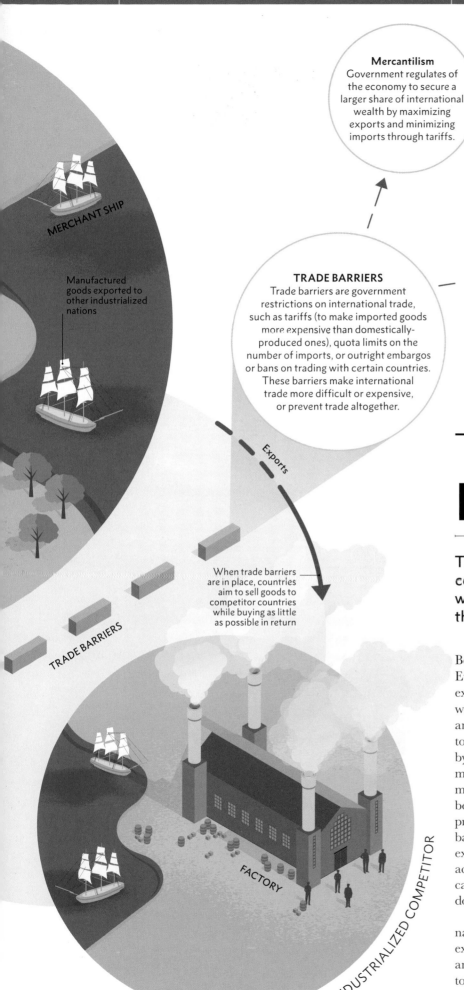

Mercantilism
Government regulates of the economy to secure a larger share of international wealth by maximizing exports and minimizing imports through tariffs.

MERCHANT SHIP

Manufactured goods exported to other industrialized nations

TRADE BARRIERS
Trade barriers are government restrictions on international trade, such as tariffs (to make imported goods more expensive than domestically-produced ones), quota limits on the number of imports, or outright embargos or bans on trading with certain countries. These barriers make international trade more difficult or expensive, or prevent trade altogether.

Protectionism
Government restricts international trade to protect domestic industries from potential rivals – tariffs, subsidies and import quotas, and exclusion from the market.

Exports

When trade barriers are in place, countries aim to sell goods to competitor countries while buying as little as possible in return

TRADE BARRIERS

FACTORY

INDUSTRIALIZED COMPETITOR

BY 1913, THE **UNITED STATES, GERMANY,** THE **UNITED KINGDOM, FRANCE,** AND **RUSSIA** PRODUCED **77 PER CENT** OF THE **WORLD'S MANUFACTURED GOODS**

THE **INDUSTRIAL ECONOMY**

The industrial revolution created new possibilities for countries to increase their wealth. Nations adapted to cope with the corresponding increase in international trade, and the pitfalls that came with it.

Before the industrial revolution, mercantilism had been the dominant European economic model. In this approach, a nation encouraged exports and discouraged imports, with the belief that the world's wealth was finite. However, the introduction of mass production on an industrial scale increased economic output, and showed it was possible to create new wealth. Industrialists realized they could make more money by importing cheap raw materials from unindustrialized countries and manufacturing them into goods they could sell to both foreign and domestic markets. With this increase in both production and profit, for a time it became beneficial for countries to trade freely with each other. Industrialists pressured governments to adopt a policy of free trade – trade without barriers or government interference, where imports are tariff-free and exports are not subsidized. This was the start of a period of great wealth accumulation, the founding of new financial institutions, and the birth of capitalism – a term coined by economist Adam Smith – which remains the dominant economic model for industrializing countries today.

However, as well as increasing the flow of goods and wealth between nations, the consequences of free trade can include economic instability, exploitation, and clashes over the sources of wealth – colonies, markets, and raw materials. To counteract this, governments create trade barriers to try and protect their interests; this can result in cyclical periods in which trade increases or decreases between nations.

Gunboat diplomacy
Samurai warriors row out to meet an American "black ship", which introduced Japan to gunboat diplomacy and made its 17th-century weaponry instantly ineffective.

THE WORLD OPENS
TO TRADE

The 19th century marked a major turning point for world trade, as industrialized nations sought to expand their commercial reach. It was not always a peaceful process, but it laid the foundations of the modern international economy.

In the 1840s, the policy of free trade – trade without government interference or tariffs on imports or exports – led to a period in which industrializing nations were able to accumulate great wealth. Factories enabled the cheap and rapid production of an unprecedented array of products for domestic and foreign markets, as a rising demand for consumer goods, in turn, fuelled more economic growth. This expansion of world trade by the industrializing powers of Britain, and later Western European countries and North America, eventually resulted in the need for each world power to protect their own economic position.

CONTROLLING MARKETS
The most rewarding and efficient form of free trade was to control both the raw materials and the markets. This was often achieved by force, as the growing disparity in technologies between industrialized nations and the rest of the world soon showed. Historically, countries such as Japan and China had been largely unwilling to import European goods: they did not need or want them. Britain imported tea from China but – other than silver acquired by selling slaves from Africa to Spanish colonists in the Americas – had nothing to offer the Chinese in exchange. With the abolition of slavery the supply of silver dried up, so Britain began selling the Chinese opium instead. China's resistance to the exploitation of its people sparked two Opium Wars in the mid-19th century.

America also adopted a policy of armed intervention in the East, regarding Japan as a backwater where its traders could open up new markets. In 1853, four American gunboats entered the prohibited waters of Edo Bay, Japan. Bristling with modern weaponry, the black ships intimidated the Japanese into opening their borders to trade with America and Europe. The

BETWEEN **1809** AND **1839**, **BRITISH IMPORTS DOUBLED** AND **EXPORTS TRIPLED**

arrival of the more technologically advanced Americans encouraged Japan's own industrialization and path to modernity.

Following their victories in the Opium Wars, the British government imposed a series of treaties on China that gave Britain favoured and unequal trading privileges. Japan signed a similar treaty with the United States, and other industrialized European powers also followed suit, imposing unequal treaties on trade with Latin America and the Middle East. Countries wishing to trade had to set low tariffs on European imports and adopt legal measures favourable to European interests.

◀ **Opium pipe**
Imports of British opium led to widespread addiction in China, resulting in the Opium Wars of 1839–42 and 1850–60. After being defeated, China was forced to open more ports to foreign trade.

▼ **The Gatling gun**
Richard Gatling justified his 1861 invention of the rapid-fire gun on humanitarian grounds. He claimed it would save lives by reducing the carnage on the battlefield and shortening the length of wars.

Hand crank, or "hopper", drops fresh ammunition into the gun's chambers using gravity. The multiple barrels turn with a hand crank on the gun's side and a solider feeds the ammunition into the top-loading "hopper"

Cyclic multi-barreled design allows a cartridge to be automatically loaded and fired from each barrel before being given a brief moment to cool, enabling rapid fire without overheating

> WHATEVER HAPPENS **WE HAVE** GOT THE **MAXIM GUN** AND **THEY HAVE NOT**.

Hilaire Belloc, Anglo-French writer and historian, 1870–1953

WAR DRIVES
INNOVATION

New innovations that increased the effectiveness of war machines made the "scramble for Africa" possible. This rapid colonization of the continent by the powers of Europe was justified by racist ideology, and had the search for raw materials at its heart.

Industrialization and the need for raw materials and new markets were important drivers of imperialism. Notions of cultural and racial superiority were also used to justify it; many 19th century Europeans believed they were duty-bound to bring civilization to the non-white world. As they increased their power and productivity at home, and abroad, European perceptions of the world begun to change. Racist thinking came to be expressed in scientific terms and the Darwinian concept of the survival of the fittest was applied to society. Europeans argued it was natural for them to displace those they considered "inferior" or "backward" races.

BATTLEFIELD BREAKTHROUGHS
Industrialization also provided the means for colonization: technological innovations were key. The steamboat and quinine, which helped prevent malaria, allowed European traders unprecedented access to the interior of sub-Saharan Africa. This opened up a treasure trove of raw materials, but trading with local economies led to crises, which prompted European

powers to annex territory. International rivalries became a factor in the land-grab that followed and, in the ensuing scramble, the borders of the continent were drawn up on maps in European board rooms. Strong armies were a crucial factor in European empire-building, and the development of new military technologies was a consequence of industrial innovation.

The machine gun, developed by Richard Gatling and perfected by Hiram Maxim, showed that in modern warfare military technology was paramount. British soldiers used the Maxim gun to slaughter over 10,0000 Sudanese Mahdists in the 1898 Battle of Omdurman, in which the British suffered less than 50 casualties of their own. The machine gun also provided a reminder that the people of Africa did not simply acquiesce to imperial rule. When Ethiopia successfully repelled Italian attempts to colonize it in 1896, it was the first time a European power had been defeated in Africa and a wounding blow to the notions of racial superiority of Europeans.

▲ **Colonial control**
Askari soldiers were African troops hired and trained by European powers. Native troops were crucial in keeping colonies under control. In Africa there were often up to 200 Askari soldiers to every seven European officers.

◄ **Winning weaponry**
Ethiopian Emperor Menilek II decimated Italian troops in 1896 using modern guns he had bought in Europe. eosaes atia.

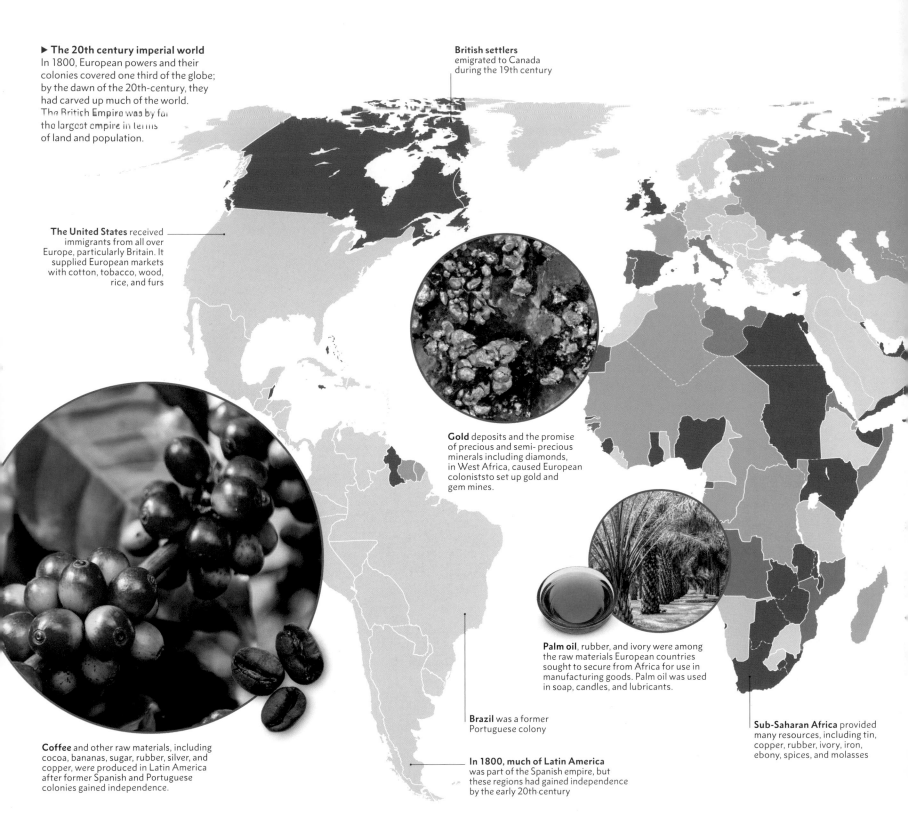

▶ **The 20th century imperial world**
In 1800, European powers and their colonies covered one third of the globe; by the dawn of the 20th-century, they had carved up much of the world. The British Empire was by far the largest empire in terms of land and population.

British settlers emigrated to Canada during the 19th century

The United States received immigrants from all over Europe, particularly Britain. It supplied European markets with cotton, tobacco, wood, rice, and furs

Gold deposits and the promise of precious and semi- precious minerals including diamonds, in West Africa, caused European coloniststo set up gold and gem mines.

Palm oil, rubber, and ivory were among the raw materials European countries sought to secure from Africa for use in manufacturing goods. Palm oil was used in soap, candles, and lubricants.

Coffee and other raw materials, including cocoa, bananas, sugar, rubber, silver, and copper, were produced in Latin America after former Spanish and Portuguese colonies gained independence.

Brazil was a former Portuguese colony

In 1800, much of Latin America was part of the Spanish empire, but these regions had gained independence by the early 20th century

Sub-Saharan Africa provided many resources, including tin, copper, rubber, ivory, iron, ebony, spices, and molasses

---

■ BRITAIN

Duration: 1603–1949

Britain began its process of overseas control through trading posts, which led to colonial expansion across the world and the largest empire in world history.

■ RUSSIA

Duration: 1721–1917

At its peak in 1866, Russia had the second-largest empire in world history, with territories in its control extending from eastern Europe right across Asia.

■ BELGIUM

Duration: 1885–1962

Belgium gained independence from the Netherlands in 1830. The Congo was its largest colony and was over 75 times as big as Belgium itself.

■ GERMANY

Duration: 1871–1918

Germany used its new navy, built to compete with Britain, to colonize parts of West Africa and the South Pacific during the late 19th century.

■ FRANCE

Duration: 1870–1916

Bruised by defeat in the Franco-Prussian war of 1870, France acquired colonial possessions in Africa, the Pacific, and Southeast Asia from 1871.

Sugar from Indian plantations became an important export for the British Empire. Once a luxury item, as sugar became available to ordinary people in Europe demand for it increased.

Nutmeg and cloves were among the spices produced in Indonesia for the Dutch empire, along with sugar and coffee.

Cotton produced in India was shipped to Britain where it was used to make textiles. Britain exported its cloth back to India, undercutting the prices of locally produced textiles.

British settlers emigrated to Australia during the 19th century, easing overcrowding and social unrest at home

COLONIAL EMPIRES GROW

Raw materials for industry, land for settlers, and markets for surplus goods were all factors that drove the imperial expansion of the 19th century, as European countries began to dominate the world.

Competition between imperial powers was fierce and colonies became a symbol of prestige. Large areas of arid, sparsely populated land were often annexed simply to prevent a rival from doing so. As political rivalries and mistrust grew in Europe, colonial wealth was used to control the empires and build up arms.

Once colonies were established, the mother country had to work out how to keep control of its new territory. Often this took the form of indirect control – collaboration with indigenous leaders in Asia and Africa was a vital part of European rule. Imperial military intervention only occurred in unstable regions or places with no pre-existing central control. However, people living in the Americas, Africa, India, and Southeast Asia often experienced racial prejudice, political oppression, and violence at the hands of imperial powers. In the Belgian Congo, the families of workers were held hostage and raped and murdered if the rubber quota was too low. Some indigenous peoples, including the New Zealand Maori and Australian Aborigines, were killed, displaced, or fell victim to European diseases.

From the early 20th century, colonized countries began to gain independence. This process picked up momentum after World War II, when European nations no longer had the wealth, means, or inclination to control far-away territories. The newly independent nations inherited none of the wealth of their past rulers, and were left to create their own institutions. Some have been highly successful; others plagued by corruption and poverty.

EUROPEAN POWERS CONTROLLED AROUND 85 PER CENT OF THE WORLD'S LAND BY 1914

ITALY
Duration: 1861–1947

Italy colonized Eritrea, Libya, and part of Somalia. The empire ended in 1947 as Italy was forced to abandon its colonies in the aftermath of World War II.

PORTUGAL
Duration: 1415–2002

The first global empire, with territories across several continents, Portugal's was the longest-lasting European colonial empire, spanning almost six centuries.

NETHERLANDS
Duration: 1543–1975

Building up indirect colonial control via the Dutch East and West India Companies before 1800, the Dutch empire reached its height during the 19th century.

JAPAN
Duration: 1868–1945

Japan demonstrated a growing military strength by defeating Russia in the 1904 Russo-Japanese war and winning Korea in the process.

SPAIN
Duration: 1402–1975

Spain gained control of large parts of Latin America by the 18th century, but by the 20th century had lost almost all of its territories.

Factory life
The working class laboured on the factory floor, supervised by their middle-class bosses, and surrounded by new machines they were often forced to clean during their lunch break.

SOCIETY TRANSFORMS

Industrialization changed every aspect of life for working people. Dangerous and unregulated working conditions existed in factories and workers often lived in overcrowded slum towns, until widespread government reforms improved the plight of this new working class.

As factories replaced farms and fields, the men, women, and children of the peasantry seeking employment were exposed to an unprecedented level of social and tecnological change.

THE PLIGHT OF THE POOR

The middle classes were the real winners of industrialization; in Britain, the 1832 Reform Bill even gave middle-class men the vote. The labouring classes suffered most. Workers toiled for at least 13 hours a day in factories, and hearing loss, lung disease, and severe injury were common. There was no legal protection for workers: the middle-class factory overseers and owners were king. It was these brutal economic inequalities that stoked the wave of revolutionary activity that broke out across Europe in 1848, mobilized in part by German philosopher Friedrich Engels, who described the misery of factory workers in *The Condition of the Working Poor*.

THE NEW CITIES

Workers lived in slum towns that grew up around factories. The rise in urbanization was everywhere: by 1850, 50 per cent of England's population were living in cities; Germany reached this level by 1900, America by 1920, and Japan by 1930. Industrial cities in every country suffered similar problems: overcrowding, pollution, a lack of running water, no waste disposal,

and unhealthy housing. These conditions all encouraged the spread of disease, and waves of cholera broke out across India, Europe, and North America. An 1832 French study into cholera showed the link between slums, poverty, and poor health, and English physician John Snow demonstrated that cholera was spread via contaminated drinking water in 1849.

Armed with this knowledge, governments began to take action, introducing sewage systems, running water, and rubbish collection into cities. Across Europe and North America, other social and political reforms were enacted. Labour laws provided protection for workers, with improved safety regulations, and education became compulsory for children.

◀ **Cholera medicine**
By the end of the 19th century, cholera epidemics no longer appeared in Europe and North America. Standards of living rose, sanitation practices improved, and permanent boards of health were established.

> 66
> THE WATER... **IN FRONT OF THE HOUSES** IS COVERED WITH A SCUM... ALONG THE BANKS ARE HEAPS OF **INDESCRIBABLE FILTH**...THE AIR HAS... THE **SMELL OF A GRAVEYARD**.
> 99
>
> **Henry Mayhew**, journalist and campaigner for better housing, 1812–1887

EDUCATION
EXPANDS

Education plays an essential part in collective learning and innovation. Realizing its importance, many governments introduced widespread reforms to make education compulsory after the mid-19th century. By 2000, 80 per cent of the world population could read and write.

▲ **Textbook learning**
The school system in America was largely private until reforms in the 1840s began to introduce public schools and standardized textbooks.

The importance of literacy has a long history. European literacy levels had risen steadily from the 16th century, especially in France, Germany, and Britain. A society that valued knowledge and ideas fitted with the Age of Enlightenment beliefs that drove industrialization. In Britain, hundreds of schools were opened in the early 18th century to cope with the rising population. However, there was great disparity between people with access to education and those without. Education had to be paid for during the 18th century and therefore it was not available to the working class. Neither was education considered important for women – working-class women were expected to work from childhood, while middle-class women were only schooled until they married.

EDUCATED NATIONS

In the 19th century, ideas about education began to change. This arose partly from Enlightenment ideals about the value of reason, knowledge, and the free exchange of ideas. Individual reformers worked to rouse popular support for new government intervention in slavery, public health, and education. Intervention was needed to appease citizens after the 1848 revolutions; the middle classes demanded reform and the working classes seemed poised to revolt. Governments realized an educated nation would keep the military strong, encourage patriotism, and reduce the desire for rebellion. From 1870, compulsory state-run school education spread across western Europe and into the northeastern states of America. Other countries outside Europe set up education systems after 1900, including China, Egypt, and Japan. These were partly created to encourage patriotism and also to imitate the institutions that had helped make the western empires so powerful.

Improved access to education has allowed world literacy to rise steadily over the last 150 years. More people than ever before can read and write – and contribute to growing networks of exchange and collective learning. However, even today, access to education is not equal; illiteracy is highest in the some of the poorest parts of the world, and also among women. In 2011, three-quarters of all illiterate adults lived in southern Asia, the Middle East, and sub-Saharan Africa. Furthermore, two-thirds of the world's 774 million illiterate adults were women.

THE INFORMATION AGE

Education is an important tool in disseminating information and knowledge at an individual level. Throughout human history, as collective learning has increased, networks of exchange have expanded and their power has grown at faster rates, enabling information to accumulate more and more rapidly. Today, we are living in what could be described as the Information Age. The Digital Revolution has led to a shift from an economy driven by traditional industry to one based on computerized information. In this information society and knowledge-based economy, it is flows of information that

MORE THAN **83 PER CENT** OF THE **GLOBAL POPULATION** WAS **LITERATE** IN 2016

▶ **Improving child welfare**
In Britain, industrialization led to young working-class children toiling in factories and mines, until government reforms prohibited this. The Education Act of 1880 introduced compulsory schooling up to the age of ten.

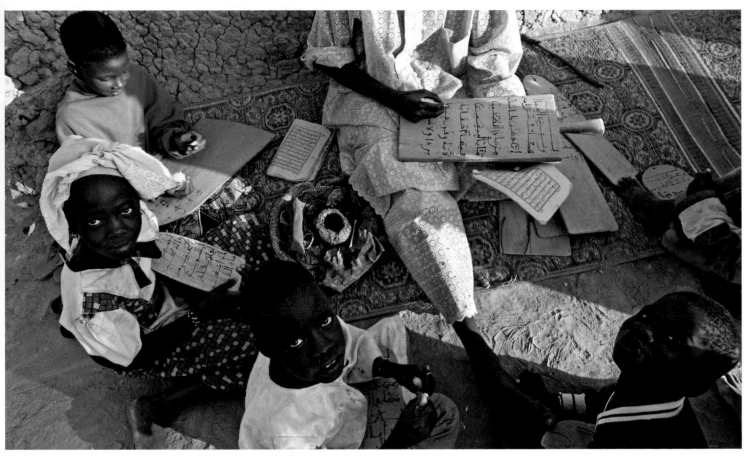

◄ **Primary education**
In 1994, the government of Malawi, Africa, introduced free primary school education, but drop-out rates remain high, especially for girls. This is often the case in many poor countries in sub-Saharan Africa, where children work to supplement the family income.

drive profit making. Globalization saw the world zones become connected, and now the control and movement of information and wealth has started to blur national boundaries even more. Of the top 100 economies of the world ranked by Gross Domestic Product (GDP) in 2009, 60 are countries and the rest are companies, many of them multinational oil and gas companies such as Sinopecand Shell, and technology and communications companies such as Apple and Samsung. Never has information been so important.

In recent years, the growth of the software and biotechnology industries has placed a new emphasis on the need for highly skilled labour. Industrialization created a system like a pyramid, with large amounts of unskilled labour at the bottom and a small number of capitalist business leaders and creative classes at the top. Education may be the key to moving towards societies in which the pyramid is inverted: if more people have access to a good level of education, they can participate in high-value jobs at the top of the pyramid, while automation reduces the need for large numbers of people to perform unskilled tasks.

THE PURSUIT OF INNOVATION

Education, as a form of collective learning, is crucial for innovation. During the 20th century, for many industrialized societies one of the main drivers of innovation was the pursuit of innovation itself – often, as in the past, with the support of governments, business, and educational institutions. During the 17th century, when the first scientific societies were founded in Europe, the British government offered incentives for innovation, and in the first century of

industrialization, it profited from major scientific and engineering breakthroughs. In the 19th century, governments and businesses realized science was a crucial source of innovation, wealth, and power, and began to take an active role in promoting and organizing scientific research. By the 20th century, innovation in science and technology had proved to be fundamental components of military, political, and economic power for industrialized nations.

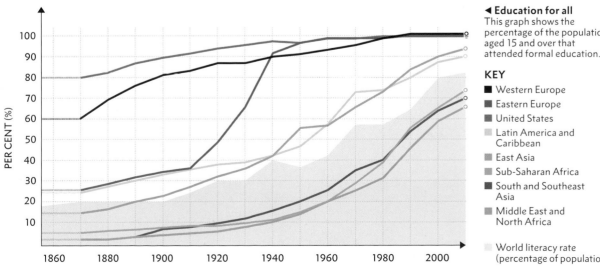

◄ **Education for all**
This graph shows the percentage of the population aged 15 and over that attended formal education.

KEY
- ■ Western Europe
- ■ Eastern Europe
- ■ United States
- ■ Latin America and Caribbean
- ■ East Asia
- ■ Sub-Saharan Africa
- ■ South and Southeast Asia
- ■ Middle East and North Africa
- ■ World literacy rate (percentage of population)

MEDICAL ADVANCES

From the late 18th century, there was a great acceleration in medical knowledge in industrializing countries, as scientific research, innovation, and disease prevention allowed people to live longer and healthier lives.

As expanding trade networks and urbanization brought people into closer contact than ever before, diseases spread. Edward Jenner's breakthrough smallpox vaccination, in 1796, was warily considered a medical miracle. During the 19th century, germ theory and the discovery of bacteria eventually led to safer surgery and an understanding of the importance of sanitation in public areas. New innovation gave physicians practical tools to help them diagnose ailments. Medical innovation and improved knowledge had a positive impact on health, especially for the very young and very old.

The 20th century was marked by an explosion in medical technology, as health systems tried to keep up with the epidemics, famines, and wars of the modern age. Scientific research of the new millennium led to stem cell research, the sequencing of the human genome, and the ability to create new life. The internet made details of these medical breakthroughs widely accessible, as well as providing an ever-growing resource for the sharing of medical knowledge – for both practitioners and patients.

Ether is used first as an anaesthetic, revolutionizing pain management for surgical patients, 1846. It is replaced by chloroform.

Chloroform inhaler

Germ theory, which states that a specific disease is caused by a specific organism, is demonstrated by Louis Pasteur in the 1850s. Pasteur goes on to produce vaccinations for rabies and anthrax.

Reforms in hygiene and patient-care introduced by Florence Nightingale in 1854, during the Crimean War, lead to modern nursing and sanitation in hospitals.

DRUGS AND ANAESTHESIA

INSTRUMENTS, INNOVATIONS AND TECHNOLOGY

Stethoscope

Stethoscope, invented by Rene Laennec in 1816, enables doctors to listen to the sounds from a patient's chest. It remains a vital diagnostic tool.

Ignaz Semmelweis proves surgeons with unwashed hands spread infection, 1847.

Aspirin synthesized, 1852, a new medicine that relieves suffering caused by disease.

DISCOVERIES AND BREAKTHROUGHS

1800

Carbolic acid spray

GERMS, DISEASES, AND VACCINES

Carbolic acid is first used as an antiseptic by Joseph Lister, in 1865, to kill germs and reduce the risk of infection.

The bacteria that cause tuberculosis and cholera are identified by Robert Koch in the 1880s, helping him found bacteriology – the study of bacteria.

Sterilization of surgical instruments is introduced by Ernst von Bergmann, in 1886, to prevent the spread of infection.

Smallpox vaccination is developed by Edward Jenner, "The Father of Immunology", 1796, and vaccination becomes widespread, saving many lives.

1775

First "test tube" baby is born, 1978, after the in-vitro fertilization of an egg outside the body, enabling people who could not conceive to have children.

Commercial magnetic resonance imaging (MRI) scanners, which use magnets and radio waves to form an image of a patient's body and organs, aid diagnoses of internal abnormalities, 1981.

Highly active antiretroviral therapy (HAART) to control HIV infection introduced, 1996. By 2010 it has led to a marked drop in the AIDS-related mortality rate in many western countries.

Human Genome Project paper identifying the 20,000–25,000 genes in human DNA, 2003, is an unprecedented resource and basis for research.

Computerized axial tomography (CAT) scanner developed by Godfrey Hounsfield, 1970. It allows doctors to locate abnormalities such as tumours in patients.

First successful heart transplant carried out by South African physician Christian Barnard, 1967. Today over 3,500 heart transplants are performed each year.

Birth control pill for women released onto the American market, 1960, leading to greater female control over family planning and the "sexual revolution".

DNA is described by James Watson and Francis Crick, 1953, leading to a greater ability to diagnose diseases early on.

Cardiac pacemaker

Cardiac pacemaker produced, 1958. It is an important innovation that uses electrical pulses to regulate the heart beat.

SURGICAL PROCEDURES

2000

A human ear is produced on a 3D printer using injections of living cow cells in 2014, leading scientists to suggest they may be able to make implants from a patient's own cells.

Ebola vaccine produced after outbreak in West Africa kills thousands, 2015. It is predicted to help prevent the spread of the disease in the future.

Dolly the Sheep, the first mammal to be cloned from an adult cell, 1996, brings scientists closer to the theoretical capability of cloning human life.

The first rib cage transplant made using a 3D printed titanium chest prosthetic, 2015, allows doctors to make an exact custom fit for the patient.

Electron microscope

Electron microscope is invented in 1931, allowing doctors to see bacteria and viruses for the first time.

The antibiotic penicillin, accidently discovered by Alexander Fleming in 1928, leads to the mass production of antibiotics, improving the health of millions.

X-rays are discovered by German physicist Wilhelm Rontgen, 1895, changing the way doctors examine patients. X-rays as radiation therapy are eventually used to treat cancer.

1900

German Paul Ehrlich releases drug treatment for syphilis in 1910 – a major breakthrough in chemotherapeutic medicine.

The "ABO" blood groups are described by Karl Landsteiner, 1900, leading to safe blood transfusions.

Ronald Ross discovers that mosquitoes carry malaria and publishes his findings in 1897. This allows him to develop "vector control" to help eradicate malaria-carrying mosquitoes.

THE AMERICAS

PACIFIC ISLAND SOCIETIES

FOUR WORLD ZONES
By the start of industrialization in the 18th century, European explorers had already connected the four world zones.

AFRO-EURASIA

AUSTRALASIA

INDUSTRIALIZED ZONE
UNINDUSTRIALIZED ZONE

1900
The four world zones had become two zones: an industrialized zone, made rich through mass-production, and a poorer unindustrialized zone that was exploited for raw materials, labour, and land.

Transport
Falling transportation and communications costs underpin international trade from 1820 onwards. The price of inland transportation drops by 90 per cent between 1800 and 1910; transatlantic transport costs fall by 60 per cent between 1870 and 1900.

ROAD TO
GLOBALIZATION

The merging of the world into two zones resulted in a worldwide exchange network of trade, capital, migration, culture, and knowledge in a process known as globalization.

Globalization is not a modern concept: global exchange networks expanded greatly after the Age of Discovery, which spanned the 15th–18th centuries and opened the new world to the old. During this period, money, people, crops, ideas, and diseases travelled between the two worlds, mostly to the benefit of the countries of Western Europe. This model of globalization sped up during 19th-century imperialism, and, by the end of the century, large colonial empires connected specialized regions of industry and agriculture within a new world economy focused on accumulating capital.

Alongside industrial technologies, including the telegraph and railways, the new organizational structures of the modern state were introduced to the unindustrialized world, including legal systems and state bureaucracy. As countries in the unindustrialized zone developed distinctive specializations – like the growing and exporting of tea – they did so under a system that came with its own rules, regulations, and language. After decolonization in the 20th century, those colonies able to grow their own economies did so with the guidebook left behind by empire.

By the 21st century, innovation in communications technology had become as important as transportation in creating modern globalization: cheap and efficient containerization contributed to the rise of China as an economic superpower, and fibre optics and broadband helped establish India as a global services hub. The innovations continue today, as ever more advanced smartphones connect the world's population, and a new global culture begins to emerge.

Trade agreements
Decolonized countries begin to make trade agreements based on mutual advantage. Many of these countries adopt a free-trade model, which leads to a new transnational economic dynamic.

LATE 20TH/EARLY 21ST CENTURY
Many unindustrialized nations become cogs in a global manufacturing machine, assembling products from raw materials shipped in from around the world.

THE **COUNTRY** THAT IS **MORE DEVELOPED INDUSTRIALLY** ONLY **SHOWS** TO THE **LESS-DEVELOPED** THE IMAGE OF ITS OWN **FUTURE**.

Karl Marx, German philosopher, economist, and sociologist, 1818–83

Resources

In the 19th century, industrial powers introduce free-market capitalism to the world. Empires seize resources, subordinate labour, and turn the globe into a vast agricultural resource for western Europe.

Migration

Innovative new forms of transport help to increase the migration and movement of peoples around the world. The Irish potato famine and overcrowding in Britain lead to mass emigration to the colonies, along with imperial bureaucrats and migrant workers.

Cultural exchange

The movement of people creates opportunities for cultural exchange in all areas of life, including social customs; academic and business culture; religious and political ideologies; literature, music, and art; clothes and beauty; eating customs and food.

Financial institutions

The rise of powerful financial institutions, such as the International Monetary Fund, leads to investment deals for industrializing countries, which come with obligations attached. This creates a more integrated global financial system.

New players

The fall of the Soviet Union and the opening of China bring new economic players to the global capital market, resulting in a surge of international transactions and investment in post-communist economies.

Foreign investment

Trade agreements encourage multinational corporations from industrialized nations to invest directly in unindustrialized economies. This prompts increased privatization and greater foreign ownership of assets in unindustrialized countries.

AFTER WORLD WAR II

Modern globalization begins as capitalism and liberalizing of trade create new world economies increasingly controlled by multinational corporations and powerful financial institutions.

Movement

The removal of trade barriers and even cheaper transportation expands human migration for work purposes. This leads to a larger cultural exchange and the rising economy of remittances – money sent from a foreign worker back to their home country.

Cultural homogeneity

The rise of a global services economy, improvements in communications technology, and the spread of multinational corporations all help promote cultural homogeneity, where brands, music, television, and food are found and recognized all over the world.

Industrial development

Global capitalism enables the industrialization of many countries in the unindustrialized zone and the creation of wealth through the manufacture of cheap consumables for the market. This leads to more employment opportunities and a reduction of people living in poverty.

▼ **Engine of change**
A petrol-fuelled combustion engine was built by Karl Benz to power his "horseless carriage" in 1885. The following year, he created the Benz "Patent-Motorwagen" – the world's first automobile. It shared many features with cars today.

The water tank cools the engine. This new invention, as well as two others – an electric ignition and differential gear – are found in every car driven today

The steering handle turns the front wheel to control direction, while the engine powers the two back wheels

The surface carburettor, invented by Benz, is a device that blends air and fuel. Benz used the oil byproduct benzine as a fuel and the carburettor mixed air with benzine vapour. It could hold 4.5 litres (1 gallon) of fuel

A crankshaft with a large horizontal flywheel that is used to start the engine

ENGINES SHRINK THE WORLD

Transport played a key part in the spread of industrialization. In the last two centuries, railways, steamships, and aeroplanes – and innovations in communication – have vastly increased the rate and speed at which people exchange goods, ideas, information, and technology.

By the late 19th century, railway tracks crisscrossed Europe and America, greatly accelerating the exchange of goods, people, and ideas, as well as making travel more widely available. Rail networks lowered the cost of moving goods between the manufacturer, retailer, and buyer, which, in turn, reduced the cost of consumer goods. The ability to move raw materials and manufactured goods across land and sea at relatively rapid speeds and low costs was as significant to the success of early industrial economies as it is today.

NEW TRANSPORT CONNECTIONS

Just as coal fuelled 19th-century railways, the transport revolution of the early 20th century would not have been possible without the wide scale availability of fossil fuels. Innovative new uses of oil and gas included the invention of the internal combustion engine – which burned oil – and led to the development of automobiles and jet planes. In 1913, entrepreneur Henry Ford devised an assembly line to mass-produce the first affordable motorcar. This was the start of consumer capitalism, as workers became the target market for goods they were making, which would once have seemed like luxuries.

Ford's vision to put a car on every driveway transformed modern Western society as governments built roads and traffic systems to accommodate cars. In the 1950s, oil-fuelled cars, buses, and trucks became vital to the transportation of

goods and people. Commercial air travel took off after World War II, as wartime aviation experts turned their attentions to creating a peacetime aviation industry. This sped up the transport of people and mail. People began to travel more for a variety of reasons, including business and leisure, which increased networks of exchange. Innovations in transportation drove growth and in turn led to more innovation.

In the early 1960s, humans invented rockets that could carry them into space. The Soviet Union was first to launch a human into space, and in 1969 the United States landed a man on the moon. As the world became increasingly accessible – with more goods, people, and ideas being exchanged than ever before – it also began to appear much smaller.

▲ **Cars for the masses**
The introduction of fast and efficient assembly lines in factories reduced production costs and enabled goods, such as the Ford Model T, to be sold at affordable prices.

IF I HAD ASKED PEOPLE **WHAT THEY WANTED**, THEY WOULD HAVE SAID **'FASTER HORSES'**.

Henry Ford, American industrialist and founder of the Ford Motor Company, 1863–1947

British postal delivery service, made available from 1635, uses horse-mounted postmen to deliver mail, allowing people who are living in different places to relay information at a reasonable speed and with some degree of predictability.

1780

POSTAL SERVICE

Royal Mail stage coaches are protected by guards from 1784, creating a more secure British postal service.

VISUAL SIGNALLING

1800

Semaphore is invented by Claude Chappe, 1792. It allows messages to be conveyed by waving flags, and is the first telecommunications system of the industrial age.

TELEGRAPH AND TELEPHONE

Telegraph system developed by Samuel Morse, 1837, sends messages via electrical telegraph lines using Morse code, revolutionizing long-distance communication.

Uniform Penny Post, 1840, allows letters to be sent for one penny, bringing an affordable postal service to people in the United Kingdom and Ireland.

Transatlantic cable, 1866, enables eight words a minute to be transmitted between America and Europe. Messages had previously taken 10 days by ship.

NEWS AND BROADCASTING

Typewriter invented by Charles Thurber, 1843, becomes widely used in offices and business communication.

Foreign post offices are opened in Chinese ports in 1844 following the Opium Wars. This lays the foundation for China's first national mail service.

TIMELINES

NEWS **TRAVELS FASTER**

The desire to communicate and connect with those around us is an important part of the human story. The technology we use to do this has changed vastly since our ancestors began painting their stories on cave walls, largely due to innovations that date from the 18th century.

The cornerstone of any form of communication is its ability to bring people closer together, and in the 21st century the World Wide Web has completely reshaped the way billions of people create and share information on every topic imaginable. And where early forms of telecommunication, such as the telephone, allowed for one-to-one correspondence, today's online world is geared towards wide – often global – dissemination. This can include anything from a concise political comment on Twitter to a lengthy news article updated in real time.

Perhaps more than anything, it is speed that now defines communication. News that once took days or even weeks to deliver by letter on a ship or train can now be transmitted via email or a Facebook post in a matter of seconds. Alongside this rapid exchange of data comes the sheer volume of information: with 24-hour television news coverage now ubiquitous, and social media in the hands of billions of smartphone users, global communication networks today are more complex and varied than ever before.

Signal lamps utilizing a form of Morse code, 1867, allow British naval ships to transmit messages across long distances.

Telephone

Telephone, patented by Alexander Graham Bell in 1876, becomes the most widespread communication system of the modern age.

Phonograph, invented by Thomas Edison, 1877, is the first device to both record and play back sound, transforming the music industry.

Telegraph

Wireless telegraph, invented by Guglielmo Marconi in 1895, is the first step towards modern, long-distance radio.

Rotary printing press becomes widely available, 1843, and paves the way for industrial-scale printing, especially at newspapers.

Telstar 1 satellite beams television, phone calls, and fax messages across the Atlantic Ocean for the first time in 1962, opening up new and faster methods of global communication.

Telstar 1

Live footage of the Moon landing in 1969 is broadcast to over 100 million TV viewers around the world.

Mobile phone

Pre-cellular mobile telephone service is launched in the USA in 1946; unlike mobile phones today, the phones were usually built inside cars and trucks.

Fifteen-minute television newscasts begin in the USA in 1948, making news more widely available across the country.

ONLINE WORLD

A message is delivered between computers in 1969 by the Projects Agency Network. This paves the way for the invention of email.

First handheld mobile phone, weighing 2kg (4.4lb), is released in 1973, signalling the start of reliable mobile telephony.

Cable News Network (CNN) begins 24-hour satellite news in 1980, ushering in a new era of round-the-clock news coverage.

Radio broadcasts are made in over 15 countries in 1939, from Vatican City to the Soviet Union, leading to a growing worldwide audience of radio listeners.

BBC offers first regularly scheduled television service in 1936, which includes sports, dramas, and cartoons.

Global Positioning Satellite (GPS) is launched in 1987, making satellite-led navigation possible.

The first online transatlantic chat, 1988, occurs between users in Finland and the USA, giving birth to the modern chat service.

Wi-Fi symbol

World's first national broadcasting organization, the British Broadcasting Corporation (BBC), is founded in 1927, to provide a television and radio service.

World Wide Web, launched by Tim Berners-Lee in 1989, today allows billions of people to communicate with each other.

Wi-Fi, or Wireless internet connectivity, becomes available in 1999, paving the way to remote online access.

WikiLeaks, a "whistle-blowing" website, releases thousands of classified documents about world governments in 2010.

First true television images are projected in 1926 by inventor John Logie Baird.

Google, the internet search engine, is launched in 1998, promising a wider data search capability and faster speeds.

Baird television

2000

Wikipedia, a free, multilingual web-based encyclopedia founded in 2001, allows online users the freedom to edit its content.

Skype – an application that enables users to make free phone and video calls over the internet – is launched, 2003.

Facebook, an online social networking service that lets users communicate and share information with friends globally, opens to the public in 2006.

Apple iPhone, launched in 2007, has a large multi-touch screen as its main means of interaction, not a keypad or stylus.

WhatsApp has over one billion users by 2016, making it the most popular global text-messaging application for smartphones.

...phone exchange set up in Great Britain in 1879 allows ...one calls to be connected between different users.

First transcontinental telephone call made in 1915 between Alexander Graham Bell in New York and Thomas A. Watson in San Francisco.

1900

BBC television station, 1936

First radio broadcast of voice and music is transmitted by inventor Reginald Fessenden in the USA, 1906.

iPhone

SOCIAL NETWORKS EXPAND

The first telephone, invented in 1876, connected two callers across seas and continents. Today, innovation has led to the creation of the smart-phone, which can connect to wireless internet. This technology has resulted in the largest and most complex exchange network ever created.

The late 20th and early 21st centuries saw the arrival of breakthrough digital and communications technologies, each of which plays an important function in connecting people and spreading information and ideas. The internet disseminates news and information; social media connects individuals and enables them to organize; mobile phones make it possible to photograph and record what is happening and share it with a global audience. Social networking has become a global phenomenon: in 2015, of the 3.2 billion online users, 2.1 billion had social media accounts. At the most basic level, people use social media to keep in touch or to share their views with the world, but it has also grown to support diverse networks and even protest movements.

Unlike conventional news channels, the spread of ideas and images via social media can be beyond any authority's control. Social networks can be used to motivate individuals to support a collective. This was seen during the Arab Spring uprisings against the leaders of Tunisia, Egypt, Bahrain, and Libya. In Tunisia, in 2011, spontaneous protests broke out when street vendor Mohamed Bouazizi set fire to himself after being harassed by government officials and mobile phone footage of the protest was posted on Facebook. Sharing this footage encouraged others to join in, and the subsequent riots were coordinated via Twitter.

Countries with less developed transport and communications infrastructures are also able to access social networks. They not only benefit from this technology but are able to innovate using it. In Kenya, an application called M-Pesa was invented to allow users to transfer, deposit, and withdraw funds via their smartphone. This enables them to send money directly to their village or remote family in minutes rather than the days it would take to travel.

> BY GIVING **PEOPLE THE POWER TO SHARE** WE ARE MAKING **THE WORLD MORE TRANSPARENT**.
>
> **Mark Zuckerberg**, co-founder of Facebook, 1984–

▼ **Expanding networks**
Since the invention of the first mobile phone in 1973, the speed of technological innovation increased and resulted in the creation of an array of devices that connect people all over the world in different ways.

Multimedia messaging enables people to send colour messages and animations, and eventually photos and videos

Cheaper mobile phones connect people in developing countries

1973
CALLS

TEXT
1992

1996
INTERNET

The invention of the mobile phone makes it possible to make calls anywhere

Mobile phones become small enough to hold in one hand, making them much more portable

Text messaging makes it possible to communicate in situations when voice calls are not available

Mobile phones become mini computers with increased functionality that allows users to connect to the internet

◀ Crowdfunding initiatives
Social media platforms have provided a new way for groups and individuals to secure investment. Crowdfunding has supported anything from arts projects to innovative new products, such as a 3D printer.

▲ Political activism
Social media provides direct access to history-making events as they occur. It played a central role in the 2011 Occupy protests around the world from Wall Street, in New York, to Hong Kong as activists used social media both to organize themselves and to keep the world updated.

▲ New opportunities
Cheap mobile phones in countries with little or no landline infrastructure transformed communications. In Africa, 3G internet coverage has enabled new trade, online banking, and access to information about health and medicine, reducing the need for people to travel long distances.

◀ Saving lives
Medical appeals, such as campaigns for organ donation, often receive a generous response. In 2016, a plea on social media dramatically increased the stem cell donor list when internet users united to help a girl with leukemia, using the hashtag "Match4Lara".

Smartwatches, such as the Apple Watch, allow wearers to make calls and send e-mails from their wrist

Blackberry Messenger enables video and voice calls as well as instant messaging via the internet

E-mail is available on smartphones, meaning people can send e-mails on the move

Apple's iPhone, 2007, uses a multi-touch screen allowing users to zoom in and view content in more detail

4G internet enables faster data transfer speeds, enabling people to send and receive information quicker than ever before

2000

CAMERA

Amazon's Kindle, originally designed for reading eBooks, connects to wireless internet

Cameras make it possible to photograph and video events as they occur

Laptops, like Apple's Macbook Pro, are able to make video calls using free applications, such as Skype, connecting people across the world

| 1750 | THE INDUSTRIAL REVOLUTION BEGINS | 1789 | DECLARATION OF THE RIGHTS OF MAN | 1830 | STEAM AGE | 1869 | DNA ISOLATED | 1880 | ELECTRICAL AGE | 1914 | WORLD WAR I | 1930S | GREAT DEPRESSION |

GROWTH AND
CONSUMPTION

The 20th century was characterized by the sharp acceleration in the pace and scale of change. Industrialization and economic growth increased the ecological power of humans over the biosphere and led to extraordinary population growth and consumption of Earth's resources.

The extraordinary pace of change during the 20th century marked an entirely new period in human history and in the history of human relations with other species and with Earth itself. Population growth is a measure of a species' ecological power, as it is dependent on there being enough resources to support it. Over the last 250 years, the human population has been through a period of spectacular growth: in 1800, there were 900 million people in the world; by 1900 there were 1.6 billion; by 2000 there were 6.1 billion; and today the world population has reached over 7 billion. At the same time, people started living for longer and the average life expectancy doubled during the 20th century. This exceptional growth is partly because new innovation has increased our collective control over the resources of the biosphere. The acceleration of technological change is the primary cause of this transformation: innovation has made it possible to provide enough resources to sustain a growing population. One area where innovation and technological change has been crucial is food production.

INNOVATIONS IN FOOD
Since 1900, food production has outpaced population growth and there has been a six-fold increase in grain production. This is because crops began to be farmed on an industrial scale: massive fossil-fuel-driven machines dug dams and irrigation canals. Chemical fertilizers increased the productivity of the land and enabled an area of arable land to produce around three times more food. Scientific innovation in the 1970s led to the creation of genetically modified grains that were engineered with useful genes from other species to produce crops that need less fertilizer or contain natural protection against pests.

In the agrarian era, most people were farmers and only a tiny elite – less than 5 per cent of the population – consumed luxury goods. Today, around 35 per cent of the global workforce works in agriculture and produces enough food to support the non-farming communities in industrialized nations, where a new, much larger global middle class enjoys unprecedented wealth and consumer goods.

PALAEOLITHIC ERA 2,000 KILOCALORIES

AGRICULTURAL ERA 10,000–12,000 KILOCALORIES

MODERN ERA 200,000 KILOCALORIES

▼ **Unlocking more energy**
New innovations in the early 20th century made it possible to harness the power of oil and natural gas, making more energy cheaply available than ever before. Compared to our ancestors in the Palaeolithic era, our energy consumption is around 100 times higher, and most of this energy comes from fossil fuels.

AS A **SPECIES** WE ARE USING **24 TIMES** AS MANY **RESOURCES** AS WE **USED 100 YEARS AGO**

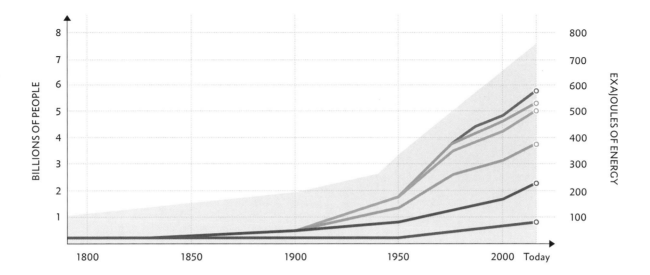

▶ Fuel consumption
Population growth has increased steadily in line with global energy use as humans unlocked the power of new forms of energy over time.

KEY
■ Wood
■ Coal
■ Oil
■ Natural gas
■ Hydro-electric
■ Nuclear
▢ Population growth

RISING CONSUMPTION

During the second half of the 20th century, rates of innovation accelerated so rapidly, and were so widespread, that the world was entirely transformed. One consequence of this change was consumer captialism: populations of industrialized regions enjoyed high levels of wealth and material affluence. In 1900, oil lamps, steam-powered trains, and unrefrigerated goods were the norm. Within just 50 years, pipes and cables brought electricity into homes, providing light and heat and powering domestic technologies that have transformed modern life: washing machines, dishwashers,

encouraged investment in produ ction and research. For example, the synthesis of plastic, a cheap new material, cut the costs of production. As more people were able to purchase once-expensive consumer goods, the cost of production fell, and even more people were able to buy them.

Today, not only are there more people than at any other point in human history, but they are also consuming more than ever before: the average consumption of each individual person is rising dramatically, all made possible by the energy from fossil fuels. Meanwhile, consumer products are cheaper, easier to purchase, and more

12 times from 1913 to 1998. However, this growth has not always been equal: by 1900, the world had been divided into those countries that had industrial economies and those that did not (see pp.336–37). Industrialization raised the wealth of Europe and North America but led to a rapid decline in the wealth of East Asia.

Meanwhile, resources such as food are not distributed equally: 800 million people in the world, mostly people living in poor undeveloped countries in Asia and sub-Saharan Africa, do not have enough to eat. At the same time, around one-third of all food produced each year is wasted.

▼ Waste products
In 1900, the world produced about 0.5 million tonnes (0.55 million tons) of solid waste per day. In 2000, this had increased six-fold to around 3 million tonnes (3.3 million tons) per day.

INFINITE GROWTH OF MATERIAL CONSUMPTION IN A FINITE WORLD IS AN IMPOSSIBILITY.

Ernst Friedrich Schumacher, German economist, 1911–77

radios, televisions, stereos, telephones, and computers gradually became everyday items that were frequently marketed and sold to the workers who produced them. Advertising (see pp.316–17) and marketing convinced consumers to buy these products and bank loans made them available to those who could not otherwise afford such goods.

The fossil fuel revolution also brought electricity into factories, where further technological innovation meant that methods of production became cheaper. This made goods more affordable and expanded markets, which, in turn,

disposable, all of which leads to huge amounts of waste. This waste includes materials such as plastics and electronic waste from computers, mobile phones, and televisions. The mass-manufacture of these items produces greenhouse gas emissions, and more emissions are created during the process of disposing of them.

UNEQUAL GROWTH
One widely accepted measure of growth is Gross Domestic Product (GDP), which measures the total production of all countries. World GDP increased almost

Burning coal can cause acid rain, which damages soil

Burning coal produces greenhouse gases and contributes to global warming

Used in steel and cement production

FACTORY

Dangerous to mine

Used to generate electricity for domestic use

More abundant than the other fossil fuels

COAL MINE

ELECTRICAL SUBSTATION

POWER STATION

IMPACT OF COAL

◀ Coal

Coal is cheaper to extract than the other fossil fuels and still relatively abundant: around 70 countries worldwide have coal reserves that are financially worth recovering. The biggest reserves are in the United States, Russia, China, and India. However, burning coal releases greenhouse gases that damage the environment and contribute to global warming.

▼ Oil

The most versatile fossil fuel, oil is also the one scientists predict we are running out of the fastest: some estimates say resources will run dry in just 55 years if we continue to use it at the current rate. Top producing oil countries include Saudi Arabia, Russia, the United States, Iran, and China.

IMPACT OF OIL

Used for diesel to fuel vehicles, which can pollute cities

Cleaner burning than coal but still releases harmful greenhouse gases

Oil is manufactured to make chemicals, synthetic rubber and plastics

FACTORY

Used for central heating systems

JUST AS **FOSSIL FUELS** FROM **CONVENTIONAL** SOURCES ARE **FINITE**... THOSE FROM **DIFFICULT SOURCES** WILL ALSO **RUN OUT**.

David Suzuki, Canadian scientist and environmental activist, 1936–

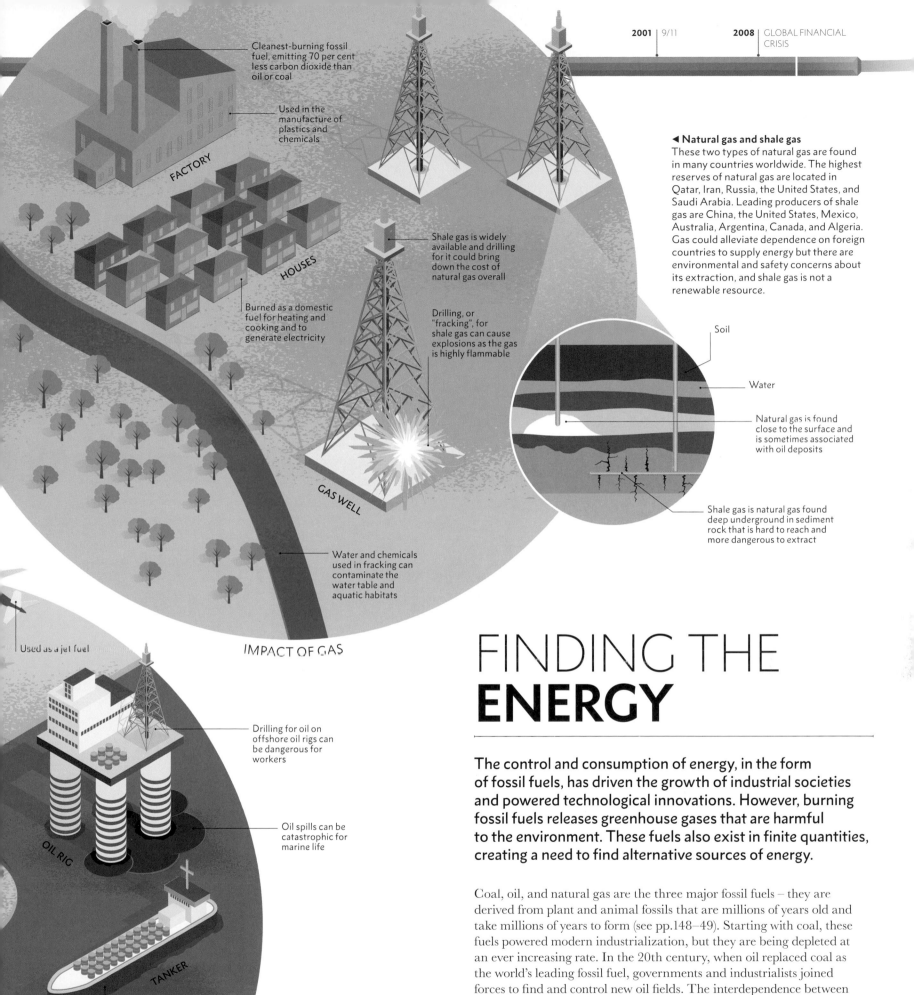

Cleanest-burning fossil fuel, emitting 70 per cent less carbon dioxide than oil or coal

Used in the manufacture of plastics and chemicals

FACTORY

HOUSES

Shale gas is widely available and drilling for it could bring down the cost of natural gas overall

Burned as a domestic fuel for heating and cooking and to generate electricity

Drilling, or "fracking", for shale gas can cause explosions as the gas is highly flammable

GAS WELL

Water and chemicals used in fracking can contaminate the water table and aquatic habitats

IMPACT OF GAS

Used as a jet fuel

Drilling for oil on offshore oil rigs can be dangerous for workers

Oil spills can be catastrophic for marine life

OIL RIG

TANKER

Easy to store and transport, especially in liquid form

◄ **Natural gas and shale gas**
These two types of natural gas are found in many countries worldwide. The highest reserves of natural gas are located in Qatar, Iran, Russia, the United States, and Saudi Arabia. Leading producers of shale gas are China, the United States, Mexico, Australia, Argentina, Canada, and Algeria. Gas could alleviate dependence on foreign countries to supply energy but there are environmental and safety concerns about its extraction, and shale gas is not a renewable resource.

Soil

Water

Natural gas is found close to the surface and is sometimes associated with oil deposits

Shale gas is natural gas found deep underground in sediment rock that is hard to reach and more dangerous to extract

FINDING THE ENERGY

The control and consumption of energy, in the form of fossil fuels, has driven the growth of industrial societies and powered technological innovations. However, burning fossil fuels releases greenhouse gases that are harmful to the environment. These fuels also exist in finite quantities, creating a need to find alternative sources of energy.

Coal, oil, and natural gas are the three major fossil fuels – they are derived from plant and animal fossils that are millions of years old and take millions of years to form (see pp.148–49). Starting with coal, these fuels powered modern industrialization, but they are being depleted at an ever increasing rate. In the 20th century, when oil replaced coal as the world's leading fossil fuel, governments and industrialists joined forces to find and control new oil fields. The interdependence between governments, energy companies, and the supply and control of oil shapes world politics today. Meanwhile, shale gas, a form of natural gas, is predicted to become an important new source of energy. It is found domestically in many countries, and may reduce or even eliminate their potential dependence on foreign nations for energy.

NUCLEAR
OPTIONS

During the 20th century, a global network of scientists discovered ways to harness nuclear energy, and in World War II deployed it with devastating immediate and long-term effects. In 2016, nuclear power provided almost 15 per cent of the world's electricity.

Warfare often drives innovation. The atomic bombs dropped on the Japanese cities of Hiroshima and Nagasaki in 1945 demonstrated the terrifying power of the world's ultimate weapon. It remains the most devastating technology unleashed by one industrialized power on another, and the fear it inspired – that any nation with a bomb could destroy another at the touch of a button – helped to create the Cold War that dominated the late 20th century.

◄ **Radioctive energy source**
Uraninite is a highly radioactive ore of uranium that is mined to provide an energy source that powers nuclear plants.

in 56 countries worldwide, where they were used for research and training, materials testing, medicine, and industry.

ALTERNATIVE ENERGY SOURCE

During the 1950s, concerns about an overreliance on fossil fuels brought peacetime usage of nuclear energy to the fore. The first electricity-producing nuclear power plant opened in the Soviet Union in 1954 and the industry spread rapidly in the 1960s. Nuclear power became even more politically important when skyrocketing prices brought about by the Middle East oil crises of the 1970s caused countries, such as France and Japan, to reduce their reliance on fossil fuels. By the year 2000, nuclear power accounted for 80 per cent of France's electricity and 40 per cent of Japan's.

Nuclear power has other important civil and commercial uses. By 2016, 240 smaller nuclear reactors were in operation

ENVIRONMENTAL THREATS

The pros and cons of nuclear power remain a topic of heated debate. There are concerns that any country building a nuclear reactor has the power to create a nuclear weapon. Arguments that nuclear power stations have lower emissions than those run by fossil fuels are met by concerns about the disposal of radioactive waste and the toxic pollution created by mining uranium. Safety is also a concern, after serious accidents occurred in Fukushima, Japan, in 2011, and Chernobyl, Ukraine, in 1986. Chernobyl affected over 16,316,900 hectares (40,320,000 acres) of land and there are 148,274 invalids on the Chernobyl registry, while Fukushima displaced over 160,000 people. Nuclear accidents also devastate rural areas, as contaminated land can no longer be used for agriculture. Engineers are working on developing safer and more efficient power stations for the future.

A WORLD **FREE OF NUCLEAR WEAPONS** WILL BE **SAFER AND MORE PROSPEROUS**.

Ban Ki-moon, Secretary-General of the United Nations, 1944–

Atmospheric weapons test
Nuclear weapons have been tested above ground, underground, and underwater. Over 2,000 nuclear explosions were detonated worldwide between 1945 and 1996.

ENTERING THE
ANTHROPOCENE

Human activity has become the most influential factor shaping life on Earth. The impact of industrialization and the pressures exerted by humankind have led to changes to the atmosphere, ecosystems, and biodiversity, while depleting many of Earth's resources. This has led scientists to propose that we have entered a new geological epoch: the Anthropocene.

▼ Burning fossil fuels
Industrialization was powered by the burning of coal, which released billions of tonnes of carbon dioxide into the atmosphere. After the 1880s, oil and gas drove further economic growth and released more carbon dioxide.

In 2000, Dutch scientist Paul Crutzen coined the term "Anthropocene" to describe a new geological epoch. He argued that the biosphere had been transformed by humans rather than by natural geological and climatic processes that defined previous epochs. Earth bears permanent signs of this human activity: airborne black carbon – the main component of soot produced by burning fossil fuels and biomass – is trapped in glacial ice; fertilizer chemicals linger in the soil; and plastics pollute both earth and water. All of these are likely to leave a fossil record for future generations to discover. Population growth, more intensive agriculture, the destruction of biodiversity, and industrialization are among the main causes of environmental damage: they have completely reshaped Earth's ecology and biology.

The history of Earth is divided into geological time scales: epochs are periods spanning thousands of years. If the Anthropocene is officially accepted it will follow the Holocene epoch, which began after the last Ice Age around 11,700 years ago, when humans colonized new territories and populations first began to grow. As the species at the top of the food chain, humans began to make their mark on the world's fauna 50,000 years ago when they hunted many large mammals to extinction.

Following the Ice Age, people started to settle in communities and began to develop agriculture. Scientists believe that deforestation to clear land for crops around 8,000 years ago released greenhouse gases into the atmosphere and created a spike in carbon dioxide (CO_2) levels. The effects of farming also changed the land; geologists can find agriculture's signature in European rock dating back to 900 CE.

During industrialization in the 19th century, Europe once again left an environmental mark and Crutzen believed that the Anthropocene started at this time. Other scientists suggest the Anthropocene began in the atomic era of the 1950s and the "Great Acceleration" that followed, which saw the rapid growth of economies, populations, and energy consumption. The Great Acceleration came after the detonation of the atomic bomb, the first nuclear weapon, which left a radioactive marker in sediments across the world, and marks the rise of truly global impacts caused by humans on the planet.

INDUSTRIAL IMPACT

While there is still some debate about the Anthropocene, few dispute the impact of industrialization upon the environment. Even in the early stages of Britain's industrial revolution, thick smog from the coal-burning factories spread into the atmosphere and created widespread health problems. These issues continued into the 20th century: a 1952 coal-fog left 4,000 dead from respiratory diseases in London in four days. In the United States, smog

SINCE THE **INDUSTRIAL REVOLUTION,** THE LEVEL OF **CO₂ ON EARTH** HAS **INCREASED** BY **34 PER CENT**

caused by car exhausts in California led to the discussion of a new environmental term: greenhouse gases.

Greenhouse gases, such as carbon dioxide and water vapour, occur naturally in small quantities in Earth's atmosphere and prevent heat escaping into space. Without them, Earth would be a frozen, arid planet. But in the last 250 years, intensified human activity – primarily burning fossil fuels for use in industry or electricity and transportation – has led to the highest concentrations of CO_2 in the atmosphere for around 800,000 years.

Carbon dioxide levels remained below 280 parts per million for thousands of years, but since the industrial revolution, they have risen at an increasing rate. Accelerating after the 1950s, they reached around 400 parts per million in the early 21st century. This is the main cause of global warming: a gradual increase in Earth's average temperature. More greenhouse gases trap more heat in the atmosphere and prevent it escaping into space.

Scientists suggest a 50 per cent reduction in global CO_2 emissions is needed by 2050 to prevent a global warming catastrophe. Global warming has already had serious effects, including glacial melting, a rise in

fertilizers and sewage can leak into waterways and contaminate freshwater, which eventually flows into the sea where it can create a dead zone. This is where algae form: when they sink to the sea floor and decompose, oxygen is removed from the water. The low levels of oxygen cause marine animals to leave or die. At the same time, around 80 million tonnes (88 million tons) of plastic litter have been dumped in the world's oceans, and around eight million more are added daily. Millions of animals and birds die annually when they mistake this plastic for food.

Every day, species' extinctions are continuing at up to 1,000 times or more

recovery from natural disasters. Even the extinction of a creature as small as a bee has a knock-on effect. Bees are the major pollinator of around one third of the world's food crops, but their numbers are in decline and severe food shortages are predicted as result of their dwindling populations.

SINCE 1992, THE NUMBER OF **PROTECTED SITES** WORLDWIDE HAS **INCREASED TWENTY-FOLD**

> ❝ OUR **PLANET** IS BEING **TRANSFORMED** – NOT BY NATURAL EVENTS, BUT BY THE ACTIONS OF **ONE SPECIES: MANKIND**. ❞

 Sir David Attenborough, 1926–

sea levels, ocean acidification, warming surface temperatures, extreme weather, and the destruction of ecosystems.

Ecosystem destruction is also caused by widespread deforestation that began during the 19th century to provide wood and raw materials for industrialization. Trees were replaced with crops, such as coffee and tea, which could be grown on one plot of ground over consecutive years. Today, deforestation accounts for around one fifth of greenhouse gas emissions, as plants and trees absorb CO_2 during photosynthesis. Halting deforestation and replanting forests would help to reduce CO_2 levels.

DECLINING BIODIVERSITY

Chopping down forests has destroyed various ecosystems. As humans increasingly exploit the land, we leave less to sustain all other species, leading to a decline in wildlife diversity and abundance. Large numbers of plants and animals were destroyed in Africa, India, and the Pacific Islands in the 19th century during deforestation for industrialization.

Meanwhile, increasingly high levels of pollutants in the world's oceans have devastated marine life. Agricultural

the natural rate due to human population growth, habitat conversion, urbanization, and over-exploitation of natural resources. In 2015, a study by the International Union for Conservation of Nature (IUCN) assessed 80,000 animal species and found nearly 25,000 of them to be under threat of extinction. If current trends continue, the Earth is on course for a sixth mass extinction on a scale not seen for 65 million years, since the extinction of the dinosaurs.

The threat to biodiversity is the result of land-use changes, pollution, climate change, and rising CO_2 concentrations, and is now a matter for serious concern. Each creature has a supporting role in Earth's biosphere, which is an interdependent global ecosystem. This ecosystem provides essential services such as clean water, fertile soils, pollution absorption, storm protection, and

REVERSING THE DAMAGE

Attempts are being made to help undo the centuries of human environmental damage. Since the 1970s, hundreds of environmental protocols and treatises have been adopted internationally; the countries signing up to them have agreed to implement targets linked to environmental concerns, but with varying degrees of success.

More recently, a set of 17 Sustainable Development Goals were adopted by the United Nations in 2015, which are expected to frame the policies of 193 nations until 2030. They aim to "end poverty, protect the planet, and ensure prosperity for all" by promoting "sustainable industrialization". This may become a defining theme for future generations to ensure that environmental sustainability and protecting the world's ecosystems remain top priorities.

> ❝ THE **CLIMATE CRISIS** IS THE **GREATEST CHALLENGE HUMANITY** HAS EVER **FACED**. ❞
>
> **Al Gore**, American politician and environmentalist, 1948–

CLIMATE **CHANGE**

Earth's climate has fluctuated dramatically throughout its 4.5 billion year history, but scientists can now prove that human activities – such as burning fossil fuels and clearing land for agriculture – are also contributing to climate change.

Climate change is a long-term shift in weather conditions identified by changes in temperature, precipitation, winds, and other indicators. Climate science began over 100 years ago, when scientists first suggested that burning fossil fuels may cause global warming, which, in turn, contributes to climate change. In 2016, humans emitted carbon dioxide (CO_2) into the atmosphere 10 times faster than at any point in the last 66 million years, causing Earth to be at its warmest for 1400 years.

The effects of global warming have been monitored for decades: they include global temperature rises, the shrinking of glaciers and ice sheets, the thinning of the ozone layer, acidification and warming of the oceans, and rising sea levels. By comparing data on these events with past records, scientists try to predict the future impact of global warming. Climate-change data is gathered by chemists, biologists, physicists, oceanographers, and geologists. They compare statistics on Earth's temperatures, weather, and greenhouse gases by feeding data into computerized climate change models. Air samples are analyzed to gauge the level of CO_2 in the atmosphere caused by natural sources compared to that of fossil fuels. Similar readings made from air bubbles trapped in Antarctic ice cores that are hundreds of thousands of years old tell us about past changes in Earth's climate (see pp.174–75). Plant fossils from Earth's crust tell us about species distribution during different atmospheric periods, which may indicate how they could react to higher levels of CO_2 in the future.

ozone hole increased during 1980s

1979

1987

1998

2015

▲ Ozone depletion

The ozone layer stretches across the Earth's upper atmosphere and absorbs most of the Sun's ultraviolet radiation. In the 1970s, robotic satellites showed a hole in the ozone layer. In 1987, the Montreal Protocol agreed to prohibit ozone-depleting chemicals, but the ozone hole is only predicted to return to 1980 levels by 2070.

Global temperature rise

To record global temperatures scientists take air measurements from satellites, ships, and meteorological stations and then analyze the data. These measurements reveal that the average global temperature is 0.8°C (1.4°F) warmer than it was in 1880. In 2015, this caused heatwaves in Asia and Europe, flooding in Africa, droughts in South America, and an increase in extreme weather events: global storms, cyclones, and typhoons.

Rising sea levels

The Maldives are at risk

Tidal gauge readings, ice core samples, and satellite measurements have shown the global mean sea level has risen by 7cm (2¾in) in the last century. This rise is due to melting glaciers and polar ice caps, and the expansion of sea water as it warms. Rising sea levels have devastated low-lying coastal habitats, including a number of Pacific Islands.

Shrinking sea ice

Satellite images of the ice caps in Greenland and Antarctica reveal that as temperatures rise they are shrinking at a rate of 13.4 per cent per decade. Sea ice reflects sunlight back into space. Without sea ice, the ocean absorbs 90 per cent of the sunlight, which warms the water, adds to the Arctic temperature rise, and causes more melting in a process known as a positive feedback loop.

Sea ice at the smallest extent recorded, 2012

Ocean acidification

Scientists study ice core samples and the chemical composition of fossilized sea creatures assess the ocean's acidity over time. The acidity of the ocean's surface has risen by 30 per cent over 200 years, as increased CO_2 in the atmosphere has been absorbed by the sea. Acidification prevents creatures such as corals, mussels, and oysters from absorbing the calcium carbonate they need to maintain their skeletons.

Warming oceans

Using robotic floats, scientists are able to show that the world's oceans have warmed by around 0.11°C (0.2°F) between 1971 and 2010. This has led to the destruction of ecosystems such as coral reefs. In 2016, warming ocean temperatures caused a global coral bleaching event. This is where coral lose the colourful algae that give them pigmentation and provide them with oxygen and nutrients. If the stress continues, the bleached coral will die.

Bleached coral

▼ **Endangered elements**
The periodic table of endangered elements shows the 44 elements facing supply restrictions in the future as well as the 17 Rare Earth Elements, three of which are also endangered.

KEY
■ Limited availability – future risk to supply
■ Rising threat from increased use
■ Serious threat in the next 100 years
■ Rare Earth Element

Lithium is used for the lithium-ion batteries that power personal electronics and electric cars today because they store more energy (in the same amount of space) than other technologies

Hafnium has a very high melting point, which is why it is used to make control rods for nuclear processors and nuclear submarines. It is also used as an insulator in microchips and found in computer circuitry.

Neodymium is used in the magnets that power mobile phones, electric car engines, and wind turbines. Without it, magnets would be 90 per cent weaker and up to 100 per cent larger, making green energy less efficient.

ELEMENTS UNDER THREAT

The chemical elements that make up Earth occur on our planet in finite quantities. Of the 118 elements that have so far been identified, around 44 are considered endangered because demand for use in technology is predicted to outstrip supply.

Coal and oil are not the only natural resources at risk from current demand. Supplies of elements – including Rare Earth Elements (REEs) with magnetic, luminescent, and electrochemical properties vital for the latest technology – are also under threat. The reasons vary: some, like helium, occur in finite non-renewable quantities. Others are hard to access: REEs are often widely dispersed and mixed with other minerals, which makes mining an expensive proposition, and refining them can create quantities of toxic waste. In addition, countries with economically viable mines may prefer to secure these resources for domestic use in medical and military equipment rather than export them to competing nations. As with oil, these countries are in a strong position to manipulate prices and protect their market share by controlling availability; it is possible to recycle REEs from old or obsolete electronics, such as computers and phones, but cheaper to extract them afresh. Technology may not work as well without them, but high prices and low supplies give manufacturers an incentive to innovate and create alternative products that use fewer – or no – REEs and endangered elements, and promote the sustainable use of what we have left.

IN 2010, **CHINA CONTROLLED 95 PER CENT** OF THE WORLD'S **RARE EARTH PRODUCTION**

Indium is used to make the touch-screen glass found in smartphones. It comes from zinc mines as it occurs in such small amounts that mining it is impractical. If the demand for zinc declines, it will have an impact on the availability of indium.

Phosphorus is an important ingredient in agricultural fertilizers. It is also used in everyday items, such as matches. Europe has started recycling phosphorus as a step towards a more sustainable supply.

Helium is the second most abundant element in the Universe, but on Earth our extractable supplies are declining. It has many uses, including in MRI scanners

Solar-powered supertrees
Singapore's Gardens by the Bay, an innovative and energy-efficient space, contain supertrees inspired by their natural counterparts. They contain photovoltaic cells that convert sunlight into energy and use it for lighting.

THE QUEST FOR
SUSTAINABILITY

Coal, oil, and gas have powered over 250 years of industrial progress, but these fossil fuels are in limited supply. Switching from non-renewable to renewable sources of energy could lead to greater energy security and help to protect the environment.

In 2013, more than 80 per cent of the world's energy came from coal, gas, and oil, while only 19 per cent came from renewable energy sources. Researchers are seeking new forms of renewable energy as a matter of urgency.

GREEN TECHNOLOGY

The most common sources of renewable power are water, solar, wind, geothermal – which harnesses heat from Earth, such as hot springs – and biomass fuels created by burning decaying plant or animal material. Each has limitations. The construction of wind farms, solar panels, hydroelectric dams, and tidal barriers is expensive, and geothermal power is only available in volcanic areas. Burning biomass emits carbon dioxide, but it is carbon neutral when it is part of a sustainably managed programme – for example, if new trees are planted to absorb the carbon dioxide released. Furthermore, new renewable technologies are developing fast and costs are coming down. With knowledge and experiences shared through global networks we may be able to innovate to overcome the current limitations.

Many countries already use renewable energy. In Brazil, sugar cane is made into the biofuel ethanol; the country's gasoline includes a blend of 18–27 per cent ethanol. Nearly 40 per cent

◀ **Electric car**
Instead of running on oil, electric vehicles are powered by a rechargeable battery, which means they emit less carbon dioxide.

of Denmark's energy comes from wind power, over 26 per cent of Germany's power comes from renewables, and some Chinese and Indian villages heat biomass material to generate electricity. In 2016, over 60 per cent of global energy investment went into renewables, and green energy is predicted to overtake electricity generated by fossil fuels by 2030.

Renewable energy could create hundreds of thousands of jobs. It could also enable many countries to develop the long-term domestic energy security essential in the industrial world, and insulate them from the fluctuating prices of imported fuels. However, industrializing countries, such as China and India, continue to rely on coal. Fossil fuel subsidies are often high, which makes them cost effective. Despite these barriers to investment, renewables are catching up and, in some cases, are already cheaper than fossil fuels.

> " WE NEED TO ULTIMATELY **MAKE CLEAN, RENEWABLE ENERGY** THE **PROFITABLE** KIND OF **ENERGY**. "

Barack Obama, President of the United States (2009–2017), 1961–

WHERE **NEXT?**

Big History provides a unique perspective on the trends and themes that connect the story of humans. Can we use them to predict the future? Nothing is certain, but the themes of population growth, innovation, energy, and sustainability look set to recur for the next hundred years.

Population growth and innovation are the signatures of our success as a species. Our 18th-century ancestors combined thousands of years of collective learning with new agricultural technologies to put an end to the Malthusian crises that periodically reduced agrarian populations. Astonishing industrial innovation gave many people access to goods, services, and a quality of life previously unimaginable. Technological growth in the last century has outstripped that of all human history. Many of today's innovations, such as smartphones and the internet, would have seemed impossible as recently as the early 1980s. These technologies have connected the world in the most complex collective network ever known.

However, progress has come at a cost. It has led to increasing consumption of the dwindling resources of water and

age. Today we are on the cusp of the sixth wave: sustainability, the great theme of our time. It aims to provide a high standard of living for the rising global population – predicted to reach 10 billion by 2050 – while reducing our reliance on fossil fuels and using remaining resources efficiently. The ability to harness new forms of energy has defined past thresholds of human history; now our relationship with energy may determine the fate of our species.

There are signs that trends are shifting. Population growth rates have slowed in industrializing countries, such as India and China. This may be because economically developed countries tend to produce fewer children. But these children tend to be more highly educated, and as they join the billions of potential innovators already connected through the modern global communications network, this may be

BIG HISTORY STUDIES THE HISTORY OF EVERYTHING, OFFERING A WAY OF MAKING SENSE OF OUR WORLD AND OUR ROLE WITHIN IT.

David Christian, Big History historian, 1946–

fossil fuels; it has brought about the mass-extinction of many plant and animal species; and it has led to an exponential rise in greenhouse gas emissions. It is now up to the global collective to reverse this damage and develop a less environmentally harmful existence for future generations.

A SUSTAINABLE FUTURE

The industrial revolution is sometimes described as the first in a series of waves of innovation: the first era of mechanization was succeeded by innovations from the steam age, the electrical age, the aviation and space age, and most recently the digital

the key to saving our planet. Never before has collective learning been so accessible, integrated, and important.

The collective hub has already created important green innovations: electric cars, biofuels, solar-powered desalination of water, and zero-emission buildings, whose total energy consumption does not result in greenhouse gas emissions. In this sense, the near future is a place of limitless potential. The 21st century may be remembered as the dawn of global sustainability, attained through green innovation and powered by renewable energies. In a future still unwritten, all things are possible.

Innovation to predict climate change
The Orbiting Carbon Observatory detects where carbon dioxide is absorbed and how much is in the atmosphere, with the aim of improving predictions of climate change.

INDEX

References in *italics* refer to illustrations and
photographs, those in **bold** indicate the main
information for the topic.

green energy 357
greenhouse gases 345, **350–351**, 352
Greenland 174, 176
Gross Domestic Product (GDP) 333, 345
guano (fertilizer) 248
gunboat diplomacy *324*
gunpowder 284
Gutenberg, Johannes 264
Guth, Alan 34

H

habitable zones (planets) 77
habitats 112, 116, 140, **186–187**
    arid *147, 152*, 153, 272
    coastal *152*, 158
    grasslands *168*, 169
    ocean 128, 128–129, 154
        marine 351
        reef 138, 139
    rainforest 158, *233*
    swamp *148*, 153
Hadean Era **78**, 79, 82, *102–103*
Hadrian's Wall 86, *286*
hafnium 354
Haikouichthys 130
haloes (dark matter) 48
Hammurabi, King of Babylon 262
hands, evolution of *142, 143, 186–187*
Han dynasty 263, **294–295**
harvests 20, *233*, **236**, *249*
hearths *216*
Heezen, Bruce 91, 94
hekat 250
heliocentrism 24–25
helium 38, 63, 355
    formation in stars 44, 56, 58
Hennig, Emil Hans Willi 173
herbivores 115, *135*, 169
    dinosaurs 154
herding animals 169
Herschel, William *26*
Herto skull *198*
Hess, Harry Hammond 91
hierarchy, of society *258*, 259
hieroglyphs 254, 267
Higgs boson particles 34, **37**, *37*
high mass stars 57
Hinduism 18, *19*, 275
Hipparcos Satellite 27
hippopotamus 170–171, *171*
Hohle Fels *Venus* 212, *213*
Holmes, Arthur 91

Holocene period 220, 226, 350
Homer 284
Hominins **184–185**, 211, 220–221
    breeding of 196, 197, 201
    burial practices 218
    dispersal from Africa 194–195
    evolution of **186–187**, *189*, 202
    within the primate family 183
Homo antecessor 194, 195
Homo erectus 184, 185, 187, 216
    brain size of *189*
    dispersal of *194*, 195
    intelligence of 202, **206, 207**, 211
Homo ergaster 186
Homo floresiensis 185, 199, 214
Homo habilis 184, 185
    brain size of *189*
    dispersal of *194*, 195
    intelligence of **206**, 211
Homo heidelbergensis 188, 195
Homo neanderthalensis 184, *189*
    see also Neanderthals
Homo sapiens 198, **199**, *199*
    burial practices of **218**, 221
    clothing of 214
    culture and language of 202, 203, 204
    dispersal of *194*, 195
    evolution of 189, *189*, 201
    intelligence of **206, 207**, 220
    interbreeding with other Hominins
        190, **196–197**
    within primate family 183, *183*
honeybee 165
hoofed mammals 167, *168*, 170, *171*
Hooker Telescope 30, *31*
horses *169*, 246, *297*
    domestication of 284
    use in trade *295*
horticulture 232
household possessions *316*, 317
Hoyle, Fred 32
huarango trees 272
Hubble, Edwin 29, **30**, 32, *33*
Hubble Space Telescope *27*, 50–51
Human Genome Project 335
human rights 318–319
human sacrifices 277
humans *see Homo sapiens*
hummingbird hawk-moth *164*
hunter-gatherer groups *210*, 211
    belief systems of 274
    competing with farmers **232**, 242
    diet and health of 190, **293**
    social networks within 204
    settlements of 228, **230–231**

Hutton, James 86
Huxley, Thomas Henry 111
hydroelectric energy 357
hydrogen 38, 63
    formation in stars 44, 56, 58–59
    formation of life 102, 114
hyenas *168*
hyoid bones *192*, 202, *202*

I

Iapetus Ocean 138
ice ages **176–177**, 220, 226
    Bering Strait 195
ice cores 174–175
Iliad, Homer *214*, 284
"Imilac" meteorite 72
imperialism *see* colonization
import trades 323
Inca Empire 248, 250, 274
India
    continental shift of 158
    development of writing 266
    and globalization 336
    imperialism in 288
    renewable energy in 357
    worship in 274, 275, 319
    see also Indus civilization
indium 355
Indohyus 170, 171
Indus civilization *246*, 266, 269
industrialization 304, *305*, **308–309**,
    310–311
    effects on environment 350
    globalization of 312
    leading to consumerism 316–317
    social impact of 331
    wealth of industrialists 314, 323
inflation (cosmology) 35
inflation (economics) 291, 299
Information Age 332
inner core, Earth's 80, *80*
insects **142**, *143*
    pollination by 160, **164–165**
interglacial periods **176**, 177, 190
internal combustion engines
    338, 339
internet 341, 342
interstellar cloud *68*
invertebrates 135, **141**, 158
    marine 162
iron, as raw material 217, 280, 281
Iron Age 281

irrigation systems 248, **268–269**, 271
Islam 274, 275, 295
Islamic Golden Age 267
islands, formation of 84, 85, *93*
isotopes 38, 72
Israel 216
Italy 320, 329

J

Jack Hills, Australia 88, 89, *89*
James Webb Space Telescope
 (JWST) 27
Japan 331, **348**
 Buddhism in 275
 development of writing 267
 education reform in 332
 imperial power of 329
 industrialization in 309, **313**
 Jomon civilization *230–231*, 231
 trade markets 299, *324*, 325
jawless fish 130
jaws, evolution of 132, *134*, **135**
Jefferson, Thomas 318
jellyfish 126
Jenner, Edward 334
jewellery *190*, 208, 214
 by metallurgy 280, 281
Jomon civilization *230–231*, 231
Judaism 274
Jupiter *74*, 75
Jurassic period 154, 163
justice 262–263
Justinian, Roman Emperor 263

K

Kaapvaal Craton 85
Kalahari bushmen *189*, *210*
katydid *109*
Kenya 211, 342
Kepler, Johannes 25
Kepler-452 system 77
keratin 153
kings **261**, 262–263, 271, 274
 pharaohs *258*, *261*, *261*
 grave goods of 277
kinship 204, 262
Koran 263
Kuiper Belt 75
Kushan Empire 294

L

labour (birth) 201
labour laws 331
lactose tolerance 246
Lafayette, Gilbert du Motier,
 Marquis de 318
Lagerstätte 138
Lamarck, Jean-Baptiste 111
land ownership **262**, 274, 314
language **202–203**, 216, 320
 capabilities of Neanderthals 192
 development of 204
 extinction of 297
Large Hadron Collider (LHC) *36*, 37
Large Magellanic Cloud 60
larynx 202
Last Universal Common Ancestor
 (LUCA) *113*
Late Devonian mass extinction 135
Late Heavy Bombardment **75**, 80, 100
Latin 173, **264**, 287
Lau event 162
Laurasia 158
lava *102*
Lavoisier, Antoine-Laurent de 63
law and order 262–263
Law of Octaves 63
layers, rock *86*, *87*
leather 207, 214
Leavitt, Henrietta Swan *28*, 29
Legalism 263
Lemaître, Georges *32*
liberty 318
Lidgettonia 145
life expectancy 344
light 32, 47, 50
 from stars **44–45**, 60
 see also telescopes
light-years **29**, 50
lignin 137, 141, 148
lignite 148
limbs
 evolved from fins 132, *141*
 wings evolve from 142, *143*
linen 214, 278
Linnaeus, Carolus
 (Carl von Linné) 172
lions *168*
literacy 267, **332**, *333*
lithic mulching 272, *272*
lithium 354
llamas *234*
lobe-finned fish 141

Locke, John 318, 320
London 304
looms 278, 309
Lord of Sipán *276*, 277
low mass stars *57*
Lyell, Charles 86
Lystrosaurus 159

M

machine guns *326*, 327
Magellan, Ferdinand 298
magma *79*, *84*, **92**, 94
magnesium 59
magnetic field 80, *81*, 91
magnetic resonance imaging
 (MRI) scanners 335
magnolias 160
Maillet, Benoît de 86
maize *234*, *242*, 253
 domestication of 236, *237*
malaria 327
male organisms *123*, 124, 240
Malthus, Thomas 253
Malthusian cycles 253
mammals 147, **166–167**
 extinctions of 163
 evolution of 133, 142, 147
 for domestication 240
 hoofed *168*
manioc *296*
mantle, Earth's 80, 84, 92
manufacturing industries
 308–309, 310, 312, 345
 assembly lines *339*
 workers conditions *330*, 331
manure 248
manuscripts 267
Māori people 18, 329
mapping, world *90*
Mariana Trench 94
marine habitats 351
marine life 140, 158, 351
Mars 24, *74*
marsupials 158, 167
Marx, Karl 319
mass spectrometer 88
Maxim, Hiram 327
Max Planck Institute for Astrophysics,
 Germany *61*
Maya civilization
 astronomy in 18
 rulers of *260*, 261

protostars 56
protosuns 68, *68*
Prototaxites 101
protowings *143*
Prussia 312, *312*
pterosaurs 142, *142, 143*
Ptolomy, Claudius **22–23**, 24, 25
Puerto Rico Trench 94, *94–95*
pumpkins *242*
pure metals 280
pyramids, Egypt 250

Q

Qianlong coin *290*
Qin dynasty 263
Qin Shi Huang, Emperor 277
quantum mechanics 28, 47
quarks **34**, 35, 37
quasars 38

R

racism 320, 327
radiation 38, 45, 49
   from the Sun 68, 69, *114*
radioactive waste 348
radioactivity 86
radio broadcasts 341
radiometric dating 72, 86, 88, *88*
radio telescopes 26
railways **308–309**, 313, 339
rainforest habitats 158, *233*
Raleigh, Sir Walter 297
Ram Mohun Roy, Raja 319
Rare Earth Elements (REEs) 355
Raven, Peter 165
Ray, John 172, 173
records, written 264–265
   calendars 244
recycling *221*, 355
Red Deer Cave people *194*
red giant (stars) *57*
redshifts 29, *29*, 30
reef habitats 138, 139
reflectors (telescopes) 26, *26*
Reform Act (1832) 317
Reform Bill (1832) 331
reforms, social 311, 320, 331
refractors (telescopes) 26
re-ionization 45

Relativity, General Theory of 32, 38,
   47, *47*
religions 86, 274–275, 295
   attitudes to law 263
renewable energy 357
reproduction
   of plants 145, 160, 165
   of protocells *107*
   sexual 111, **120–121**, 124
reptiles 153, **154–155**, 162–163
   evolution into birds and mammals 156, 167
   evolution of eggs 147
   winged 142
Republic of Letters 319
reservoirs *268*, 269
respiratory systems 114, *137*
respiration, aerobic 116
retail 316, 317
revolution, political 314, 318, 331
Rheinische Zeitung 319
rhizoids 137
ribosome *113*
rice *243*, 253
   domestication of 236, *236*
Richmond Union railway 313
rickets 293
Rights of Man, Paine 318
ritualistic burials 218
RNA 104, 104–105, 106
road networks 287, *287*, 294, **339**
rock erosion 86, *87*, 88
rock (cave) paintings 208, 209, 212–213
   depicting hunting scenes *188, 227*
   story-telling through *203*
rocky planets 71
"rogue" planets 75
Roman alphabet 264
Roman Catholic Church 24, 25, 264
Roman Empire *286*, **287**, 294
   coal mining in 307
   development of laws and justice 263
   fall of 288
   food and famine in 250, 253
   religion in 274, 275
   trade in 291, 294
   views on afterlife 277
Rosetta Stone 266
Ross, Ronald 335
royal authority **261**, 262–263
Royal Mail 340
r-process 59
rule of law 262
rulers **261**, 262, 291
   chieftains 259, 277
   monarchies 304, 318, 320

Russia 328
   see also Soviet Union
Russian Chemical Society *62*
Rutherford, Ernest 28, *29*

S

sacrifices
   human 277
   religious 274, 275
Sahelanthropus tchadensis 183, *184*, 186
salinization 272
Samurai warriors *324*
San bushmen *189, 210*
sanitation 334
Sargon of Akkad *288, 288*
satellites (communication) 341
Saturn *74*
sauropods 154
savanna habitat *168*
scala naturae 172
scanning electron micrograph (SEM) *136*
Schrödinger, Erwin *29*
screw pump (Archimedes' screw) *269*
scribes *258*
sculpture 208, *212*
   see also carvings, art
scurvy 293
sea crossing, earliest 195, 206
sea-floor spreading 91
sea levels 86, 176, 352
seasons 82
secondary products, of animals 246
seeds 101, 158, 160
   in early farming 236
   evolution of 144–145
seismic waves *80*
seismology 95
semaphore 340
semi-domesticated animals 240
Semmelweis, Ignaz 334
sensory organs 126
settlements
   city states 270–271
   towns 256–257
   villages 220, 228–229, 230–231
sexual reproduction 111, **120–121**, 124
shaduf lifting system *269*
shale gas 347
shamanism *209*, 275
Shang Yang, Lord 263
Sharia law 263
sharks 130–131, 135, 162

ACKNOWLEDGMENTS

The publisher would like to thank the Big History Institute for their enthusiastic support throughout the preparation of this book – especially Tracy Sullivan, Andrew McKenna, David Christian, and Elise Bohan. Special thanks to the writers: Jack Challoner, Peter Chrisp, Robert Dinwiddie, Derek Harvey, Ben Hubbard, Colin Stuart, and Rebecca Wragg-Sykes.

DK would also like to thank the following:
Editorial assistance: Steve Setford; Ashwin Khurana; Steven Carton; Anna Limerick; Helen Ridge; Angela Wilkes; and Hugo Wilkinson.
Design assistance: Ina Stradins; Jon Durbin; Saffron Stocker; Gadi Farfour; and Raymond Bryant.
Additional illustrations: KJA artists; Andrew Kerr.
Image retoucher: Steve Crozier.
Picture Research: Sarah Smithies.
Proofreader: Katie John.
Indexer: Elizabeth Wise.
Creative Technical Support: Tom Morse
Senior DTP Designer: Sachin Singh.
DTP Designer: Vijay Kandwal.
Production manager: Pankaj Sharma.

PICTURE CREDITS

The publisher would like to thank the following for their kind permission to reproduce their photographs:

(Key: a-above; b-below/bottom; c-centre; f-far; l-left; r-right; t-top)

1 Corbis: EPA.
2 Dorling Kindersley: Oxford University Museum of Natural History.
8–9 Getty Images: Fuse.
19 Getty Images: De Agostini.
20–21 Corbis: EPA.
20 Corbis: EPA (bc).
21 123RF.com: Boris Stromar (tr).
© LDA Sachsen-Anhalt: Juraj Lipták (cr).
22–23 Bridgeman Images: Private Collection.
23 Alamy Stock Photo: Patrizia Wyss (tr).
26 Dorling Kindersley: The Science Museum, London (cl). **Fraunhofer:** Bernd Müller (ca). **Science Photo Library:** David Parker (br). **Thinkstock:** Photos.com (tl).
27 Alamy Stock Photo: PF-(bygone1) (bc); RGB Ventures (crb). **Corbis:** Design Pics / Steve Nagy (tl).
28 Alamy Stock Photo: Granger, NYC (cra).
30–31 Science Photo Library: Royal Astronomical Society.
30 Carnegie Observatories – Giant Magellan Telescope: (clb).
32 Getty Images: Bettmann (bl).
36–37 © CERN: Maximilien Brice.
37 © CERN: T. McCauley, L. Taylor (cra).
38 NASA: ESA, J. Jee (University of California, Davis), J. Hughes (Rutgers University), F. Menanteau (Rutgers University and University of Illinois, Urbana-Champaign), C. Sifon (Leiden Observatory), R. Mandelbum (Carnegie Mellon University), L. Barrientos (Universidad Catolica

de Chile), and K. Ng (University of California, Davis) (bl).
38–39 ESA: and the Planck Collaboration (t).
45 ESO: M. Kornmesser (https://www.eso.org/public/images/eso1524a/) (tr).
46 Corbis: The Gallery Collection (cla).
47 Mark A. Garlick / www.markgarlick.com.
48–49 Image courtesy of Rob Crain (Leiden Observatory, the Netherlands), Carlos. Frenk (Institute for Computational Cosmology, Durham University) and. Volker Springel (Heidelberg Institute of Technology and Science, Germany), partly based on simulations carried out by the Virgo Consortium for cosmological simulations: (c). **Rob Crain (Liverpool John Moores University) & Jim Geach (University of Hertfordshire):** (b).
49 NASA: H. Ford (JHU), G. Illingworth (UCSC / LO), M.Clampin (STScI), G. Hartig (STScI), the ACS Science Team, and ESA (tr).
50 NASA: ESA, and Z. Levay, F. Summers (STScI) (cb).
50–51 NASA: ESA / G. Illingworth, D. Magee, and P. Oesch, University of California, Santa Cruz; R. Bouwens, Leiden University; and the HUDF09 Team.
51 NASA: illustration: ESA; and Z. Levay, (STScI) image: T. Rector, I. Dell'Antonio / NOAO / AURA / NSF, Digitized Sky Survey (DSS), STScI / AURA, Palomar / Caltech, and UKSTU / AAO (cra); ESA and John Bahcall (Institute for Advanced Study, Princeton) Mike Disney (University of Wales) (br).
59 123RF.com: Yuriy Mazur (tc). **NASA:** ESA, M. Robberto (Space Telescope Science Institute / ESA) and the Hubble Space Telescope Orion Treasury Project Team (crb).
60 Getty Images: John Livzey (bl). **Science Photo Library:** Konstantinos Kifonidis (tc).
60–61 Science Photo Library: Konstantinos Kifonidis
61 Science Photo Library: Konstantinos Kifonidis (tl, tc, tr).
62–63 Dorling Kindersley: The Science Museum, London / Clive Streeter.
68–69 ESO: L. Calçada / M. Kornmesser.
70 Alamy Stock Photo: Stocktrek Images, Inc.
72 ESA: Rosetta / NAVCAM – CC BY-SA IGO 3.0 (bl).
72–73 Heritage Auctions.
73 Alamy Stock Photo: dpa picture alliance (br). **Science Photo Library:** Chris Butler (crb).
76–77 ESA: D. Ducros, 2013.
79 Mark A. Garlick / www.markgarlick.com: (br).
82 Kevin Snair, Creative Imagery: (b).
83 Kevin Snair, Creative Imagery.
85 Getty Images: The Asahi Shimbun (cra).
86 Science Photo Library: Royal Institution Of Great Britain (bl); Sheila Terry (tr).
87 Alamy Stock Photo: Stefano Ravera.
88 Library of Congress, Washington, D.C.: David G. De Vries Call No: HAER CAL,41-MENPA,5–31 (c).
88–89 J. W. Valley, University of Wisconsin-Madison.

89 Alamy Stock Photo: B Christopher (tr); World History Archive (br).
90 Alfred-Wegener-Institute for Polar and Marine Research: (bl). **Science Photo Library:** UC Regents, National Information Service for Earthquake Engineering (c, ca).
90–91 Copyright by Marie Tharp 1977/2003. Reproduced by permission of Marie Tharp Maps LLC, 8 Edward St, Sparkill, NY 10976: (t).
92 Alamy Stock Photo: Nature Picture Library (clb).
100 Dorling Kindersley: Hunterian Museum and Art Gallery, University of Glasgow (c). **FLPA:** Frans Lanting (bl).
101 Dorling Kindersley: Hunterian Museum and Art Gallery, University of Glasgow (cla).
103 Peter Bull: based on original artwork by Simone Marchi.
105 Science Photo Library: A. Barrington Brown, Gonville and Caius College (b).
106 Alamy Stock Photo: World History Archive (ca).
108 Getty Images: Tom Murphy / National Geographic (b).
108–109 Piotr Naskrecki.
110 Alamy Stock Photo: Natural History Museum, London (t).
112 Science Photo Library: Professors P. Motta & F. Carpino, Sapienza – Università di Roma (bl).
114 Science Photo Library: Wim van Egmond (cl).
114–115 Anne Race.
115 NASA: SeaWiFS Project / Goddard Space Flight Center and ORBIMAGE (br).
120 Ardea: Auscape (bl).
122 Getty Images: Carolina Biological (cl). **Shuhai Xiao of Virginia Tech, USA:** (cra, cr).
123 Shuhai Xiao of Virginia Tech, USA.
124 Jurgen Otto.
125 Science Photo Library: Eye of Science (br).
126 Xiaoya Ma: Xianguang Hou, Gregory D. Edgecombe & Nicholas J. Strausfeld / doi:10.1038 / nature11495 fig 2 (bl).
134 Corbis: Scientifica.
136–136 Science Photo Library: Martin Oeggerli.
137 Chris Jeffree: (bc).
138 Corbis: Jonathan Blair (bl, clb, bc).
138–139 The Sedgwick Museum of Earth Sciences, University of Cambridge.
139 Alamy Stock Photo: Stocktrek Images, Inc. (br).
142 Robert B. MacNaughton: (bl).
144–145 Dorling Kindersley: Natural History Museum, London.
148–149 Alamy Stock Photo: imagebroker.
149 Dorling Kindersley: Natural History Museum, London (bc).
150–151 Deutsches Bernsteinmuseum: (b).
150 Alamy Stock Photo: Agencja Fotograficzna Caro (c).

152 **Colorado Plateau Geosystems Inc:** © 2016 Ron Blakey.

156–157 **Science Photo Library:** Natural History Museum, London.

158–159 **Colorado Plateau Geosystems Inc** © 2016 Ron Blakey.

162–163 **Alamy Stock Photo:** dpa picture alliance (c).

163 **Dorling Kindersley:** Jon Hughes (cra); Natural History Museum, London (tc). **Science Photo Library:** Mark Garlick (cb).

164–165 **123RF.com:** Timothy Stirling.

165 **FLPA:** Biosphoto / Michel Gunther (b).

166 **Roger Smith:** Iziko South African Museum (cl).

167 **Dorling Kindersley:** Jon Hughes (tl).

172 **Alamy Stock Photo:** Natural History Museum, London (b).

173 **TopFoto.co.uk:** Ullsteinbild (ca).

174 **Getty Images:** National Geographic / Carsten Peter (br).

176 **Colorado Plateau Geosystems Inc** © 2016 Ron Blakey (b).

182–183 **Getty Images:** Andrew Rutherford.

184–185 **Kennis & Kennis / Alfons and Adrie Kennis:** (all).

186 **123RF.com:** Stillfx (cr). **Science Photo Library:** MSF / Kennis & Kennis (bl).

187 **123RF.com:** Oleg Znamenskiy (cl). **Alamy Stock Photo:** RooM the Agency (cr).

188 **Alamy Stock Photo:** Heritage Image Partnership Ltd (t).

189 **Alamy Stock Photo:** Nature Picture Library (tr).

190 **Alamy Stock Photo:** dpa picture alliance (bl). **Luka Mjeda:** (cra).

191 **Science Photo Library:** S. Entressangle / E. Daynes.

192–193 **Alamy Stock Photo:** Natural History Museum, London.

192 **Kenneth Garrett:** (clb). **Djuna Ivereigh www. djunapix.com:** (c).

193 **Getty Images:** National Geographic / Ira Block (br).

194 **Alamy Stock Photo:** National Geographic Creative (bc). **Darren Curnoe:** (cra). **Science Photo Library:** MSF / Javier Trueba (clb).

197 **Robert Clark:** (b).

198 **Alamy Stock Photo:** age fotostock (t); Hemis (bl).

199 **Kennis & Kennis / Alfons and Adrie Kennis**.

200–201 **Alamy Stock Photo:** Pim Smit.

202–203 **Getty Images:** Print Collector (b).

203 **Alamy Stock Photo:** Premaphotos (t).

204 **Alamy Stock Photo:** Arterra Picture Library (clb).

204–205 **RMN:** Grand Palais / Gérard Blot.

205 **RMN:** Grand Palais / Gérard Blot (crb).

206 **Dorling Kindersley:** Natural History Museum, London (cr); Robert Nicholls (tr). **Getty Images:** FyeEm / Daniel Koszegi (cb). **Wim Lustenhouwer / Vrije Universiteit University Amsterdam:** (crb). **Museum of Anthropology, University of Missouri:** (cla). **Science**

Photo Library: P. Plailly / E. Daynes (bc). **SuperStock:** Universal Images Group (c).

207 **Alamy Stock Photo:** Granger, NYC (cra). **Science Photo Library:** John Reader (c). **Muséum de Toulouse:** Didier Descouens/Acc No: MHNT PRE.2009.0.203.1/ https://commons.wikimedia.org/wiki/File:Pointe_ levallois_Beuzeville_MHNT_PRE.2009.0.203.2.fond.jpg (cla). **João Zilhão (ICREA/University of Barcelona):** (tr).

208 **Alamy Stock Photo:** Heritage Image Partnership Ltd (cl). **Getty Images:** Field Museum Library (crb). **Pierre-Jean Texier:** (tc).

209 **akg-images:** Pictures From History (bc). **Alamy Stock Photo:** Arterra Picture Library (tl, tr); Natural History Museum, London (cra). **Joel Bradshaw, Honolulu, Hawaii:** (ca). **Dorling Kindersley:** University of Pennsylvania Museum of Archaeology and Anthropology (br).

210–211 **Alamy Stock Photo:** John Warburton-Lee Photography.

211 **Alamy Stock Photo:** Cindy Hopkins (crb).

212–213 **Alamy Stock Photo:** EPA / Guillaume Horcajuelo (b).

213 **Paleograph Press, Moscow:** (tr). **© urmu:** © uni tübingen: photo: Hilde Jensen (cla).

214 **Getty Images:** De Agostini (bl). **Lyudmilla Lbova:** (tr).

215 **Science Photo Library:** S. Entressangle / E. Daynes

216 **Alamy Stock Photo:** Penny Tweedie (bl). **Institut Català de Paleoecologia Humana i Evolució Social:** (ca).

216–217 **Bridgeman Images:** (t).

217 **Alamy Stock Photo:** EPA (cla). **Dorling Kindersley:** Board of Trustees of the Armouries (cra). **Rex by Shutterstock:** Isifa Image Service sro (bl).

218 **Science Photo Library:** Natural History Museum, London (bc).

218–219 **Kenneth Garrett**.

220 **Ardea:** Jean-Paul Ferrero.

226–227 **Alamy Stock Photo:** Archivio World 4.

229 **Corbis:** John Warburton-Lee Photography Ltd / Nigel Pavitt (br).

231 **Alamy Stock Photo:** Peter Horree (bc).

232 **Dorling Kindersley:** Museum of London (cl).

232–233 **SuperStock:** Universal Images Group.

234 **Getty Images:** Bloomberg (ca); Morales (crb).

235 **Alamy Stock Photo:** Nigel Cattlin (clb); Danita Delimont (tr). **Dreamstime.com:** Jaromír Chalabala (cla)

236 **Getty Images:** Markus Hanke (ca).

238 **Corbis:** Imagebroker / Frank Sommariva. **Science Photo Library:** Ami Images (clb); Steve Gschmeissner (bl); Scimat (cb, bc).

238–239 **Science Photo Library:** Ami Images.

239 **Dreamstime.com:** Fanwen (tr).

240 **Alamy Stock Photo:** Kip Evans (bl).

242 **Alamy Stock Photo:** Chuck Place (cra). **Dreamstime.com:** Branex | (tl).

243 **123RF.com:** Samart Boonyang (cr). **Alamy Stock**

Photo: Tim Gainey (cra). **Dreamstime.com:** Sergio Schnitzler (bc); Elena Schweitzer (tc).

244 **SuperStock:** De Agostini (b).

244–245 **Science Photo Library:** David R. Frazier.

245 **Alamy Stock Photo:** Sputnik (tr).

246 **Corbis**.

246–247 **Alamy Stock Photo:** India View.

248–249 **The Trustees of the British Museum**.

249 **Alamy Stock Photo:** The Art Archive (tl).

250 **Photo Scala, Florence:** Metropolitan Museum of Art (cl).

250–251 **Alamy Stock Photo:** Bert de Ruiter.

252–253 **Alamy Stock Photo:** Yadid Levy.

253 **Getty Images:** AFP (cb).

254 **The Trustees of the British Museum**.

254–255 **The Trustees of the British Museum**.

255 **akg-images:** Erich Lessing (cra). **Bridgeman Images:** Tarker (cr). **Reuters:** Chinese Academy of Science (br).

256 **Getty Images:** De Agostini (tc, cb).

257 **Corbis:** Nathan Benn (tc); Ottochrome / Nathan Benn (tr).

259 **Artemis Gallery:** (tl).

260–261 **Alamy Stock Photo:** Dennie Cox.

261 **Corbis:** Sandro Vannini (br).

262 **Alamy Stock Photo:** Glasshouse Images (br).

264 **Alamy Stock Photo:** Prisma Archivo (bc).

264–265 **Alamy Stock Photo:** The Art Archive.

266 **Alamy Stock Photo:** Eye35 (tl). **Bridgeman Images:** Louvre, Paris, France (cb). **Corbis:** Gianni Dagli Orti (clb). **Getty Images:** De Agostini (bl).

267 **Alamy Stock Photo:** Holmes Garden Photos (tc). **Bridgeman Images:** British Library (tr). **Wikipedia:** (br).

270 **Alamy Stock Photo:** Interfoto (b).

272 **Alamy Stock Photo:** age fotostock (b).

272–273 **Getty Images:** Yann Arthus-Bertrand.

275 **Alamy Stock Photo:** imagebroker (b).

276–277 **Alamy Stock Photo:** Heritage Image Partnership Ltd.

277 **The Trustees of the British Museum:** With kind permission of the Shaanxi Cultural Heritage Promotion Centre, photo by John Williams and Saul Peckham (cb).

278 **Corbis:** Burstein Collection (b).

278–279 **Bridgeman Images:** Museum of Fine Arts, Boston, Massachusetts, USA / Julia Bradford Huntington James Fund.

280 **akg-images:** (tr); Erich Lessing (cr). **Alamy Stock Photo:** Edwin Baker (ca).

281 **Alamy Stock Photo:** Ancient Art & Architecture Collection Ltd (c). **Bridgeman Images:** Museo del Oro, Bogota, Colombia / Photo © Boltin Picture Library (tr). **Dorling Kindersley:** Gary Ombler (c) Fort Nelson (bc); University of Pennsylvania Museum of Archaeology and Anthropology (clb). **Dreamstime.com:** Xing Wang (cla)

282–283 **Bridgeman Images:** South Tyrol Museum of Archaeology, Bolzano, Wolfgang Neeb (b).

282 **South Tyrol Museum Of Archaeology – www.**

iceman.it: (ca); Reconstruction by Kennis & Kennis © South Tyrol Museum of Archaeology, Foto Ochsenreiter (3) (tr).
283 Bridgeman Images: South Tyrol Museum of Archaeology, Bolzano, Wolfgang Neeb (cra). **South Tyrol Museum Of Archaeology – www.iceman.it.**
284 Getty Images: De Agostini (clb).
284–285 Alamy Stock Photo: 505 Collection.
286–287 Alamy Stock Photo: Clearview.
287 The Trustees of the British Museum.
288 Photo Scala, Florence: (ca).
288–289 Alamy Stock Photo: Peter Horree.
290 Dorling Kindersley: University of Pennsylvania Museum of Archaeology and Anthropology (t). **Numismatica Ars Classica NAC AG:** Auction 92 Pt 1 Lot 152 (bl); Auction 59 Lot 482 (bc); Auction 72 Lot 281 (br).
291 Alamy Stock Photo: Anders Ryman (b). **RMN:** Grand Palais (musée du Louvre) / Franck Raux (tr).
292–293 Bridgeman Images: Galleria Regionale della Sicilia, Palermo, Sicily, Italy.
293 Corbis: Demotix / Demotix Live News (cb).
294–295 Getty Images: AFP (b).
295 Dorling Kindersley: Durham University Oriental Museum (tc).
296 Alamy Stock Photo: John Glover (bl). **Getty Images:** De Agostini (cla); Clay Perry (clb).
297 Alamy Stock Photo: Melvyn Longhurst (crb). **Getty Images:** EyeEm / Cristian Bortes (cra); Tim Flach (br). **Science Photo Library:** Eye of Science (cr).
298 Courtesy of The Washington Map Society www.washmapsociety.org: original research published Fall 2013 issue (#87) of The Portolan, journal of the Washington Map Society (b).
299 Bridgeman Images: Pictures from History (t). **The Trustees of the British Museum.**
304–305 Getty Images: Robert Welch
307 Alamy Stock Photo: North Winds Picture Archives (br).
308 Science & Society Picture Library: Science Museum (tr).
308–309 SuperStock: Science and Society Picture Library (b).
309 Alamy Stock Photo: Granger, NYC (tr). **Getty Images:** Transcendental Graphics (br).
310 123RF.com: Jamen Percy (cla). **Alamy Stock Photo:** Granger, NYC (c, bc); Historical Art Collection (HAC) (tr). **Dorling Kindersley:** The Science Museum, London (cra).
311 Alamy Stock Photo: Chronicle (cr); Niday Picture Library (cl); North Winds Picture Archives (cb); Photo Researchers (cla).
312 Alamy Stock Photo: Liszt Collection (tr). **Getty Images:** Bettmann (cb); SSPL (ca).
312–313 Cyfarthfa Castle Museum & Art Gallery, Merthyr Tydfil: © Mervyn M. Sullivan (c).

313 Alamy Stock Photo: (cb); North Winds Picture Archives (cla). **Getty Images:** Hulton Archive (ca). **Library of Congress, Washington, D.C.:** LC-USZ62-136561 (br). **Science & Society Picture Library:** NRM / Pictorial Collection (clb).
315 Alamy Stock Photo: The Print Collection (br).
316–317 TopFoto.co.uk: The Granger Collection (b).
316 akg-images: Les Arts Décoratifs, Paris / Jean Tholance (tr).
317 Alamy Stock Photo: Granger, NYC (br); Pictorial Press Ltd (tc).
318 Corbis.
319 Corbis: (bc).
320 Alamy Stock Photo: Lebrecht Music and Photo Library.
320–321 Alamy Stock Photo: Chronicle.
324 The Art Archive: British Museum, London.
325 Science & Society Picture Library: Science Museum (br).
327 akg-images: Interfoto (tr). **Bridgeman Images:** Private Collection / Archives Charmet (b).
328 123RF.com: Saidin B. Jusoh (crb); Pornthep Thepsanguan (cl). **Photoshot:** John Cancalosi (ca).
329 Corbis: Richard Nowitz (clb). **Getty Images:** John Wang (tl).
330–331 SuperStock: ACME Imagery.
331 Science & Society Picture Library: Science Museum.
332 Alamy Stock Photo: Granger, NYC (tr); Thislife Pictures (b).
333 Getty Images: Aldo Pavan (t).
334 Alamy Stock Photo: North Winds Picture Archives (tr); Photo Researchers (bc). **Science & Society Picture Library:** Science Museum (ca, crb, clb). **Science Photo Library:** Science Source / CDC (bl).
336 Science & Society Picture Library: National Railway Museum (tr).
337 Alamy Stock Photo: The Art Archive (tc); Lebrecht Music and Photo Library (tl); David Wells (bl); Cultura Creative (RF) (br). **Getty Images:** The LIFE Images Collection / James Whitmore (cl).
338 Alamy Stock Photo: Motoring Picture Library.
339 Alamy Stock Photo: Motoring Picture Library (cr).
340 Alamy Stock Photo: Granger, NYC (bc). **Corbis:** Araldo de Luca (br). **Science & Society Picture Library:** Science Museum (cb). **TopFoto.co.uk:** The Granger Collection (ca).
341 Alamy Stock Photo: The Art Archive (clb); Granger, NYC (tl); Everett Collection Historical (bc); D. Hurst (br). **Getty Images:** Bloomberg (cra). **NASA:** (tr). **Science & Society Picture Library:** National Museum of Photography, Film & Television (cb); Science Museum (ca).
342 Alamy Stock Photo: Annie Eagle (5/b). **Flickr.com:** Portal GDA/https://www.flickr.com/photos/135518748@N08/23153369341/in/photolist-

BgZ548 (6/b); roach/https://www.flickr.com/photos/mroach/4028537863/sizes/l (4/b). **Science & Society Picture Library:** Science Museum (1/b, 2/b).
343 123RF.com: Adrianhancu (8/b); svl861 (ca); Norman Kin Hang Chan (5/b). **Alamy Stock Photo:** D. Hurst (4/b); Visions of America, LLC (tl); Frances Roberts (cra); Oleksiy Maksymenko Photography (3/b, 6/b). **Amazon.com, Inc.:** (7/b). **Getty Images:** Business Wire (2/b). **Rex by Shutterstock:** Langbehn (1/b). **Science Photo Library:** Thomas Fredberg (c).
344 ESA: NASA.
345 Getty Images: Yann Arthus-Bertrand (br).
348 Science Photo Library: Dirk Wiersma (c).
348–349 Getty Images: Galerie Bilderwelt.
350 Getty Images: EyeEm / William McClymont (bl).
351 Rex by Shutterstock: London News Pictures.
352 Alamy Stock Photo: Global Warming Images (bc). **NASA**.
353 Alamy Stock Photo: Reinhard Dirscherl (br). **NASA:** Goddard Space Flight Center Scientific Visualisation Studio (cra).
354 Alamy Stock Photo: fStop Images GmbH (tr). **Getty Images:** Davee Hughes UK (bl).
355 123RF.com: Andrii Iurlov (cra). **Dreamstime.com:** Emilia Ungur (cb).
356–357 Alamy Stock Photo: Sean Pavone.
357 Alamy Stock Photo: Oleksiy Maksymenko Photography (ca).
358–359 Alamy Stock Photo: Stocktrek Images, Inc.

Cover images: Front: 123RF.com: Andrey Armyagov fcrb, Igor Dolgov crb; **Alamy Stock Photo:** Granger, NYC. cb/ (Map); **Bridgeman Images:** Biblioteca Monasterio del Escorial, Madrid, Spain cb; **Dreamstime.com:** Constantin Opris crb/ (Industry), Imagin.gr Photography clb/ (Acropolis), Sergeypykhonin cb/ (Steam); **Neanderthal Museum:** clb; **Science Photo Library:** Pascal Goetgheluck; Back: **123RF.com:** Nikkytok fclb, Pablo Hidalgo crb, Sergey Nivens fcrb; **NASA:** cb/ (Solar system), JPL-Caltech / UCLA cb, JPL-Caltech / University of Wisconsin-Madison / Image enhancement: Jean-Baptiste Faure clb; **Science Photo Library:** Pascal Goetgheluck.

All other images © Dorling Kindersley.
For further information see: **www.dkimages.com**